Eat, Drink & Sleep Smoke-free 1993

HEADWAY BOOKS

First published in 1991 by Catherine Mooney and Headway Books
Saddlers Cottage, York Rd, Elvington, York, YO4 5AR

This 3rd edition published 1993

© Catherine Mooney, 1993

ISBN 0 9513045 8 5

Printed by The Redwood Press, Melksham, Wilts.

Designed and typeset on Rank Xerox Ventura by Lisa Pickering

For dad

Perfectos, finos.....

ACKNOWLEDGEMENTS

It has been a very great privilege for me to work in conjunction with ASH as editor and publisher of *Eat, Drink and Sleep Smoke-free*. More than any other work I have ever been involved in - this has been a team effort. I would like to thank everyone at ASH who has been associated with the project, but my especial thanks go to Zuzana Eisler without whom this book would never have happened: she has worked - apparently tirelessly - on almost every aspect of the guide to ensure that it meets the highest standards. We couldn't have produced it without her. Thankyou, too, to David Pollock, ASH's director, for his help, advice and support. On the home-front I would like to thank Beverley McJannett my wonderful secretary who has gone way above and beyond the call of secretarial duty in ensuring that the administrative organisation behind the production of the book has gone smoothly. Special thanks, too, to Christopher, my free-lance amanuensis.

Catherine Mooney.

Introduction

Do you mind if I smoke? That is becoming an increasingly rare question. Non-smokers - and even many smokers - certainly do mind if anyone smokes around them. This is what the *Eat, Drink and Sleep Smoke-Free* guide is about. Here we provide you with nearly 2000 hotels, guest houses, restaurants and even pubs, where you can find smoke-free air. Some of these establishments have gone as far as to ban smoking completely, while others at least provide a no-smoking area. It is for you to choose which best suits your needs.

Of course, although we have made a great deal of progress in achieving smoke-free air over the past few years, ASH is not complacent. We will not consider our work finished until non-smoking is the norm in society, with designated areas provided for smoking only where necessary and possible. Just as public health campaigners in the latter half of the last century considered their goal to be a clean water supply and the elimination of cholera, so we have a goal of clean air and the elimination of diseases induced by passive smoking.

Ultimately, we believe that we will see legislation introduced in the United Kingdom that will guarantee non-smokers the right to breathe smoke-free air. We believe that the pressure from non-smokers, who form the majority of the population will be too great for the Government to resist. The Government is already showing signs of weakening. In 1991 they brought out a Code of Practice and in their Health White Paper in 1991 they said that if satisfactory progress was not made by voluntary means then "if necessary . . . . legislation will be introduced."

In the meantime, we will look carefully at legislation protecting non-smokers in other nations. In the autumn of 1992 French non-smokers welcomed the introduction of a law to protect them from passive smoking. One often quoted survey showed 84% approval for the law. We shall look very carefully at the enforcement of that law and learn the lessons for the time when the UK follows suit. But there are many other examples which are already long established and working well. For example, New York City has had minimum standards applying to the provision of smoke-free air for some years - and it is working well.

Before any law is introduced in the United Kingdom, however, we will need to campaign for change. ASH has already made a good start, by producing reliable information to help employers, restaurateurs, bus operators, banks and others to go smoke-free. Our work was given a boost by the courageous and vigourous campaign mounted by Roy Castle, who has lung cancer caused by passive smoking. Roy's highly public fight against his illness and against its cause - passive smoking - has earned him the admiration of many. He has also shown how vital it is to protect non-smokers from passive smoking. He is a prime example of the dreadful consequences of being forced to breathe in other people's tobacco smoke. That is why we are currently planning our *Breathing Space* campaign - a consumer driven campaign for smoke-free air which we hope will enlist the vast army of non-smokers to press for change. Contact us for further news of this unique venture.

By buying this guide you have stated your preference for smoke-free air. We hope that you enjoy visiting the places listed here. We also hope that you will work with us towards a smoke-free society.

David Pollock

Director ASH

Passive Smoking Basics

The Health Risk:

Passive smoking - breathing other people's smoke

- *Can cause lung cancer in non-smokers.* The Government's Independent Scientific Committee on Smoking and Health concluded in March 1988 that passive smoking leads to several hundred lung cancer deaths in the United Kingdom each year. The lung cancer risk from passive smoking is more than 100 times greater than that from exposure to asbestos in buildings.

- *May cause heart disease*: the evidence is mounting of this suspected link.

- *Can seriously affect the health of young children.* Wheezing, coughs, bronchitis, asthma, middle ear and upper respiratory tract infections are all more common among the children of smokers. Recent estimates suggest that 17,000 under-fives are admitted to hospital every year because their parents smoke. Up to 25% of cot deaths could also be attributable to parental smoking.

- *Can harm unborn babies.* Babies born to non-smoking mothers who have been exposed to environmental tobacco smoke tend to weigh less than babies born to unexposed mothers. Their average weight lies between that of the babies of non-smoking women reportedly unexposed to passive smoking and that of the babies of women who smoke.

- *Exacerbates respiratory problems in adults.* Non-smokers exposed to passive smoking can suffer from a range of non-fatal but unpleasant respiratory ailments, and can have existing breathing problems, such as asthma, made much worse.

- *Passive smoking exposes the non-smoker to a large number of toxic chemicals and substances.* Examples include formaldehyde (used for preserving dead bodies), arsenic (a deadly poison), benzene (used for dry-cleaning), ammonia (strong disinfectant), nicotine (insecticide) and nickel (widely used in industry for metalwork and plating). All these substances end up in non-smokers' lungs - some of them in greater concentrations even than smokers receive.

Times are changing:

Non-smokers are in the majority - 7 out of 10 of the population do not smoke.

Most people would welcome smoke-free air. Opinion polls show that:

- 82% of the population agree that passive smoking is a health hazard (*NOP 1990*)

- 87% of the general population and 77% of smokers agree that people who do not smoke should have the right to work in air free of tobacco smoke (*EOS Gallup 1992*)

- 97% of non-smokers and 70% of smokers think that all restaurants should provide no-smoking areas (*NOP 1989*)

- 66% agree that there should be no smoking on public transport (NOP 1987)

- When asked which change in pubs people would most like to see, no-smoking rooms came top of the list - above longer and more flexible opening hours! (*Which? Magazine, 1988*)

Other countries, for example Belgium, Australia, Canada, France, Italy and almost all states in the USA, have actually passed laws that ensure public place of various sorts - restaurants, schools, offices etc. - are smoke-free. More and more countries are introducing such legislation.

No-smoking rules are almost always readily observed and welcomed by the overwhelming majority of people, wherever such rules are introduced.

About ASH

Action on Smoking and Health (ASH) was founded in 1971 by the Royal College of Physicians. It strives by education and by advocacy of effective controls to reduce the toll of diseases, disability and death caused by smoking. It is a charity and draws on the suppport of many eminent persons, particularly in the medical profession.

ASH maintains a comprehensive database of information on all aspects of smoking - medical, social, commercial, industrial - and of tobacco control measures and smoking cessation methods, both at home and worldwide. It publishes a special bulletin twice a month intended primarily for health professionals.

ASH campaigns for better control of tobacco. The main steps required are:

- to ban all tobacco advertising and promotion, including tobacco sponsorship of the arts and sport
- Regular tax increases to produce a constant rise in the real price of cigarettes
- Laws to make public indoor places smoke-free as a protection against the dangers of passive smoking
- a major campaign of health and education

ASH Workplace Services is a consultancy offering advice to employers on how to introduce smoking policies at work. It offers professional consultancy, seminars and a detailed manual.

ASH supporters receive in return for their subscription a quarterly newsletter and briefings on ASH's campaigns plus special offers on ASH books and merchandise.

For further information write to:

Action on Smoking and Health
109 Gloucester Place
London W1H 3PH
Tel: (071) 935 3519
Fax: (071) 935 3463

ASH Scotland	*ASH Wales*	*ASH Northern Ireland*
8 Frederick Street	*372a Cowbridge Road*	*Ulster Cancer Foundation*
Edinburgh	*Canton*	*40 Eglantine Avenue*
EH2 2HB	*Cardiff CF5 1HF*	*Belfast BT9 6DX*
Tel: 031 225 4725	*Tel: 0222 641101*	*Tel: 0232 663281*
Fax: 031 220 6604	*Fax: 0222 641045*	*Fax: 0232 660081*

W.Isles

Highlands

Gramps.

Tayside

Cent.

Fife

Loth.

Strath.

Borders

Dumf. & Gall.

The
N. East.

Cumbria
&
the
N. West

Yorks. & Humb.

Clwyd

Gwynedd

East Midlands

Powys

Central
England

East Anglia

Dyfed

Gwent

Glamorgan

Thames
& Chilts.

Lond.
& M'sex

South East

The South West

The South

Orkneys and Shetlands

Contents

HOW WE COLLECTED OUR INFORMATION

Eat, Drink & Sleep Smoke-free 1993 was compiled from information received on detailed questionnaires which were completed by participating establishments in 1992. It has not been possible to verify the information that has been given by visiting each place and accordingly the information provided in this book is presented in the good faith that it is correct but with the recommendation that customers check with a particular establishment before booking to ensure that the provision meets their requirements and has not altered since the information was compiled. Inclusion in the guide is based solely on merit. No establishments have paid any charge for listing - but those which have editorial comment and/or an illustration have paid a small charge for the extra space.

HOW TO USE THIS BOOK

This guide is divided into five sections: *England, The Channel Islands, Northern Ireland, Scotland* and *Wales.* The *England* section of the book is divided into 11 principal areas in which the English counties within these areas are listed alphabetically; hotels and guest houses are listed within each county section under an alphabetical list of cities, towns and, if they are especially significant, villages. Establishments themselves are listed alphabetically by name under their city, town or village heading.
Scotland, Wales, Northern Ireland and *The Channel Islands* are smaller sections so it was not thought necessary to divide them into area by area sections. Instead the regions within *Scotland, Wales* and *N. Ireland* (and the islands for *The Channel Islands*) are listed alphabetically and within that format the listing is exactly the same as for the English entries.

The information given about each establishment is largely self-explanatory but the following should be noted:

- The prices for B. & B. are per person per night and represent the cheapest high season price offered by each establishment - this is usually based on the price of a couple sharing a room, and it should be noted therefore that single rooms may cost significantly more than the B. & B. price given. Prices are correct at the time of going to press but it is impossible to guarantee that prices will not have increased by the time you use this book. We therefore strongly advise you to check with any establishment before booking.
- The reference to access for the disabled is based on the information we have been supplied with by the establishments. It has not been possible to verify the extent of the provision for those with varying degrees of physical disability - whether a room has wheelchair access, for instance. It is advisable to check that the establishment meets your requirements before booking.

HOW TO HELP US TO MAKE THE BOOK BETTER

I hope very much that *Eat, Drink & Sleep Smoke-free 1993* helps you to find a hotel, guest house, restaurant or pub - with clean air! I welcome any comments or suggestions you may have for making this a more useful and helpful publication - in particular I invite recommendations about hotels, guest houses, restaurants or pubs that you feel should be included in next year's guide. If we are able to use your recommendations we will enter your name in a prize draw - and you could be one of five lucky (and helpful) readers to win a copy of next year's guide!

The South West

Avon
Accommodation

BATH

Aaron House: Number Ninety Three, 93 Wells Road, Bath, BA2 3AN (0225) 317977
Within easy walking distance of the city centre, B.R. & coach stations. ETB commended.
Open all year. No smoking in the house. Special diets by arrangement. Children welcome. En suite, tea/coffee-making & T.V. in all bedrooms. Credit cards. B. & B. from £19.

Bathhurst Guest House, 11 Walcot Parade, Bath (0225) 421884
Beautiful terraced Georgian house with 6 spacious guest rooms, just a short stroll from the Roman Baths & antique shops in the city centre.
Open all year ex. Xmas & New Year. No smoking in the house. Vegetaran & other diets by arrangement. Children welcome. Pets by arrangement. 2 en suite rooms. TV & tea/coffee-making in rooms. B. & B. £15.50-18.

Devonshire House, 143 Wellsway, Bath, Avon, BA2 4RZ (0225) 312495
19th C. house incorporating antiques shop, offering all the comforts of home. Well-appointed, spacious bedrooms. B'fast of your choice in comfortable Victorian dining room. Secure car parking.
Open all year. No smoking in the house. Vegetarian & other diets by arrangement. Children welcome. En suite, beverage-making & TV in all bedrooms. B. & B. from £19.

Grove Lodge Guest House, 11 Lambridge, London Rd, Bath, BA1 6BJ (0225) 310860
An elegant Georgian House built in 1788, set in beautiful gardens, offering well-proportioned single, double and family rooms.
Open all year. No smoking in the house. Vegetarian & coeliac diets by arrangement. Licensed. Children welcome. Tea/coffee available on request. T.V. in all bedrooms. B. & B. from £17.50

Haydon House, 9 Bloomfield Park, Bath, BA2 2BY (0225) 427351

From the outside Haydon House looks like many another unassuming Edwardian detached house so typical of the residential streets of Bath. Inside, however, 'an oasis of tranquility and elegance' prevails; certainly the proprietor, Magdalene Ashman, has done everything possible to make your stay - so near and yet so far from the tourist throng of Bath - a truly happy and welcome one: rooms are tastefully decorated (lots of Laura Ashley and soft furnishings) and, although breakfast is the only available meal, this too has a little special something added (porridge is served with whisky and muscavado sugar, for instance, and a fresh fruit platter is available for less staunch appetites).
Open all year. No smoking in the house. Vegetarian breakfast avail. Children by arrangement. En suite, TV & tea/coffee-making in bedrooms.
Credit cards. B. & B. from £25 (3 for the price of 2 mid-Nov. to mid-Mar.).

Holly Lodge, 8 Upper Oldfield Park, Bath, BA2 3JZ (0225) 424042 Fax: (0225) 481138
Holly Lodge is a large Victorian house set in its own grounds and enjoying magnificent views over the city of Bath. The house has been extensively renovated and beautifully decorated in recent years but with an eye to retaining all the period features of the original building (marble fireplaces, ceiling cornices, *etc*) so that the original architectural elegance is maintained. Breakfast is the only meal available at Holly Lodge but guests dine in a charming room which has views of the city and gives diners a chance to contemplate which of Bath's 80 fine restaurants they will choose for their evening meal. Facilities are also available for small conference parties.
Open all year. No smoking in the house. Vegetarian & other diets by arrangement. Children by arrangement. En suite, tea/coffee-making, T.V. and phone in all rooms. Credit cards. B. & B. from £34.

Kinlet Villa Guest House, 99 Wellsway, Bath, BA2 4RX (0225) 420268
Kinlet is an attractive guest house situated within easy walking distance of Bath city centre.
Open all year. No smoking in the house. Special diets avail. Children welcome. Tea/Coffee-making & T.V.
in all bedrooms. B. & B. from £15. ETB 2 Crowns Commended.

Meadowland, 36 Bloomfield Park, Bath, BA2 2BX (02250 311079

Meadowland is a large family residence standing in about ½ acre of secluded grounds, including lovely gardens and private parking, in the beautiful Georgian city of Bath. Entirely non-smoking, it has been elegantly furnished and decorated throughout (Meadowland has been awarded a Highly Commended status by the ETB), and the spacious, colour-coordinated en suite bedrooms offer accommodation of the highest standard including remote control TV, a hair dryer and trouser press; there is a large comfortable lounge, with a selection of books and magazines, for guests' use. Breakfast is the only meal to be offered at Meadowland, but there are several imaginative choices and special diets can be accommodated by arrangement; there are a number of good restaurants within easy reach to which your host will gladly direct you for your evening meal. Sporting and other leisure activities can also be arranged for you should you so wish. Non-smokers only, please.
Open all year. No smoking in the house. Vegetarian & other diets by arrangement. Wheelchair access "yes,
with help." Children welcome. En suite, TV & tea/coffee-making in bedrooms. Credit cards. B. & B. from £25.

The Old Red House, 37 Newbridge Rd, Bath, Avon (0225) 330464
Romantic Victorian guest house with stained glass windows and canopied beds. B'fast is served in a sunny conservatory - hearty or healthy, the choice is yours. Private parking.
Open all year. No smoking in the house. Vegetarian standard. Other diets by arrangement. 1 ground floor room.
Children welcome. Pets by arrangement. En suite, TV & tea-making in rooms. Access, Visa. B. & B. £17.50.

The Old School House, Church Street, Bathford, Bath, BA1 7RR (0225) 859593

The Old School House, pleasantly situated within the conservation area of the village of Bathford, has only recently been converted to use as a private hotel: for the previous decade it was a private home and since 1839 it was the village school. Accommodation is in most pleasantly appointed rooms (some with views over the beautiful Avon Valley with its wooded hillsides) and there are 2 ground floor rooms suitable for the less mobile; guests dine by candlelight (24 hrs notice for dinner, please) on superb cuisine typically featuring a home-made soup or feta cheese salad followed by Salmon Steak with Asparagus Sauce and a selection of tempting desserts. Bath is just 3 miles away and the energetic may choose to visit it via the towpath walk along the canal.
Open all year. Smoking banned throughout. Special diets: any (within reason) on request. Licensed. Disabled
access: 2 ground floor, level-entry bedrooms available. En suite bathrooms, tea/coffee-making and T.V. in all
bedrooms. Credit cards accepted. B. & B. from £29.50. ETB Highly Commended. AA Selected 4Qs.

Parkside Guest House, 11 Marlborough Lane, Bath, BA1 2NQ (0225) 429444
Large, spacious Edwardian house on the fringe of Bath's famous Royal Victoria Park. Wholefood & organic ingredients in cooking. Bedrooms are spacious and have been furnished and decorated with an eye to lightness and comfort. Large, attractive garden for guests' use in clement weather.
Open all year. No smoking in the house. Vegetarian, vegan & other diets by arrangement. Children: over 5s
only. Pets by arrangement. 3 rooms en suite. Tea/Coffee-making & T.V. in all bedrooms. B. & B. from £17.50.

Somerset House, 35 Bathwick Hill, Bath, BA2 6LD   (0225) 466451
Fine Regency house 1m from Bath centre; excellent food made from home-grown produce.
Open all year. No smoking in the house. Vegetarian & other diets by arrangement. Licensed. Children: over 10s only. En suite & tea/coffee-making in all rooms. T.V. lounge. Credit cards.

Sydney Gardens Hotel (B. & B.), Sydney Road, Bath, BA2 6NT   (0225) 464818/445362
The Sydney Gardens Hotel is a spacious Italianate, Victorian house which lies in a unique parkland setting on the fringe of Bath's magnificent city centre; it has been carefully refurbished in keeping with its period and now offers a very high standard of accommodation to guests. Each of the 6 guest bedrooms have been decorated with taste and charm, and enjoy beautiful views (those to the rear and West overlook the trees of Sydney gardens, one of Bath's oldest and loveliest parks). Breakfast is served in an elegant dining room and, although no evening meal is available at the hotel, there are numerous excellent restaurants in Bath and the walk to the city centre via the park and along Great Pulteney Street is an enjoyable five minutes' stroll. Car parking is available.
Open all year ex. Xmas & Jan. No smoking in the house. Children: over 4s only. Pets by arrangement. En suite, tea/coffee-making, T.V. & telephone in all bedrooms. Visa, Mastercard, Eurocard. B. & B. only from £32.50.

21 Newbridge Road, Bath, BA1 3HE   (0225) 314694
Attractive Victorian family house, with spacious rooms and views, 1m from Bath centre on the A4 road to Bristol. Healthy b'fast alternative on request.
Open Feb. to Nov. No smoking in the house. Vegetarian, vegan, dairy free and gluten free diets available. Children welcome. Tea/coffee-making available. TV lounge. B. & B. from £17.

BRISTOL

Arches Hotel, 132 Cotham Brow, Cotham, Bristol, BS6 6AE   (0272) 247398
Victorian house offering B. & B. within easy reach of Bristol centre. Healthy b'fast options.
Open all year, ex. Xmas. No smoking in the house. Vegetarian & other diets by arrangement. Children welcome. Pets by arrangement. Tea/coffee-making & TV in all bedrooms. Credit cards. B. & B. around £17.

Courtlands Hotel, 1 Redland Court Rd, Redland, Bristol, BS6 7EE (0272) 424432
Small, family-owned hotel overlooking tree-lined park just north of city centre.
Open all year. Separate area of dining room for smokers. Vegetarian & other diets by arrangement. Licensed. Children welcome. Most rooms en suite. TV, phone & tea/coffee-making in bedrooms. B. & B. from £27.

Moorledge Farm, Moorledge Lane, Chew Magna, Nr Bristol, BS18 8TL   (0272) 332383
Attractive 17th C. farmhouse in lovely rural setting.
Open Mar. to Oct. No smoking in the house. Vegetarian. Children welcome. B. & B. from £12.50.

Vicarage Lawns, Bristol Rd, West Harptree, Bristol, BS18 6HF (0761) 221668

Vicarage Lawns is is a comfortable country home which stands amidst an acre of lovely walled gardens in the pretty village of West Harptree at the foot of the Mendip Hills. Accommodation is in exceptionally well-appointed and tastefully decorated bedrooms (all with garden views), one of which has a spa bath and most of which have en suite facilities; a wholesome breakfast is offered to guests (evening meals can be provided by prior arrangement). The tranquil rural setting of Vicarage Lawns, with its proximity to Chew Valley Lake with its fishing, wildlife and lovely walks, makes it a perfect choice for a relaxing away-from-it-all break; additionally you will find yourself within easy reach of Bath, Bristol, Wells, Cheddar and Weston-Super-Mare.
Open all year. No smoking in the house. Vegetarian & other diets by arrangement. Children welcome. En suite in some rooms. Tea/coffee making & T.V. in bedrooms. T.V. in lounge. B. & B. from £13.50.

WESTON-SUPER-MARE
Moorlands Country Guest House, Hutton, BS24 9QH   (0934) 812283
Open Jan. to Nov. No smoking in dining room. Vegetarian & other diets by arrangement. Licensed. Disabled access. Children welcome. En suite, tea/coffee-making & T.V. in some bedrooms. Amex. B. & B. from £16.

Purn House Farm, Bleadon, Weston-super-Mare, BS24 0QE (0934) 812324

Purn House Farm is a 17th C. creeper-clad building which forms part of a 700 acre arable/dairy farm at the foot of Purn Hill, one of the western points of the Mendip Hills; it has been comfortbly furnished throughout in traditional style to complement the original features - such as the oak-panelled walls in the dining room and lounge - and there is a recreation room with table tennis, darts and other games. Good, home-cooking with plenty of home-produced vegetables and meat, is the order of the day in the Purn House dining room, and special diets can be accommodated by arrangement. In spite of its rural setting you are just 7 miles from J21 or 22 on the M5 from which, within an hour's drive, you may visit the Cheddar and Wookey Hole Caves, Wells Cathedral, the ruins of Glastonbury Abbey, and Bath; the nearest sandy beach is just 1½ miles away and riding, trekking, fishing, golf and sailing can all be enjoyed locally.

Open Mar. to Nov. No smoking in the house, ex. in public lounge. Vegetarian & other diets by arrangement. Wheelchair access. Children welcome. En suite, TV& tea/coffee-making in rooms. B. & B. from £15, D. £6.

Restaurants

BATH

Bath Sports and Leisure Centre, North Parade, Bath (0225) 63645
Open 9.30 - 7.30. L. around £5. No smoking in 50%. Vegetarian. Licensed. Disabled access. Children.

Canary, 3 Queen Street, Bath (0225) 424846
Open 9 - 7. D. around £7. 50% no smoking. Vegetarian. Licensed. Disabled access. Children. Access, Visa.

Circles Restaurant, Jollys, House of Fraser Ltd, Milsom Street, BA1 1DD (0225) 462811
Open Mon. to Sat. 9 - 5, plus late night Thurs. 100 no-smoking seats. Vegetarian. Licensed. Disabled access.

Clarets, 7a Kingsmead Square, Bath, BA1 2AB   (0225) 466688
Stylish restaurant with pleasing decor; offering a wide range of imaginatively prepared dishes.
Open Mon. to Sat. 12 - 2, 5.30 - 11. No smoking in 1 room. Vegetarian. Licensed. Children. Credit cards.

The Crown Inn, 2 Bathford Hill, Bathford, Bath, BA1 7SL (0272) 852297
Situated at the bottom of Bathford Hill, this charming pub is known to have been on this site since 1757. Excellent food: 'not a fast food restaurant', freshly prepared to order.
Serving food 12 - 2, 7 - 9.30. Smoking banned in Garden Room. Vegetarian standard. Disabled access 'easy', but no W.C facilities for wheelchair users. Children welcome. Pets by arrangement. Access, Visa, Amex.

Demuth's Restaurant & Coffee House, 2 North Parade Passage, Abbey Green. (0225) 446059
Vegetarian restaurant serving meals prepared from fresh, sometimes organic, ingredients.
Open Mon. to Sat. 9.30 - 6, Sun. 10 - 5. L. & D. around £5. No smoking throughout. Vegetarian. Licensed.

Hands Dining and Tearoom, 9 York Street, Bath, BA1 1NG (0225) 463928
Charming small restaurant situated in a Georgian House (with most of the Georgian features intact) serving a wide variety of freshly prepared meals throughout the day.
Open 9.30 - 5.30. L. from around £2.50. No smoking throughout. Vegetarian. Licensed. Disabled access.

Huckleberry's, 34 Broad Street, Bath (0225) 464876
Vegetarian and wholefood café/restaurant.
Open 9 - 4.30 (Fri. 9 - 9). Prices 'reasonable'. No smoking in 1 of 2 dining rooms. Licensed. Children.

Old Orleans, 1 St Andrews Terrace, Bartlett Street, Bath (0225) 333233
Open 11 - 11. D. from £10. 55% no smoking. Vegetarian. Licensed. Disabled access. Children welcome.

The Pump Rooms, Stall Street, Bath (0225) 444477/88
Smoking banned in 50% of restaurant. Vegetarian standard. Licensed. Children welcome.

Sally Lunn's House, 4 North Parade Passage, Bath, BA1 1NX (0225) 461634

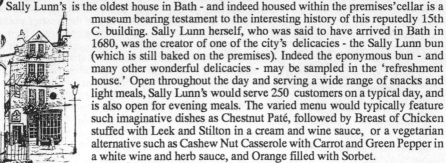

Sally Lunn's is the oldest house in Bath - and indeed housed within the premises' cellar is a museum bearing testament to the interesting history of this reputedly 15th C. building. Sally Lunn herself, who was said to have arrived in Bath in 1680, was the creator of one of the city's delicacies - the Sally Lunn bun (which is still baked on the premises). Indeed the eponymous bun - and many other wonderful delicacies - may be sampled in the 'refreshment house.' Open throughout the day and serving a wide range of snacks and light meals, Sally Lunn's would serve 250 customers on a typical day, and is also open for evening meals. The varied menu would typically feature such imaginative dishes as Chestnut Paté, followed by Breast of Chicken stuffed with Leek and Stilton in a cream and wine sauce, or a vegetarian alternative such as Cashew Nut Casserole with Carrot and Green Pepper in a white wine and herb sauce, and Orange filled with Sorbet.

60 seats. Open 10 - 6 for daytime menu, 6 - 10.30 for dinner menu. Closed Monday evenings. D. around £11. No smoking throughout. Vegetarian and vegan standard. Licensed. Children welcome. Credit cards for evening meals. Booking essential Sat. & Sun. evenings.

BRISTOL

Cherries, 122 St Michaels Hill, Bristol, BS2 8BU (0272) 293675
Open from 7, last orders 10.30. Prices D. from £7. 50% no smoking. Licensed. Disabled access.

China Palace Restaurant, 18A Baldwin Street, Bristol, BS1 1SE (0272) 262719
Open 12 - 2.30, 6 - 11.30. Separate area for smokers. Vegetarian. Licensed. Children welcome.

The Coffee Shop, John Lewis Partnership, The Horsefair, BS1 3LS (0272) 279100
Open 9 - 5, Mon. to Sat. No smoking. Vegetarian. Disabled access: lift available. Children.

Debenhams, 1-5 St James Barton, Bristol, BS99 7JX (0272) 291021
Intermission: friendly self-service family restaurant serving popular snacks & lunches.
Open store hours. No smoking. Vegetarian. Disabled access. Children very welcome. Credit & debit cards.

The Mendip Gate Guest House and Tea Room, Bristol Rd, Churchill (0934) 852333
No smoking. Vegetarian, diabetic & low-fat diets standard. Disabled access only to dining room.

Michael's, 129 Hotwell Road, Bristol (0272) 276190
Open 7 - 11. D. around £20. No smoking. Vegetarian standard. Licensed. Children welcome.

Millward's Vegetarian Restaurant, 40 Alfred Place, Kingsdown (0272) 245026
Small vegetarian restaurant offering creative imaginative food, winner of Vegetarian Restaurant of the Year 1990-91; good wine list including organic choices.
Tues. to Sat. 7 - 10.30 p.m. No smoking. Special diets on request. Licensed. Wheelchair access. Access, Visa.

WESTON-SUPER-MARE

The Corn Dolly Restaurant, 134 High St, Worle, Weston-Super- Mare (0934) 510041
Open 9 - 4. Main course around £3. No smoking throughout. Vegetarian. Children welcome.

Pubs & Wine Bars

BATH

The Crown Inn, 2 Bathford Hill, Bathford, Bath, BA1 7SL (0272) 852297
Smoking banned in Garden Room.

The Old Green Tree, Green St, Bath (0225) 448259
Smoking banned in part of pub. Vegetarian & gluten-free standard. Licensed. Disabled access.

Cornwall
Accommodation

BODMIN

Mount Pleasant Moorland Hotel, Mount Village, Nr Bodmin, Cornwall, PL30 4EX (0208) 82342

This peaceful country village hotel is hidden away in the heart of Cornwall amidst some of its most beautiful scenery in an area of Outstanding Natural Beauty surrounded by farmland and trees; parts of the hotel date from the 17th C. and some of the original building's character can still be seen in, for example, the beamed ceiling in the bar. The hotel has been comfortably furnished throughout: 6 of the 7 bedrooms have en suite facilities, and all have been decorated in a light, airy style. The food is the best of Cornish home-cooked fare - there are free-range eggs for breakfast from the hotel's own hens! - and guests may enjoy relaxing in the sun lounge (the sun set over unspoilt countryside is truly spectacular) or enjoy a drink in front of the Cornish stone fireplace in the bar. In spite of its secluded rural setting, Mount Pleasant is within an hour's drive of both the North and South Cornwall coasts (even Land's End is within a day's outing); those seeking a little gentle holiday activity closer to hand will find that golf, fishing, sailboarding, pony-trekking, swimming and tennis may all be enjoyed locally.

Open Easter to Sept. inc. No smoking in the dining room, bedrooms & lounge. Vegetarian & other diets by arrangement. Licensed. Children welcome. En suite, TV & tea/coffee-making in rooms. D., B. & B. from £25.

CRACKINGTON HAVEN

Crackington Manor, Crackington Haven, EX23 0JG (08403) 397/536

Peaceful hotel splendidly situated amongst the spectacular cliff scenery of Crackington Haven & the North Cornwall Coastal Path. Excellent food. Gym, sauna, solarium & pool.

Open all year. No smoking in the house. Vegetarian standard. Other diets by arrangement. Licensed. Disabled access. Children welcome. En suite & tea/coffee-making in bedrooms. T.V. lounge. B. & B. from £23, D. £10.

FALMOUTH

Bradgate Guest House, 4 Florence Place, Falmouth, TR11 3NJ (0326) 314108

Georgian town house in quiet residential street overlooking harbour and bay.

Open Mar. to Dec. No smoking in the house. Vegetarian & other diets by arrangement. Children welcome. Pets by arrangement. 1 room en suite. Tea/coffee-making in bedrooms. T.V. in lounge. B. & B. from £13.50.

Tresillian House Hotel, 3 Stracey Road, Falmouth, TR11 4DW (0326) 312425/311139

Tresillian House is a small, friendly, family run family-run hotel which is situated in a quiet road near the main sea front and close to the beach and coastal walks at Falmouth. The 12 comfortable, en suite bedrooms have each been tastefully decorated and furnished with a good range of amenities including colour TV, hair dryer, radio intercom and baby listening service. The cooking is excellent: traditional food is served in generous portions, in an attractive dining room with lovely garden views, and after-dinner coffee is served in the comfortable lounge. Falmouth is a perfect fishing town with one of the world's deepest natural harbours and, for those wanting to spend a day lazing on its lovely beaches, the proprietors will prepare picnic lunches on request.

Open Mar. to Oct. Smoking banned in dining room and in one lounge. Vegetarian, diabetic, gluten-free and low-fat diets by arrangement. Licensed. Children welcome. En suite, tea/coffee-making & T.V. in all bedrooms. Access, Visa. D., B. & B. from £24. ETB 3 Crowns Commended.

ISLES OF SCILLY

Covean Cottage Guest House, St Agnes, Isles of Scilly (0720) 22620

Charming family-run guest house overlooking the sea on the peaceful island of St Agnes.

Open Jan. to Nov. No smoking in dining room; separate cottage reserved for non-smokers. Vegetarian and other diets by arrangement. Not licensed (but bring your own). Disabled access: 1 ground floor bedroom. Children: over 12s only. En suite & TV in 3 bedrooms. Tea/coffee-making in bedrooms. L., B. & B. from £21.

Carnwethers Country Guesthouse, Pelistry Bay, St Marys, TR21 0NX (0720) 22415

Carnwethers Guest House, at one time the farmhouse for Pelistry farm, stands in an acre of lovely grounds (complete with croquet lawn and heated swimming pool) amidst the most natural and unspoilt part of St Mary's, high above beautiful and secluded Pelistry Bay. Carnwethers is situated away from the hustle and bustle of St Mary's - and as such enjoys the peace and tranquillity of the off islands - but the little town is close enough for guests to enjoy its many amenities. The original farmhouse has been tastefully modernised and extended over the years and now boasts eight very comfortable guest rooms - all with excellent facilities. There is also a very pleasant lounge which is divided into two parts - one for reading and for conversation, and the other housing a general library, including Scillonian subjects, (there is also a VCR with videos about the island). A traditional English Breakfast and 4-course dinner are offered - the latter accompanied by a selection of 60 or so modestly priced wines.

Open 1st Apr. to 15th Oct. Smoking banned in dining room, games room, TV lounge & public rooms. Licensed. Children: over 7s only. En suite, TV & tea/coffee-making in bedrooms. Half board from £32.

LOOE

⊗ Coombe Farm, Widegates, Nr Looe, Cornwall, PL13 1QN (05034) 223

Coombe Farm is a delightful 8-bedroomed country house which stands amidst 10 acres of lawns, meadows, woods, streams and ponds with magnificent views down an unspoilt wooded valley to the sea. The house itself has been carefully furnished with antiques, paintings and bric-a-brac, and in cooler weather there are open log fires in the dining room and lounge; each of the comfortable bedrooms has lovely country views. Meals are served in a candlelit dining room with views down the valley to the sea, and the food matches the setting: everything is home-cooked and a typical evening meal would feature home-made soup with crusty rolls, followed by honey roast duck with apple sauce and fresh seasonal vegetables, and a refreshing dessert such as fresh fruit salad and clotted cream; coffee or tea is served in the dining room or lounge. There are 3 acres of lawns in which guests can play croquet, lounge in the sun with a cool drink, or perhaps take a dip in the outdoor heated pool; additionally there is a snug, stone outhouse which has been converted to a games room with snooker, table tennis or a variety of board games.ETB 2 Crown Highly Commended.

Open Mar. to Oct. inc. No smoking in the house. Vegetarian & other diets by arrangement. Licensed. Wheelchair access to dining rom, lounge & 5 ground floor bedrooms. Children: over 5s only. Pets: guide dogs only. En suite, TV & tea/coffee-making in all bedrooms. B. & B. from £16.50 - 22.50. D. £10.50. Bargain breaks avail.

⊗ The Gulls, Hannafore, West Looe (0503) 262531

The Gulls is aptly named: it stands high up in a fabulous position directly opposite the main bathing beach with uninterrupted, panoramic views of East and West Looe, the harbour, river, sea and the spectacular Cornish coastline sweeping round to Rames Head. It is a small, family-run hotel - and as such offers friendly, personal service and has a warm, informal atmosphere: the care extends to the food, which is home-cooked from fresh local ingredients and served to you in a lovely dining room which, again, has panoramic sea views. The Gulls has many regular guest who return year after year - lured very probably by the prospect of being able to relax on the patio and the lounge and just watch the yachts and boats in the harbour and the changing moods of the river. They have chosen a lovely town in which to holiday: Looe has a fascinating history from 1154 - when it first appeared on records - through the smuggling era of 1760 and right up to the present day.

Open all year. No smoking in the hotel. Vegetarian & other diets by arrangement. Licensed. Children & pets welcome. En suite in some rooms. TV & tea/coffee-making in bedrooms. B. & B. from £19.50.

MARAZION

Ⓝ **Castle Gayer, Leys Lane, Marazion, TR17 0AQ (0736) 711548**

Impressive Victorian house, built on a peninsula & with spectacular views of St Michael's Mount & the rugged coastline as far as Lizard Point. Bedrooms have superb views of the Cornish coast.

Open all year. No smoking in the house. Vegetarian & other diets by arrangement. Not licensed, but ice and lemon provided for drinks on request. En suite , TV & tea/coffee-making in all bedrooms. B. & B. from £22.50.

Ⓝ **Old Eastcliffe House, Eastcliff Lane, Marazion, TR17 OAZ (0736) 710298**

Originally built for the wealthy mine owning Michell family, this fine old Georgian residence stands in a charming walled garden which slopes gently to the sea, and enjoys a most dramatic and uninterrupted view of St Michael's Mount. Beautifully decorated and with lots of character (brass beds, log fires, interesting antiques...) it is the place to come if you're in search of peace; it is also the place to come if you are looking for a good breakfast: your generous hosts, the Haverys, offer a splendid morning meal with lots of choices, including home-baked ham with Oxford Sauce (a house speciality) and smoked haddock with poached egg, as well as the usual traditional Great British Breakfast options.

Open Easter to end Sept. No smoking in dining room and in bedrooms. Vegetarian & other diets by arrangement. Children welcome. En suite in some rooms. Tea/coffee-making in bedrooms. T.V. in lounge. B. & B. from £17.

NEWQUAY

Ⓝ **Sheldon, The Haven for Non-Smokers, 198 Henver Road, TR7 3EH (0637) 874552**

Small, friendly guest house. Emphasis on the use of fresh ingredients: bread, rolls and pastries baked fresh each day; home-made marmalade.

Open June to Aug. inc. No smoking in the house. Children: over 10s only. T.V. lounge. B. & B. from £100 p.w.

PADSTOW

Ⓝ **Trevone Bay Hotel, Trevone, Padstow, PL28 8QS (0841) 520243**

The Trevone Bay Hotel is a small, friendly family-run hotel which stands overlooking the beach just 2 miles from the picturesque fishing port of Padstow, enjoying panoramic views of the beautiful coastline from the sandy beach of Trevone Bay across to Trevose Head. Under the personal supervision of Sue and Andrew Hamilton since 1985, the hotel has a friendly relaxed atmosphere and recently received a Commended status from the English Tourist Board. All 13 en suite bedrooms are comfortably furnished and the family rooms are generously proportioned; cots and highchairs can be provided for younger guests. The food is excellent: everything is home-baked by Sue - including the bread rolls - and fresh local produce and home-grown vegetables are used wherever possible; there is a reasonably priced wine list and a cosy bar open each lunch time and evening. There is everything you could possibly want for a relaxed family holiday at the Trevone, including a large, pleasant garden overlooking the bay and three separate lounges - one with TV - so children can play without disturbing other guests.

Open Easter - Oct. No smoking throughout. Vegetarian & other diets by arrangement. Licensed. Children & pets welcome. En suite & tea/coffee-making in bedrooms. TV in lounge. D. B. & B. from £145 per week.

PENRYN

Prospect House, 1 Church Rd, Penryn, TR10 8DA (0326) 373198

Built as a 'gentleman's residence'around 1830 & standing within pretty walled rose garden, on the edge of Penryn. Elegant surroundings & excellent food.

Open Jan. to Dec. No smoking in dining room. Vegetarian diets by arrangement. Children: over 12s only. Pets by arrangement. En suite in most rooms. Tea/coffee making. T.V. on request. B. & B. from £22.

PENZANCE

 Penalva Guest House, Alexandra Road, Penzance (0736) 69060

Small, private hotel in pleasant tree-lined avenue.

Open all year; no evening meals Jul. & Aug. No smoking in the house. Vegetarian & other diets by arrangement. Children welcome. En suite in 5 rooms. Colour TV & tea/coffee-making in bedrooms. B. & B. from £11. D. £8.

PERRANPORTH

 Beach Dunes Hotel, Ramoth Way, Reen Sands, Perranporth, TR6 0BY (0872) 573824

Beach Dune Hotel is a small, friendly, family-run establishment which, as its name suggests, is situated in sand dunes with panoramic views of the sea, beach and beautiful surrounding countryside. The hotel has been comfortably furnished and a wide variety of well-equipped en suite bedrooms are available - some on the ground floor; additionally there is a hotel annexe with 3 purpose-built holiday suites - each with their own entrance - which are suitable for holidaying families or honeymooners. The hotel has several other excellent leisure amenities for guests - including an indoor swimming pool and squash court - and it has the further advantage of adjoining an 18-hole golf course (there is a 30% fee reduction for guests staying at the hotel).The food is good - and reasonably priced - and there is a well-stocked residents'bar. With its easy access to the 3 miles of Perrans sandy beach and the hotel's own spacious lawns and patios, the Beach Dunes Hotel is an ideal holiday base, and is an excellent centre for touring. Private parking.

Open Easter - Oct. No smoking in dining room. Vegetarian & other diets by arrangement. Licensed. Ground floor rooms. Children: over 4s only. En suite, TV, D.D. phone & tea/coffee-making in bedrooms. Access, Visa. B. & B. from £25.50, D. B. & B. from £31.43.

PORTSCATHO

Roseland House Hotel, Rosevine, Nr Portscatho, TR2 5EW (0872580) 644 Fax: (0872580) 801

18 bedroom hotel set in 6 acres of National Trust and Heritage Coast; wonderful sea views.

Open all year. No smoking in dining room. Vegetarian & other diets by arrangement. Licensed. Some rooms disabled access. Children. En suite, tea/coffee-making & T.V. in rooms. Credit cards. D., B. & B. from £36.50.

REDRUTH

Sycamore Lodge Guest House, Primrose Terrace, Portreath, TR16 4JS (0209) 842784

Delightful old house in quiet situation. Ideal for walking, touring and golfing. Good food & courteous service from Pam & Roger Pattinson.

Open all year. No smoking in the house. Children: over 7s only. Tea/coffee-making. TV lounge. B. & B. £15-16.

ST BLAZEY

 Nanscawen House, Prideaux Road, St Blazey, Nr Par, PL24 2SR (0726) 814488

Nanscawen House was, until 1520, the home of the Nanscawen family and it stands in five acres of beautiful grounds and gardens which include an outdoor heated swimming pool and whirlpool spa. Surrounded by beautiful mature trees, it is approached by a private drive and its splendid southerly aspect gives indication of the many wonderful walks which are to be enjoyed through the nearby quiet country lanes and the Luxulyan Valley. The house itself has been beautifully furnished and appointed: each of the spacious guest bedrooms has its own en suite bathroom with spa bath and enjoys lovely views of the surrounding grounds or gardens. The food is excellent: all meals have been home-prepared from fresh ingredients (many culled from the extensive garden), and the dishes, which vary from season to season, reflect a menu which has

endeavoured to revive some old-fashioned and often-forgotten recipes, as well as to introduce some new ideas. Prices include afternoon tea!
Open all year ex. Xmas. No smoking in the house. Vegetarian by arrangement. Residential license. Children: over 12s only. No pets. En suite, TV & tea/coffee-making in all bedrooms. Access, Visa. B. & B. from £27.50.

ST COLUMB

 Brentons Farm, Goss Moor, St Columb, TR9 6WR (0726) 860632
Small farm close to the A30; free-range eggs, home-baked rolls.
Open Feb. to end Nov. No smoking in the house. Vegetarian & other diets by arrangement. Children welcome. Tea/coffee on request. T.V. B. & B. from £12.

ST IVES

 Boswednack Manor, Zennor, St Ives, TR26 3DD (0736) 794183
Open all year. No smoking in the house. Vegetarian. Vegan by arrangement. Children welcome. 2 en suite rooms. Tea/Coffee-making in bedrooms. B. & B. from £13.50, D. £6.

 Craigmeor, Beach Road, St Ives, TR26 1JY (0736) 796611
Small, friendly guest house with uninterrupted views over lovely Porthmeor Beach.
Open Mar. to Oct. No smoking in the house. Vegetarian & other diets by arrangement. Children welcome. Pets by arrangement. Tea/Coffee-making in bedrooms. T.V. in lounge. B. & B. from £14.

Woodcote Vegetarian Hotel, The Saltings, Lelant (0736) 753147
Open Mar. - Oct. No smoking in dining room, bedrooms & lounge. Vegetarian. D. B. & B. from £22.

ST NEWLYN EAST

 Trewerry Mill, Trerice, St Newlyn East, TR8 5HS (0872) 510345
Open Easter to Oct. inc. No smoking in the house. Vegetarian & other diets by arrangement. Licensed. Children: over 7s only. T.V. in lounge. B. & B. from £13.75.

TORPOINT

 The Copse, St Winnolls, Polbathic, Torpoint, PL11 3DX (0503) 30205
The Copse is an attractive farmhouse forming part of a mixed farm in the rural hamlet of St

Winnolls between Polbathic and Downderry. Although the house is in a quiet situation, you are conveniently situated just a mile from the A374 and 2 miles from the beaches of Portwrinkle and Downderry. The guest rooms are pleasantly furnished - each has a hand-washbasin as well as tea and coffee-making facilites - and there is a comfortable lounge with TV for guests'use; two en suite rooms are also available. A full English Breakfast is served - which features delicious home-produced milk - and your hosts can recommend good local places to eat in the evening. The Copse is an ideal base for touring Cornwall and South Devon and the Whitsand Bay Golf Course is just 2 miles away.
Open Mar. to Sept. No smoking in the house. Children: over 10s only. En suite in some rooms. Tea/coffee-making & T.V. in all bedrooms. B. & B. from £15.

TRURO

Marcorrie Hotel, 20 Falmouth Rd, Truro (0872) 77374
Privately owned, family-run Victorian hotel pleasantly situated in a conservation area just a few minutes'walk from Truro town centre. Ideal base for touring Cornwall. Car parking.
Open all year. No smoking in dining room & some bedrooms. Vegetarian & other diets by arrangement. Children & pets welcome. Licensed. En suite, tea/coffee-making & TV in all bedrooms. Credit cards. B. & B. from £19.

 Polsue Cottage, Ruan High Lanes, Truro, TR2 5LU (0872) 501596
Open all year. No smoking in the house. Vegetarian standard (fish may be served on request). Low-fat, vegan and diabetic by arrangement. Children welcome.Tea/coffee-making. B. & B. from £11. E.M. £7.

Restaurants

LAUNCESTON

Ⓝ The Greenhouse Vegetarian Wholefood Restaurant, Madford Ln. (0566) 773670
    Pleasant, airy, self-service restaurant serving wholefood/vegetarian dishes prepared from some organically home-grown ingredients. 1989/90 Heartbeat Award winner, North Cornwall.
46 seats. Open 10 - 4, Mon. to Sat. L. from £2. No smoking throughout. Exclusively vegetarian, with vegan and diabetic meat-free meals on request. Licensed. Disabled access: 'one front step.' Children welcome.

LISKEARD

Aze Bistro, Lower Lux St (0579) 42345
Open 11.30 - 2.30, 7 - 9.30. L. around £3.50, D. £15. 50% no smoking.

PENZANCE

Enzo Restaurant, Newbridge, Penzance TR20 8QU
Open 7 - 9.30. D. from £10. Separate room for smokers. Vegetarian. Licensed. Disabled access. Children.

The Olive Branch Restaurant, 3a The Terrace, Market Jew St, Penzance (0736) 62438
Open Summer: 10.30 - 2.30, 6 - 9 (hrs. reduced in winter). No smoking in separate dining room.

Pizza World, 96 Market Jew Street, Penzance (0736) 60678
Open 10 - 11. L. from £3.50. Separate smoke-free section. Vegetarian. Licensed. Children welcome.

POLPERRO

Ⓝ The Old Barkhouse Coffee Shop and Eating House, The Quay, (0503) 72085
Open 8am - 10pm (summer), shorter hours in winter. No smoking throughout.

PORTH LEVEN

Critchard's Seafood Restaurant, Harbour Head, Porth Leven (0326) 562407
Open 12 - 2.30, 7 - 9.30. Separate area for non smokers. Vegetarian. Licensed. Disabled access.

ST AUSTELL

The Thin End, 41a Fore Street, St. Austell (0726) 75805
Open 9 - 5, Mon. to Sat. Smoking banned in 60% of restaurant. Vegetarian standard. Licensed.

Pubs & Wine Bars

PENDOGGETT

The Cornish Arms, Pendoggett, Port Isaac, PL30 3HH (0208) 880263
The Cornish Arms is a delightful 16th C. coaching inn which is beautifully situated one mile inland

from the historic fishing village of Port Isaac on the North Cornish Coast. Accommodation is in comfortable, spacious bedrooms, and delicious freshly prepared meals are served in both the bar and the inn's excellent restaurant. With its proximity to Port Isaac, it is not surprising that fish features highly on both menus: you might be tempted by an appetiser such as whole unshelled Tiger Prawns in garlic butter followed by a main course such as Lobster Thermidore or Sole Grand Duc; a wide range of snacks are available for lighter appetites or those saving themselves for the wonderful desserts with thick Cornish clotted cream.
Open all year. Smoking banned in 50% of restaurant, the front bar and some bedrooms. Vegetarian standard, other special diets on request. Licensed. Wheelchair access. Children welcome. Pets welcome. En suite. Tea/coffee-making, phone, Satellite and T.V. in all bedrooms.

SCORRIER

Fox & Hounds, Scorrier, Nr Redruth, TR16 5BS (0209) 820205
Smoking banned in small lounge extension. Vegetarian standard. Children: over 14s only.

Devon
Accommodation

ASHBURTON

Cuddyford, Rew Rd, Ashburton, TQ13 7EN (0364) 53325

Open all year ex. Xmas. No smoking in the house. Vegetarian, vegan, gluten-free & macrobiotic diets standard. Children welcome. Pets by arrangement. Tea/coffee-making. T.V. by arrangement. B. & B. from £12. D. £7.

Middle Leat, Holne, Ashburton, TQ13 7SJ (03643) 413

Open all year. No smoking in the house. Vegetarian standard. Disabled access. Children welcome. Pets by arrangement. En suite in some rooms. Tea/coffee-making & T.V. in all bedrooms. B. & B. from £13-£16.

The Old Coffee House, 27-29 West Street, Ashburton, Devon, TQ13 7DT (0364) 52539

Beautifully situated next to the 15th C. church of St Andrews in the ancient stannary town of Ashburton, this charming 16th century Grade II listed building offers most comfortable accommodation to guests, including a guests' lounge. Ashburton, on the southern edge of Dartmoor National Park, is a perfect place from which to explore both the coastal resorts of Torbay and Torquay as well as the charms of Exeter and the unspoilt beauty of Dartmoor. Guests will be likewise pleased to discover that the Old Coffee House is open throughout the day as a restaurant serving delicious teas and snacks, in the cooking of which fresh local produce (including vegetables) have been used wherever possible.

Open all year. Smoking banned throughout. Vegetarian by arrangement. Tea/coffee-making & T.V. in all bedrooms. B. & B. from £12.50

BARNSTAPLE

Norwood Farm, Hiscott, Barnstaple (0271) 858260

Lovely old farmhouse dating back to early 17th C. Individually styled rooms with welcoming bottle of sherry & luxurious little extras. Imaginative, home-cooked dinners.

Open all year. No smoking in the house. Vegetarian. En suite, TV & tea/coffee-making in rooms. B. & B. £22.

BIGBURY-ON-SEA

Henley Hotel, Folly Hill, Bigbury-On-Sea, TQ7 4AR (0548) 810240/810331

Edwardian cottage style hotel with superb sea views; private steps through garden to excellent beach. Good walking and golf nearby; close to Dartmoor.

Open all year. No smoking in the house. Vegetarian & diabetic standard. Other diets by arrangement. Licensed. Children & pets welcome. En suite, TV, phone & tea-making in bedrooms. Credit cards. B. & B. from £20.

BOVEY TRACEY

Willmead Farm, Bovey Tracey, Nr Newton Abbot, TQ13 9NP (06477) 214

Superb 15th C. thatched farmhouse with minstrel gallery, in 32 acres of fields, woodland & streams. Guaranteed peace. Excellent home-made fare including preserves & bread.

Open all year ex. Xmas and New Year. No smoking in the house. Vegetarian & other diets by arrangement. Children: over 10s only. 1 room en suite. Beverage-making on request. T.V. in drawing room. B. & B. from £19.

BRIXHAM

Woodlands Guest House, Parkham Rd, Brixham, TQ5 9BU (0803) 852040

Victorian house on a quiet hill-road, facing east & with magnificent views of Brixham town and its famous harbour. Cold drinks fridge on the first floor landing. B. & B. only.

Open April to Oct. No smoking in the house. Vegetarian & other diets by arrangement - breakfast only. Children welcome. En suite, TV & tea/coffee making in all rooms. Credit cards. B. & B. from £17.50-£18.50.

CHAGFORD

 Helpful Holidays, Chagford, Devon, TQ13 8DF Ref 222/6 Tel: (0647) 433593 Fax: (0647) 433694
Self-catering: modern one-level apartment in moorland village within Dartmoor National Park. 3 bedrooms. Sleeps 5. Plymouth 8 miles. Non-smokers only. ETB 4 key Commended.
Open April - Nov. inc. No smoking in the house. Children welcome. Credit cards. Per week £164 - 328.

 St Johns West, Murchington, Chagford, TQ13 8HJ (0647) 432468
St Johns is a fine 19th C. granite-built house which stands against Dartmoor, some 800 feet above sea-level, overlooking the beautiful Teign Valley; there are beautiful views from the house, which has an acre of lovely gardens (numerous varieties of birds may be spotted therein) and the countryside is excellent for rambling. Accommodation is in one of two very comfortable guest rooms - (one room has an annexe for children's accommodation), and the excellent breakfast, which is prepared on the kitchen Aga, features bacon, sausage, home-made bread and free-range eggs.

Although there are lots of restaurants nearby, your hostess will be happy to cook an evening meal for you from a small selection if you let her know at breakfast.
Open all year. No smoking in the house. Special diets catered for. Children welcome. Pets by arrangement. 1 en suite room. Tea/coffee making in all rooms. B. & B. from £14-£18.

CULLOMPTON

Tredown Farm, Clayhidon, Cullompton, EX15 3TW (0823) 662421
Comfortable modern bungalow on working dairy farm high on the Blackdown Hills. To find Tredown Farm, leave the M5 at junction 26 and proceed towards Wellington, then follow the signs to Ford Street. At the top of the hill turn left, then after 300 yards, turn right.Dinner by arrangement.
Open all year ex. Xmas. No smoking in dining room & lounge. Vegetarian by arrangement. Disabled access. Children welcome. Tea/coffee-making. T.V. in lounge & 1 bedroom. B. & B. from £12.50-£15. D. £7.50.

DARTMOOR

Two Bridges Hotel, Two Bridges, Dartmoor, PL20 6SW (0822) 89581
This 18th century posting inn, set in the heart of Dartmoor some 1,000 feet above sea-level, is situated near to the junction of the two main roads over the moor and has boundless views on each side of the unspoilt beauty of this lovely National Park. In the heart of a beautiful wilderness it is therefore reassuring to discover that the atmosphere at Two Bridges is *cosy*: log fires warm footsore travellers in the beautifully furnished lounge and bar, and good home-cooked food accompanied by sensibly priced wines is the order of the day at the carvery or in the dining room (cream teas are also served daily). With some 60 acres of hotel grounds alone, holiday-makers could walk for days

within the vicinity of Two Bridges and not retrace a single path - but the proprietors organise guided National Park walks and there is riding and fishing to be enjoyed nearby (the West Dart River flows through the grounds).
Open all year. No smoking in dining room, lounge & most bedrooms. Vegetarian standard. Other diets by arrangement. Licensed. Disabled access. Children. Pets by arrangement. En suite most rooms. Tea/coffee-making & T.V. (plus satellite) in bedrooms. B. & B. from £24.50 (2-day breaks from £62.50 for D.B. & B.).

EXETER

Claremont, 36 Wonford Rd, Exeter, EX2 4LD (0392) 74699
Regency style town house in quiet part of Georgian Exeter, offering accommodation of a very high standard. Special diets catered for with advance notice.
Open all year. No smoking in the house. Vegetarian & other diets by arrangement. Children: over 5s welcome. En suite, TV & tea/coffee-making in bedrooms. B. & B. £16-22 per person per night.

Clock Tower Hotel, 16 New North Rd, Exeter, Devon, EX4 4HF (0392) 52493
Open all year. No smoking in dining room, lounge & all communal areas. Vegetarian by arrangement. Licensed. Children welcome. Pets by arrangement. En suite, tea/coffee making, T.V. & phone in rooms. B. & B. from £12.

Down House, Whimple, Exeter, EX5 2QR (0404) 822860
Elegant Edwardian gentleman's country house in 5 acres of gardens and paddocks situated amidst the quiet farmland of East Devon. Country-house-party style hospitality.
Open Apr. to Sept. No smoking in all public areas. Vegetarian & other diets by arrangement. Disabled access, & 1 ground floor ensuite room. Children. En suite, TV & tea/coffee-making in rooms. B. & B. from £15.

Fairwinds Hotel, Kennford, Nr Exeter, EX6 7UD (0392) 832911
Fairwinds Hotel is an attractive, small, modern hotel situated on the edge of the typical Devon village of Kennford just 1 mile from the end of the M5. The hotel has 8 well-appointed bedrooms - each with private facilities - and the 5 ground floor rooms make the hotel an ideal choice for those who find it difficult to get about. The menu features a wide variety of home-made dishes, and a typical evening menu selection might be Prawn Cocktail followed by Country Pork Casserole (served with fresh vegetables) and a choice of tempting home-made desserts; tea or coffee would complete the meal. The Fairwinds Hotel is conveniently situated just 4 miles from the centre of Exeter and a short drive from a variety of attractive coastal resorts, while a pleasant walk from the hotel will take you to the pretty village of Kenn, with its thatched cottages and Saxon parish church.
Open all year. No smoking in dining room, bar & some bedrooms. Special diets by arrangement. Licensed. Children welcome. En suite most rooms. Tea/coffee-making & T.V. in rooms. Access, Visa. D. B. & B. from £32.

St Davids Lodge, 65 St Davids Hill, Exeter, EX4 4DW (0392) 51613
Open all year. No smoking in most of house. Vegetarian & other diets by arrangement. Children welcome. En suite in one room. Tea/coffee-making in lounge. T.V. in lounge. B. & B. from £11.

Whitemoor Farm, Doddiscombsleigh, Nr Exeter, EX6 7PU (0647) 52423

Whitemoor Farm is an attractive 16th C. listed thatched farmhouse, with exposed beams, oak doors and staircase, set in the seclusion of its own mature garden and farmland within easy reach of Exeter, Dartmoor, the South Devon coast, Haldon Racecourse and many forestry walks. The farmhouse is warm and comfortable, with central heating and double glazing, and log fires in winter. Breakfast is a generous feast which includes home-made preserves and cordials; evening meals are available by arrangement and are also available at a nearby inn whose culinary reputation is locally acclaimed. The area is excellent for birdwatching and there is a golf course within easy reach.
Open all year. No smoking in the house.Vegetarian standard. Children & pets welcome. Tea/coffee-making in bedrooms. T.V. in guests'lounge. B. & B. from £14. D. £7.50.

EXMOUTH

Stevenstone House, Stevenstone Rd, Exmouth. Tel: (0395) 266106 Fax: (0395) 276816

Stevenstone House is a large, attractive Edwardian house standing in its own grounds in the elegant area of Exmouth which is known as The Avenues. The house has been comfortably furnished throughout - each of the spacious bedrooms has en suite facilities - and your hosts, Joe Ashford and Nicky Soden, place a great emphasis on friendly, informal, but *efficient* service: thus breakfast and evening meals are served at a time of your choosing (everything is home-cooked, incidentally, from fresh, local produce and home-grown herbs), and guests are invited to bring their own wine (no charge for corkage - and there is an aperitif on the house before dinner!). Exmouth is an understandably popular resort - with its vast sandy beaches and numerous leisure activities, such as sailing, wind-surfing, riding and golf - while those seeking to escape to unspoilt countryside will find themselves within easy reach of both Dartmoor and Exmoor.

Open all year. No smoking in the house. Vegetarian & other diets by arrangement. Not licensed, but bring your own. Children welcome (ex. babies). En suite, TV & tea/coffee-making in rooms. B. & B. from £17.50 D. £12.50.

HONITON

The Belfry Country Hotel, Yarcombe, Nr Honiton, EX14 9BD Tel: (0404) 86 234 Fax: 86579

Originally the village school serving Yarcombe and outlying towns, The Belfry was constructed in 1872 from local dressed flint and Portland stone in typical West country style; the foundation stone was laid by a descendant of Sir Francis Drake - indeed the original school was a gift from the Drakes to the village - but it has been a hotel since 1963, having been upgraded to its current high standards by the present owners, Jackie and Tony Rees. With only 6 bedrooms, their policy of offering country house hospitality has been easy to maintain and there is a relaxed, friendly atmosphere: each of the guest bedrooms has been stylishly decorated and has en suite facilities, and there is also a cosy bar and lounge. Meals are prepared from fresh local produce and varied menu options - including vegetarian - are prepared by an imaginative and competent chef.

Open all year ex. 2 weeks Feb. No smoking in restaurant/bar & discouraged in bedrooms. Vegetarian & other diets by arrangement. Licensed. Wheelchair access. Children; over 12s only. En suite, TV, phones, radio alarms, hairdryers & tea/coffee-making in rooms. Credit cards. B. & B. from £29.50. D., B. & B. from £45.50.

ILFRACOMBE

Strathmore Private Hotel, 57 St Brannock's Road, Ilfracombe, EX34 8EQ (0271) 862248

Pleasantly appointed guest house in the centre of town with easy access seafront & countryside.

Open all year. No smoking in dining room, lounge & bedrooms. Vegetarian & other diets by arrangement. Licensed. En suite most rooms. Tea/coffee-making & colour T.V. in bedrooms. Credit cards. B. & B. from £14.

Trimstone Manor Hotel, Trimstone, Ilfracombe, EX34 8NR

Old country manor standing in 55 acres with full range of indoor and outdoor leisure activities including swimming pool, sauna, spa pool, gym, steam room, putting, tennis and boating.

Open Feb. to Dec. inc. No smoking in the house. Vegetarian and some other speical diets by arrangement. Children welcome. En suite, tea and coffee making & T.V. in all bedrooms.

Two Ways, St Brannocks Rd, Ilfracombe, EX34 8EP (0271) 864017

Two Ways is a lovely, large Victorian house situated 100 yards from Bicclescombe Park on the main A361 Barnstaple Ilfracombe Road. It has been very comfortably furnished and appointed and there is an emphasis on 'good old-fashioned service' - with every modern comfort. Two Ways offers bed and breakfast and an optional evening meal: this is an excellent 4-course dinner in which a typical menu would feature Devilled Mushrooms followed by Coq au Vin with fresh vegetables, and a refreshing dessert such as fresh fruit salad and cream; coffee and mints would complete the meal. You are just 10 minutes walk from both the shop and seafront at Two Ways and your hosts will happily collect you from the station if you do not wish to bring your car.

Open all year ex. Xmas. No smoking in the house. Some special diets on request. Licensed. Children welcome. En suite in 3 rooms. Tea/coffee-making in bedrooms. T.V. in lounge & some bedrooms. B. & B. from £12.

KINGSBRIDGE

Helliers Farm, Ashford, Aveton Gifford, Kingsbridge, TQ7 4ND (0548) 550689

Dating from 1749, this small working sheep farm is set on a hillside in the heart of Devon's unspoiled South Hams countryside. Recently modernised, the farm has been converted to a most comfortable family guest house whose accommodation includes, in addition to four pleasantly furnished bedrooms, a spacious dining room, a comfortable lounge and a games room. Outside a charming little paved courtyard leads onto a water garden and, a little further down the hill, an extensive trout pool. Evening meals are not usually available but your hosts will be happy to advise you of good local eateries. The area is excellent for walking - and a number of National Trust walks begin nearby. ETB 2 Crowns.

Open all year. No smoking in the house. Children. Tea/coffee-making. T.V. lounge. B. & B. £14.50.

Burton Farm, Galmpton, Kingsbridge, TQ7 3EY (0548) 561210

Open all year ex. Xmas and New Year. No smoking in the house. Vegetarian & other diets by arrangement. Licensed. Children welcome. Some rooms en suite . Tea/coffee-making in rooms. T.V. B. & B. from £14.

Old Walls, Slapton, Kingsbridge, TQ7 2QN (0548) 580516

South-facing Georgian house with lovely gardens in the centre of Slapton village.

Open all year. No smoking in dining room, bedrooms & sitting room. Vegetarian & other diets by arrangement. Children welcome. Pets by arrangement. Tea/coffee-making. T.V. in lounge. B. & B. from £13.50. D. £7.

Start House, Start, Slapton, Nr Kingsbridge, TQ7 2QD (0548) 580254

Open all year ex. Xmas. No smoking in the house. Vegetarian & other diets by arrangement. Bring your own wine. Children welcome. Some en suite. Tea/coffee-making. T.V. sitting room. B. & B. from £15. D. £9.

LAPFORD

Nymet Bridge Country House, Lapford, EX17 6QX (0363) 83334

Peaceful 14th C. country house, surrounded by beautiful gardens, in 'Tarka Country'where abundant wildlife delights nature lovers. Charming guest lounge with inglenook; home-cooked meals using local produce served in licensed dining room.

Open all year ex. Xmas. No smoking throughout. Vegetarian on request. Licensed. All bedrooms en suite. Regret no children or pets. B. & B. from £15, with 10% discount for stays of 2 nights or more, D. opt. £7.

LYDFORD

Moor View Hotel, Vale Down, Lydford, Devon, EX20 4BB Tel: (082) 282220

Moor View was originally a farmhouse built in 1869 and it was not until the early 1980s that it

became a small hotel and restaurant; it has been very comfortably appointed - there are open fires in cooler weather - and the drawing room, bar and guest rooms have each been furnished with Victorian family pieces. The house enjoys Dartmoor as its garden to the front and magnificent views for some 30 miles of Devonshire countryside and into Cornwall at its rear; there are spectacular views of the setting sun each evening. The hotel is run by the Sharples family who do everything they can to make your stay a happy and memorable one, including providing excellent home-cooked English food, a typical 6-course evening meal featuring home-made soup followed by plaice stuffed with spinach, a choice of main dishes such as braised steak with mustard sauce, and a selection of desserts; cheese, biscuits and coffee would complete the meal.

Open all year. No smoking throughout except in bar. Vegetarian & other diets by arrangement. Licensed. Pets welcome. En suite, tea/coffee-making & T.V. in all bedrooms. Credit cards. B. & B. from £31.

LYNTON

Alford House Hotel, 3 Alford Terrace, Lynton, EX35 6AT (0598) 52359

Alford House is an elegant, Georgian-style hotel nestling on the slopes of Sinai Hill which has spectacular views out over Lynton town and the beautiful Exmoor coast. Built around 1840, the hotel has been carefully restored and refurbished and retains the charm and peaceful ambience of its original period without forsaking modern comforts and conveniences (the bedrooms - some with mahogany 4-poster beds - all have en suite facilities and have each been well-equipped with a range of amenities including colour TV and tea/coffee-making facilities). Your hosts, June and David Ronson, offer good, old-fashioned hospitality and imaginative home-cooking: fresh, local produce is used wherever possible - including

Devon lamb and Exmoor trout - and meals are served in a lovely dining room with garden views. Lynton is a charming town with much to commend it (including the unique carriage lift to its sister town, Lynmouth, and its harbour); it stands on the North Devon Coastal path from which it is possible to walk to Watersmeet, the Valley of the Rocks or Lee Bay. ETB 3 Crowns. RAC Acclaimed.

Open all year. No smoking in dining room & bedrooms. Vegetarian & other diets by arrangement. Licensed. Children: over 9s only. En suite in 7 rooms. TV & tea/coffee-making in rooms. Credit cards. D., B. & B. £30-35.

Longmead House Hotel, 9 Longmead, Lynton, EX35 6DQ (0598) 52523

This pleasant hotel is quietly situated amongst lovely level gardens near the Valley of the Rocks and is overlooked by the wooded Hollerday Hill. Accommodation is in comfortable and attractively decorated bedrooms. The evening menu is imaginative, with all home-cooked dishes prepared from fresh produce whenever possible. Dinner is served in an oak-panelled dining room with a majestic fireplace. Lynton is perched 500 feet above the Bristol Channel and is a perfect centre for exploring the natural beauties of Exmoor National Park. Not to be missed is the famous Victorian Cliff Railway to Lynmouth and the beautiful walks along the East Lynn River. Parking is available.

Open Mar. to Nov. No smoking in the house. Vegetarian, diabetic & coeliac diets by arrangement. Licensed. Children welcome. Pets by arrangement. En suite 4 rooms. Tea/coffee in rooms. T.V. lounge. B. & B. from £15.

Sylvia House Hotel, Lydiate Lane, Lynton, EX35 6HE (0598) 52391

This delightful little Georgian hotel, set in the midst of England's romantic little Switzerland, combines elegance and old fashioned hospitality - at moderate terms. The hotel is exceptionally pretty with drapes, cameos and beautiful pictures. The bedrooms - some of which have four-posters - are individually named, are mostly en suite and each has a colour TV, and beverage-making facilities. The food is exceptionally scrumptious and has been prepared from fresh ingredients which have been bought daily.

Open all year. Smoking banned in all public rooms and most bedrooms. Vegetarian and most other special diets by arrangement. Licensed. Children welcome. Pets by arrangement. En suite in most rooms. Tea/coffee-making & T.V. in all bedrooms. B. & B. from £14.

Waterloo House, Lydiate Lane, Lynton (0598) 53391

The Waterloo House Hotel is a delightful Georgian building, one of the oldest lodging houses in Lynton, in which are combined the spirit of the 19th century with all the comforts of modern day life; there are two comfortable lounges, one of which is reserved for non-smokers. Accommodation is in spacious bedrooms which have been furnished to a high standard (most have en suite facilities). Imaginative 4-course meals are served by candlelight in an elegant dining room, a typical evening meal featuring Fish Paté followed by Poultry cooked in Cider with dried fruits (with fresh vegetables), and a tempting dessert such as Rhubarb and Ginger Crumble; everything has been prepared from fresh produce. Vegetarians are most welcome and

can be accommodated by arrangement. Quietly situated in the heart of 'old' Lynton, Waterloo House is a perfect base from which to enjoy the variety of pursuits which the area offers.

Open all year. No smoking in dining room, some bedrooms & 1 lounge. Vegetarian by arrangement. Well-behaved children welcome. En suite most bedrooms. Tea/coffee making & T.V. in bedrooms. B. & B. from £16.50. ETB 3 Crowns Commended. AA Selected Award for high standards of cooking, comfort & hospitality.

MORETONHAMPSTEAD

White Hart Hotel, The Square, Moretonhampstead, TQ13 8NF (0647) 40406

Open all year ex. Xmas. No smoking in dining room. Vegetarian by arrangement. Licensed. B. & B. from £29.

NEWTON ABBOT

Cleave Hotel, Lustleigh, Newton Abbott, TQ13 9TJ (06477) 223
15th C. thatched inn in the heart of the picturesque village of Lustleigh. Huge, granite inglenook fireplace in the cosy bar & exposed granite walls.
Open Feb. to Nov. No smoking in dining room. Vegetarian standard. Other diets by arrangement. Licensed. Wheelchair access. Pets by arrangement. Tea/coffee making and T.V. in all rooms. B. & B. from £20.

Rutherford House, Widecombe in the Moor, Nr Newton Abbot, TQ13 7TB (03642) 264
Large detached house standing amidst pretty gardens in a beautiful valley just 300 yards from the centre of the famous village of Widecombe in the Moor.
Open Easter to end of year. No smoking throughout. Vegetarian, vegan and diabetic on request. Children: over 9s only. T.V. in lounge. B. & B. from £13.50.

NEWTON POPPLEFORD

Jolly's, The Bank, Newton Poppleford, EX10 0XD (0395) 68100
Friendly smoke-free establishment offering accommodation and food to both residential and non-residential guests. Predominantly vegetarian, but with a good range of meat and fish dishes.
Open all year. No-smoking throughout the house. Vegetarian standard. Most other diets by arrangement. Licensed. Children welcome. Tea/coffee-making facilities. Colour T.V's. Credit cards. B. & B. from £12.50.

NORTH BOVEY (DARTMOOR)

Slate Cottage, The Green, North Bovey, Nr Moretonhampstead, TQ13 8RB (0647) 40060
18th C. cottage offering peace and comfort, overlooking thatched houses, 13th C. church, oak-tree'd green and undulating moorland, all in a picturesque Dartmoor village.
Open all year. No smoking in the house. Vegetarian & other diets by arrangement. Children: over 12s only. TV & tea/coffee-making in bedrooms. B. & B. from £19.50, single £24.50.

OKEHAMPTON (CALL)'96

1) **Howard's Gorhuish, Northlew, Okehampton, EX20 3BT (0837) 53301**
Charming 16th C. Devon longhouse standing in 7 acres of beautiful gardens, orchards and paddocks with spectacular views of Dartmoor; excellent home-cooked food.
Open all year. No smoking in the house. Vegetarian & vegan by arrangement. Children: over 10s only. En suite in some rooms. Tea/coffee-making in bedrooms. T.V. in lounge. B. & B. from £15.

2) **Pumpy Cottage, East Week, Okehampton, Devon, EX20 2QB (0647) 23580**
Mediaeval Dartmoor cottage, formerly a yeoman farmer's long house; situated in beautiful countryside, with its own herb garden and paddock. 'Unpretentious', but comfortably furnished and with great charm. Healthy breakfast, using much home-grown and local produce.
Open May to Oct. No smoking in the house. Vegetarian on request. Children: over 5s only. B.& B. from £10.

Stowford House, Stowford, Lewdown, Okehampton, Devon, EX20 4BZ (056 683) 415
Stowford House is a charming former rectory which stands amidst peaceful gardens just a few

minutes from the old A30 and a short drive from Okehampton, Tavistock and Launceston. Your hostess, Jenny Irwin, offers a warm welcome to guests, and comfortable accommodation in beautifully appointed guest rooms (single, double and twin rooms are available). The food is outstandingly good: everything is prepared on the premises from fresh ingredients (vegetarian meals are available with advance notice), and there are three or four starters and main courses to choose from, a typical selection featuring fried Camembert with Gooseberry Preserve or Creamy Parsnip and Apple Soup followed by grilled Whole Plaice with Orange Butter or Rack of Lamb with Wine, Mint and Caper Sauce; a selection of home-made desserts, ranging from light and fruity to rich and creamy, are served after the meal - and there is the option of a generous wedge of Stilton; there is a well-stocked bar and an interesting wine list to accompany your meal. Stowford is an excellent touring base: beautiful Dartmoor and Lydford Gorge are easily reached, and the coasts of both North and South Devon are only about 40 minutes driving distance away.

Open Mar. to Nov. No smoking in dining room. Vegetarian & other diets by arrangement. Licensed. Children by arrangement. En suite, TV & tea/coffee-making in rooms. Credit cards. B. & B. £17.50, D., B. & B. £29.50.

OTTERY ST MARY

Fluxton Farm Hotel, Ottery St Mary, EX11 1RJ (040481) 2818

Once a 16th C. long house, this charming white-washed hotel is pleasantly situated in lovely farming country and stands in pretty sheltered gardens complete with stream and trout pond; almost all the bedrooms enjoy splendid views over the Otter Valley. There is a healthy emphasis in the preparation of the excellent cuisine on the use of fresh, locally purchased or home-produced ingredients: free-range eggs come from the house hens. Meals are served in a bright airy dining room (log fires in cooler weather) with candlelight in spring and autumn. You are just 4 miles from the sea and a stone's throw from the pretty country town of Ottery St Mary.

Open all year. No smoking in dining room & 1 lounge. Vegetarian & other diets by arrangement. Licensed. Children & pets welcome. En suite, TV & tea-making in rooms. B. & B. from £22.50 D., B. & B. from £28.50.

PLYMOUTH

Churston Hotel, Apsley Road, Plymouth, PL4 6PJ (0752) 664850

Hotel close to city centre and British Rail. "Arrive as guests, depart as friends!".

Open all year. No smoking in dining room & some bedrooms. Vegetarian & other diets by arrangement. Licensed. Children by arrangement. Tea-making & TV in rooms. Credit cards. B. & B. from £13.50.

Windwhistle Farm, Hemerden, Plymouth, PL7 5BU (0752) 340600

Quiet farmhouse with 2 acres of gardens. Abundance of wildlife. Home-cooking.

Open all year. Smoking banned throughout. Vegetarian and other special diets by arrangement. Licensed. No disabled access. Children welcome. Some en suite. Tea/coffee-making & T.V. in all rooms. B. & B. from £15.

SALCOMBE

Lyndhurst Hotel, Bonaventure Road, Salcombe, TQ8 8BG (054884) 2481

The Lyndhurst is a small, private hotel - formerly the harbour master's residence - which stands on the side of a hill overlooking the town and harbour and with glorious views of the estuary. All bedrooms are comfortable and very well-appointed, and the hotel has a spacious lounge (with log fire in cooler weather) and a well-stocked bar. The dining room has panoramic views over the harbour and surrounding countryside, and the excellent home-cooked meals feature a range of dishes prepared from fresh, local produce. Salcombe is renowned as a yachtsman's paradise, while the miles of safe, sandy beaches make it an excellent choice for a family holiday.

Open Feb. to Nov. No smoking in the house. Vegetarian, diabetic, & low-fat diets by arrangement. Licensed. Children: over 7s only. En suite, TV & tea/coffee-making in rooms. B. & B. from £18.50. D., B. & B. from £30.

Trennels Hotel, Herbert Road, Salcombe, TQ8 8HR (0548) 842500

Trennels Hotel is built of local stone and was at one time a Victorian sea captain's house; these days it has been carefully converted into a charming small hotel but still has the wonderful views of Salcombe Estuary that its former occupant doubtless enjoyed. The house has been very comfortably furnished and appointed and there are double, single or family rooms available: most bedrooms have en suite facilities and many have glorious harbour views. Your hosts take care to ensure that there is a very friendly and relaxed atmosphere at the Trennels Hotel and a generous breakfast is served to guests in the pleasant, airy dining room. Salcombe is the most southerly resort in Devon and stands at the mouth of a magnificent

estuary: there are miles of golden sandy beaches and, as much of the coast is owned and protected by the National Trust, there are some splendid unspoilt coastal footpaths.
Open Easter to end. Oct. No smoking in the hotel. Licensed. Children: over 4s welcome. En suite in most rooms. Tea/Coffee-making in bedrooms. T.V. in all en suite bedrooms. B. & B. from £19. ETB 3 Crowns, AA listed.

Mr & Mrs Petty-Brown, Rocarno, Grenville Rd, Salcombe, Devon   (0548) 842732
Small B. & B. in quiet residential area; friendly & warm; lovely views. Home-cooking.
Open all year. No smoking. Vegetarian by arrangement. Pets by arrangement. Children welcome. Tea/coffee-making & T.V. in rooms. B. & B. from £12.50. Dinner & picnic lunches by arrangement.

SEATON
The Bulstone, Higher Bulstone, Branscombe, Nr Seaton, EX12 3BL (0297) 80446
Open Feb. to Nov. Smoking allowed only in 1 lounge. Vegetarian & other diets by arrangement. Licensed. Children welcome. En suite in most rooms. Tea/coffee-making in bedrooms. T.V. lounge. B. & B. from £19.75.

SIDMOUTH
Applegarth Hotel and Restaurant, Church Street, Sidford, EX10 9QP (0395) 513174
Open all year. No smoking in dining room, bedrooms & lounge. Vegetarian & other diets by arrangement. Licensed. Disabled access. Children: over 10s only. En suite, tea/coffee-making & T.V. B. & B. from £17.50

Brackendale, 50 Sidford Rd, Sidmouth, EX10 9LP (0395) 516219
Open all year. No smoking in dining room, bedrooms & lounge. Vegetarian standard, other diets on request. Children: over 12s only. En suite in 2 rooms. Tea/coffee-making in bedrooms. T.V. lounge. B. & B. from £14.50.

SOUTH BRENT
The Rock, South Brent, TQ10 9JL (0364) 72185
Lovely old house overlooking Lydia Bridge and the falls; largely built in 1843, the house electricity is partly generated by water wheel!
Open Feb. to Nov. inc. No smoking in the house. Vegetarian & other diets by arrangement.Children: babies or over 8s only. Pets by arrangement. En suite in most rooms. Tea/coffee-making. T.V. B. & B. from £20.

TEIGNMOUTH
Fonthill, Torquay Rd, Shaldon, Teignmouth, TQ14 0AX (0626) 872344

Fonthill is a beautiful Georgian house which stands amidst 25 acres of private grounds on the edge of Shaldon, a delightful village on the South Devon coast. Although very well situated for visiting most parts of Devon, visitors to Fonthill come to enjoy the peace and quiet afforded by its tranquil situation. There is much to see and do locally: Shaldon itself is situated overlooking the lovely Teign Estuary where birdwatching, fishing, sailing and water skiing may all be enjoyed, and there is a tennis court in the Fonthill grounds and a golf course nearby. There are several pubs and restaurants within a short walking distance where you may enjoy an evening meal.
Open Mar. to Dec. No smoking in the house. Vegetarian & other diets by arrangement. Children welcome. One private bathroom. Tea/coffee-making in bedrooms. B. & B. from £17.50.

Leicester House, 2 Winterbourne Road, Teignmouth, TQ14 8JT (0626) 773043
Open all year. No smoking in the house. Children welcome. Pets by arrangement. En suite in 3 rooms. Tea/coffee-making & T.V. in all bedrooms. B. & B. from £10.

TIVERTON
Harton Farm, Oakford, Tiverton, EX16 9HH (03985) 209
No smoking in dining room. Vegetarian & other diets by arrangement. Not licensed, but bring your own. Children: over 4s only. Pets by arrangement. Tea/coffee-making in bedrooms. T.V. in lounge. B. & B. from £10.

Trewman's House, Cadeleigh, Tiverton, EX16 8HP (0884) 5311
Open all year. No smoking. Vegetarian & other diets by arrangement. Not licensed, but bring your own. Children welcome. 1 room en suite. Tea/coffee in bedrooms. T.V. lounge. B. & B. from £11.

TORQUAY

 The Beehive, Steep Hill, Maidencombe, Nr Torquay (0803) 314647

The Beehive is situated in the peaceful conservation area of Maidencombe. There is a friendly atmosphere and it is a totally smoke-free establishment. All room have magnificent views of the sea, coastline and valley and there is a large courtyard for car parking. There is a thatched tavern just 2 minutes'walk away (with bar snacks and a restaurant) and it is just a 4 minute walk to the cove. Dartmoor is just 30 minutes'away and you are just 10 minutes from Torquay, Shaldon and Teignmouth.

Open all year. Smoke-free establishment. TV & tea/coffee-making in bedrooms. B. & B. £15 - 16.

Bowden Close Hotel, Teignmouth Rd, Maidencombe, Torquay, TQ1 4TJ (0803) 328029

Victorian country house hotel in peaceful hamlet midway between Torquay & Teignmouth. Garden & car park. Panoramic views over Lyme Bay. Comfortable bedrooms. Close to Dartmoor.
Open all year. No smoking in dining room & lounge. Vegetarian & other diets by arrangement. Licensed. Wheelchair access to restaurant. Children & pets welcome. En suite, TV & tea/coffee-making in bedrooms. Credit cards. B. & B. from £17 - 30.

 Hotel Protea, Seaway Lane, Chelston, Torquay, TQ2 6PW Tel: (0803) 605778 Fax: (0803) 690171

Hotel Protea is a spacious, elegant Victorian villa which stands in secluded south-facing grounds overlooking Torbay. Family-owned and run, the Hotel Protea offers the ultimate in efficient, personal service thus creating an atmosphere of friendly informality in which you are able to relax and feel at home: each of the 11 spacious en suite bedrooms has been luxuriously appointed with direct dial phones, remote-control TVs, hairdryers and mini bars - and most overlook Torbay; the sunny sitting room is particularly inviting - the perfect place in which to let an hour or two pass playing chess or listening to music. The food is fabulous - everything is prepared with care from fresh local produce - and a typical evening menu would feature Fanned Melon with Raspberry Sauce, followed by home-made soup or sorbet, Roast Leg of Pork (with fresh vegetables - there are also vegetarian options), and a selection of home-made desserts; cheese, biscuits, coffee and mints would complete the meal.

Open Feb. - Dec. No smoking in the house. Vegetarian & other diets by arrangement. En suite, TV & tea/coffee-making in bedrooms. Licensed. Credit cards. D., B. & B. from £40.

Hotel Sydore, Meadfoot Road, Torquay, TQ1 2JP (0803) 294758 Fax: (0803) 294489

Hotel Sydore is an elegant Victorian villa set in its own grounds and well-kept gardens (complete with sun terrace and croquet lawn) just a short walk from the Harbour and award-winning Meadfoot beach. Accommodation is in comfortable and well-appointed rooms, and guests can choose from a good selection of dishes on the traditional evening menu. Vegetarians are exceptionally well-catered for (there is an imaginative menu with a variety of tasty options), and a typical meat-free evening meal would feature Tomato Soup with Croutons followed by Vegetable Goulash and a selection of tempting desserts.

Open all year. Smoking discouraged in dining room, smoking banned in bedrooms & sun lounge. Vegetarian standard. Other diets by arrangement. Licensed. Disabled access. Children welcome. Pets by arrangement. En suite, TV & tea/coffee-making in rooms. Credit cards. B. & B. from £17.

'Kellaton', Devons Rd, Babbacombe, Torquay, TQ1 3PR (0803) 326106
Charming Victorian residence set in its own large garden and driveway in a quiet tree-lined road close to Cary Park.
Open Feb. to Dec. 18th. No smoking in the house. Vegetarian & other diets by arrangement. Children: over 12s only. Tea/coffee-making & T.V. B. & B. from £13.50.

Millbrook House Hotel, Old Mill Road, Chelston, Torquay, TQ2 6AP (0803) 297394

 Millbrook House is a small, elegantly furnished hotel situated close to Tor Abbey Sands and Cockington Village in the Chelston area of Torquay. The charming bedrooms are all equipped to a very high standard, and there are a number of more spacious deluxe rooms available. The leisure amenities are impressive too: there is a lovely secluded garden and patio, and a mini-gym for guests' use. The dining room offers superb cuisine, prepared from fresh local ingredients and beautifully served on tables laid with linen and cut glass. A typical evening meal would feature Sherried Chicken Livers followed by Monkfish in Brandy and Cream Sauce and a selection of sweets, including home-made ice-cream; there is a helpful wine recommendation to accompany each menu.
Open all year. Smoking allowed only in the basement bar. Vegetarian and most other special diets by arrangement. Licensed. Children by arrangement. En suite, TV & tea/coffee-making in bedrooms. Access, Visa. B. & B. from £17.50. D. £9.

 **Sunnybrae, 38 Bamfylde Road, Torquay, TQ2 5AR (0803) 296073**
Sunnybrae is a small, friendly guest house, conveniently situated near to the seafront of the popular seaside town of Torquay and has achieved such a reputation during the time that Mr and Mrs May have been its proprietors that some guests have been returning season after season for 17 years! Good traditional home-cooking is a hallmark of a stay at Sunny Brae and a typical evening meal would feature soup, roast lamb with all the trimmings and home-made apple pie and custard.
Open Jun. to Sep. No smoking in the house. Children by arrangement only. Tea/coffee-making in bedrooms. T.V. in lounge. B. & B. from £10.50. D., B. & B. £14.50. Weekly rate £80 to £100 incl. D., B. & B.

 **Trees Hotel, Bronshill Rd, Babbacombe, Torquay, TQ 1 3HA (0803) 326073**
The Trees Hotel is a small, elegant licensed hotel which is peacefully situated amidst spacious lawned gardens just a short distance from the centre of Babbacombe and the beach. A family-run hotel, The Trees has a happy, friendly atmosphere and your hosts, Gwen and Stewart Ferguson, will do everything they can to make your stay a happy and memorable one. The rooms are pleasantly furnished - everything is scrupulously clean - and there is a cosy bar for pre-dinner drinks. The food is 'good, plain, Devonshire cooking', and is served in a light, airy dining room. Torquay offers a wealth of entertainments and attractions to visiting tourists and additionally there are numerous safe, sandy beaches and coves within easy striking distance.
Open all year. No smoking thoughout. Licensed. Wheelchair access. Children: over 7s only. En suite, tea/coffee making & T.V. in all rooms. Visa. B. & B. from £15. D. £5.

TOTNES

Dorsley Park Farmhouse, Higher Plymouth Road, Totnes, TQ9 6DN (0803) 863680
18th C. farmhouse which has been pleasingly converted to provide excellent accommodation just 500 yards from Totnes.
Open all year. No smoking at breakfast & in bedrooms at all times. Vegetarian & other diets by arrangement. Children welcome. Pets by arrangement. Tea/coffee. T.V. in lounge. B. & B. from £13.

Hatchlands Farm, Bluepost, Avonwick, Nr Totnes, TQ9 7LR (0364) 72224
Luxury farmhouse in panoramic countryside with plenty to see and do on the farm.
Open all year ex. Xmas. No smoking in the house. Tea/coffee making in rooms. T.V. lounge. B. & B. from £10.

The Old Forge at Totnes, Seymour Place, Totnes, TQ9 5AY (0803) 862174

No church bells

This charming stone-built hotel was converted recently from a 600 year-old smithy; it has a lovely walled garden which makes it a rural retreat in the heart of Totnes; the property has had an interesting history and has partly reverted back to its primary use - Peter Allnutt now runs a busy wrought iron business while his wife, Jeannie, runs the hotel. The highest standard of accommodation is offered to guests: the cottage-style bedrooms are prettily and tastefully furnished, and the food (served in very plentiful quantities) is prepared from the best of healthy ingredients. A typical breakfast menu features a variety of fish and vegetarian options and, in addition to four different types of bread, *two* different sorts of decaffeinated coffee are also offered. Healthily conscientious indeed. Traditional breakfasts are also available as well as fruit, yoghurts, waffles and pancakes. **Holder of AA Merit Award and ETB Highly Commended.**
Open all year. No smoking in the house. Vegetarian & other diets by arrangement. Licensed. Disabled access to some ground floor rooms. Children welcome. Pets in cars only. En suite in most rooms. Tea/coffee-making & T.V. in all bedrooms. Credit cards. B. & B. from £20.

Restaurants

ASHBURTON

The Old Coffee House, 27-29 West Street, Ashburton, TQ13 7DT (0364) 52539
For further details please see under the entry in the accommodation section.

BARNSTABLE

Heavens Above, 4 Bear Street, Barnstable (0271) 77960
'The only licensed, non-smoking, wholefood, vegetarian restaurant in Barnstaple'
50 seats. Open 10 - 3, six days, some evenings in summertime. L. around £3.50. No smoking throughout . Vegan and some other meat-free special diets on request. Licensed. Children welcome.

BIDEFORD

Banks Coffee Shop, 16 High Street (0237) 476813
Coffee shop serving home-made soup, quiches, jacket potatoes & cream teas.
Open 9 - 5. Smoking banned throughout. Vegetarian. Disabled access. Children welcome.

Sloops, Bridge Street, Bideford (0237) 471796
Open 10.30 - 2, 6.30 - 9.30; closed Mon. No smoking after 12 noon. Vegetarian standard. Access, Visa.

Thymes Restaurant, The Bakehouse, Queen Street, Bideford (0237) 473399
Vegetarian/Wholefood restaurant serving a variety of meat-free snacks and main meals.
Open 10 - 3. Only 3 smoking tables. Licensed. Children welcome.

BOVEY TRACEY

Devon Guild of Craftsmen, Riverside Mill, Bovey Tracey (0626) 2832223
Granary cafe serving teas, coffees and light lunches annexed to specialist exhibition centre and retail shop selling work of over 200 craftsmen and women; outside seating in walled courtyard.
Open 10 - 5. L. from £3.25. No smoking throughout. Vegetarian standard. Licensed. Disabled access. Children welcome (toys available). Credit cards.

CREDITON

 Wild Thymes, 100 High Street, Crediton (0363) 77 2274
Friendly little restaurant serving a wide variety of wholesome meat-free dishes.
Open all year, Tues. - Fri., 10 - 5.30, Sat. 10 - 5. No smoking throughout. Vegetarian and wholefoods exclusively. Not licensed, but you are welcome to bring your own wine. Children welcome.

DARTINGTON

 Cranks, Cider Press centre, Shinners Bridge, Dartington (0803) 862388
Open 10 - 5. Sun. only in summer. No smoking throughout. Exclusively vegetarian. Licensed. Disabled access.

EAST BUDLEIGH

 Grasshoppers, 16 High Street, East Budleigh, Budleigh Salterton, EX9 7DY (03954) 2774
Beautiful cob-walled Devon cottage; delicious Devon cream teas.
Open 10 - 5.30, Sun. 2.30 - 5.30. No smoking throughout. Vegetarian standard. Disabled access.

EXETER

Brambles, 31 New Bridge Street, Exeter (0392) 74168
Small, friendly restaurant; main stream jazz played as background music.
No smoking in 50% of restaurant. Special diets on request. Not licensed, but bring your own. Children.

The Cafe, 38 South Street, Exeter (0392) 410855
Light, airy 'conservatory' restaurant, with pleasant *al fresco* dining area, in converted chapel; excellent food. 'Thai nights'are a special feature Wednesdays & Thursdays from 7.30 p.m. with authentic menu created by Thai cooks.
Open 10.30 - 6 Mon.. to Sat. No smoking in 80% of the restaurant & there is also a large garden. Licensed. Disabled access. Children welcome. Credit cards.

Debenhams, 1-11 Sidwell St, Exeter, EX4 6NW (0392) 54911

Herbies, 15 North Street, Exeter (0392) 58473
Vegetarian restaurant in the centre of Exeter.
Open 11 - 2.30, Mon. to Fri; 6 - 9.30, Tues. to Sat; Sat: 10.30 - 4. L. from £3. No smoking in 60% rest. Exclusively vegetarian. Vegan standard. Licensed. Children welcome. Access, Visa.

 Killerton House (National Trust), Broadclyst (0392) 881691
Various tea-rooms & restaurants located in & around splendid National Trust property.
Open 11 - 5.30. L. around £3.50. No smoking in all restaurants. Vegetarian standard. Some other special diets on request. Licensed in some areas. Children welcome. Credit cards.

Mill on the Exe, Bonhay Road, Exeter (0392) 214464
Friendly pub serving excellent food.
Open 11 - 11. L. from £3, D. from £5. Separate section for non-smokers. Vegetarian. Disabled access.

EXMOUTH

Willows, 53 The Strand, Exmouth (0395) 264398
 Open 9 - 11. L. from £2. D. from £4. No smoking throughout. Vegetarian. Licensed. Children welcome.

HONITON

Honey Bees, 160 High Street, Honiton (0404) 43392
Open 9 - 5. L. around £5. 50% no smoking. Vegetarian standard. Disabled access. Children welcome.

ILFRACOMBE

The Red Petticoat Restaurant, 7 The Quay, Ilfracombe (0271) 863273
Open 10 - 10, (10 - 6. out of season). L. around £3.50. D. from £5. Separate area for non-smokers. Disabled access. Children welcome.

KINGS KERSWELL

Ⓝ Pitt House Restaurant, 2 Church End Road, Kings Kerswell (0803) 873374
40 seats. Open 7 - 9.30. L. £5 - £10. D. around £25. No smoking throughout. Licensed. Disabled access.

NEWTON ABBOT

Ⓝ Devon Guild of Craftsmen, Riverside Mill, Newton Abbot, TQ13 9AF (0626) 832223
35 seats. Open 10 - 5.30. L. around £2. Smoking banned throughout. Vegetarian standard. Licensed. Disabled access. Children welcome. Credit cards accepted.

NEWTON POPPPLEFORD

Jolly's Vegetarian Restaurant, The Bank, Newton Poppleford, EX10 0XD (0395) 687100
For further details please see under the entry in the accommodation section.

PLYMOUTH

Ⓝ Debenhams, Royal Parade, Plymouth, PL1 1SA (0752) 266666
A self-service restaurant with cheerful staff; serving popular food throughout the day.
Smoking banned throughout.

TIVERTON

Ⓝ The Angel Gallery, 1 Angel Terrace, Tiverton, EX16 6PD (0884) 254778
Art Gallery with newly re-opened restaurant serving vegetarian food with Mediterranean and world cuisine influences. Historic castle and award-winning museum nearby. Gallery open all day.
Lunch served 12.15 - 2 p.m. No smoking throughout. 2-course lunch £4.75. Vegetarian. Children welcome.

TORQUAY

Ⓝ Debenhams, 13 - 15 The Strand, Torquay (0803) 295921
A self-service restaurant with cheerful staff serving popular food throughout the day.
Open store hours. No smoking throughout. Vegetarian meals. Disabled access. Children very welcome. Credit and debit cards accepted.

TOTNES

Ⓝ Willow Vegetarian Restaurant, 87 High St, Totnes (0803) 862605
The Willow wholefood vegetarian restaurant is situated in The Narrows at the top of the charming town of Totnes. A café by day and a restaurant by night, the Willows has a lovely garden and is exceptionally customer-friendly (there is a room with toys and a childrens'table). The food is first-rate too: everything is prepared from fresh, wholefood ingredients - most of the vegetables are organic - and a typical lunch menu would feature French Onion Soup followed by Homity Pie and a range of healthy desserts, such as soya icecream or amazing Rocombe Farm Icecream made with organic milk and natural ingredients. Every week there is a special feature night and a delicious choice of reasonably priced and healthy dishes such as Indian patties in spiced yoghurt with fresh coconut chutney followed by Mushroom Stroganoff and 10 or so desserts (crunchy topped peach, cinnamon and banana pie or carob chop and mocha cake).
60 seats. No smoking throughout. Vegetarian and other special diets standard. Licensed. Disabled access. Children welcome.

Dorset Accommodation

BLANDFORD FORUM

La Belle Alliance, White Cliff Mill Street, Blandford Forum, DS11 7BP (0258) 452842

 La Belle Alliance is an elegant country house style restaurant and hotel offering first-rate accommodation and food just a short walk from the centre of the attractive town of Blandford Forum. Each of the six guest bedrooms has been individually decorated and styled and has a wide range of helpful little extras (bottled Dorset water, toileteries, magazines and books) in addition to other useful amenities (trouser press, direct dial phone). You are invited to take an aperitif in the comfortable lounge, with its attractive draped curtains, before dining in the pretty dining room (flowers and linen on the table); all dishes have been prepared from fresh ingredients (local wherever possible), and the imaginative menu, which changes seasonally, would typically feature Lettuce in Walnut Oil with grilled Goat's Cheese, followed by Fillet of Sea Bream with a Herb Crust (with Ratatouille and Red Wine Sauce) and an extraordinary selection of desserts. Blandford Forum is architecturally interesting in that it was totally rebuilt in the 30 years succeeding 1731 when it was almost completely destroyed by fire; it is, therefore, unique in England in being a whole town conceived in the high Georgian period.

Open Feb. to Dec. No smoking in dining room. Vegetarian & other diets by arrangement. Licensed. Children welcome, babies by arrangement. Pets by arrangement. En suite, TV & tea/coffee-making in bedrooms. Access, Visa, Amex. B. & B. from £29.

 Restharrow B. & B., North St, Winterbourne Stickland, Blandford Forum, DT11 0NH (0258) 880936

Restharrow is an attractive modern house which stands near the centre of the pretty village of Winterbourne Stickland near the head of the Winterbourne Valley; recently upgraded to 2 crown Highly Commended status by the ETB, the house offers every comfort and your hosts will do all they can to make you feel at home. Accommodation consists of one ground floor en suite double bedroom (ideal for a disabled person) and a first floor double room with a private bathroom; both rooms are centrally heated and have electric blankets as well as other helpful amenities. The full English breakfast includes home-made jam and home-produced honey, as well as a wide range of cereals and a cooked platter. Winterbourne Stickland has a pub (with good food), a post office, school and 13th C. church, and is situated in an area of Outstanding Natural Beauty.

Open all year. No smoking in the house. Vegetarian & other diets by arrangement. One ground floor room. Children welcome. En suite, TV & tea/coffee-making facilities in bedrooms. B. & B. from £15-18.

BOURNEMOUTH

 **The Cottage, 12 Southern Road, Southbourne, Bournemouth, BH6 3SR (0202) 422764**

The Cottage is a delightful small hotel, pleasantly located in a quiet select area of Southbourne near Bournemouth, within walking distance of the cliff-top beach lift or to the zig-zag paths which lead to 7 miles of safe, sandy beaches. Bournemouth has one of the cleanest beaches in Europe and has the warmest recorded annual sea temperature in Great Britain. Another good reason for choosing The Cottage as a holiday location is the friendly personal service offered by the resident proprietors Ronald and Valarie Halliwell, and the spotless accommodation. The Cottage is noted for fresh home-cooking; a typical evening meal consisting of Egg Mayonnaise, Roast Lamb with all the trimmings, and a home-made dessert; cheese and biscuits, coffee and mints complete the meal. Ample parking. ETB 3 Crowns Commended.

Open all year. No smoking in the house. Special diets by arrangement. Licensed. Ground floor bedroom. Children: over 4s only. En suite most rooms. Tea/coffee-making in rooms. T.V. lounge. B. & B. from £15.

Cransley Hotel, 11 Knyveton Rd, East Cliff, Bournemouth, BH1 3QG (0202) 290067

The Cransley Hotel is a 12-bedroomed establishment which stands amidst attractive gardens in a quiet tree-lined road just 0.5 miles from East Cliff with its lovely sandy beach. Each of the bedrooms has en suite facilities and has been comfortably furnished and appointed with a range of helpful amenities; a double and twin room are on the ground floor - making them a good choice for disabled guests - and there is a lovely lounge with large French windows which lead out onto a patio and southfacing garden. The food is wholesome and satisfying: a generous breakfast starts the day and the 4-course evening meal is home-prepared from fresh ingredients. Packed lunches, flask filling and other light refreshments are also available at a reasonable cost. The Cransley Hotel is within walking distance of the coach and rail stations; the town's superb shopping centre, with its department stores and arcades, is also just a short stroll away.

Open Easter - Oct. No smoking in the house. Vegetarian & other diets by arrangement. Ground floor rooms. Children & pets welcome. En suite, TV & tea/coffee-making in rooms. B. & B. from £15, D., B. & B. from £20.

Durley Grange Hotel, 6 Durley Road, West Cliff, Bournemouth, BH2 5JL (0202) 554473/290743

The Durley Grange Hotel is a large, white-washed and pantiled building, pleasingly situated in a quiet corner of the West Cliff and yet just 5 minutes walk from the sea and the town centre. It has been under the supervision of the Kirby family since 1979 and since that time has established an enviable reputation, not only as a holiday hotel, but also as a venue for banquets, receptions and conferences. Bedrooms are well-appointed with direct dial phones in addition to the usual facilities, and the dining room, with its pink tablecloths and draped curtains, is a charming place in which to dine on dishes chosen from a traditional British menu, which would typically feature such appetisers as home-made soup, followed by a choice of hot or cold main courses (Chicken Chasseur or some interesting salads) and some very tempting desserts (Walnut Cream or Mandarin Gateau). A new smoke-free conference room is available as well as an ozone treated indoor pool, sauna, solarium and whirlpool.

Open all year. Smoking banned in dining room, part of bar area, pool area and solarium. Vegetarian and diabetic diets by arrangement. Licensed. Wheelchair access. Children: over 5s only. Pets by arrangement. En suite, tea/coffee-making, T.V. and phone in all rooms. Access, Visa. Car parking. B. & B. from £26.50-£29.50.

Ferndale, 10 Pembroke Rd, Alum Chine, Bournemouth, BH4 8HE (0202) 761320

Detached Victorian residence with large en suite bedrooms. High standards of cleanliness & food. Easy stroll to shops and beach. Excellent bus services. Forecourt parking. Basic rooms also avail.

Open Mar. to Nov. No smoking ex. in TV sun lounge. Vegetarian & other diets by arrangement. Licensed. Children: over 4s only. Tea-making in all rooms. B. & B. from £13 daily, £70 weekly; Evening meal optional.

Hinton Firs Hotel, East Cliff, Bournemouth, BH1 3HB Tel: (0202) 555409 Fax: (0202) 299607

Hinton Firs Hotel is a 52- bedroomed establishment, standing amidst pine trees in a peaceful setting in the heart of East Cliff close to the sea; it is a very poular place - many of the guests are regular visitors or have been recommended by friends - and the hotel has a relaxed, informal atmosphere. Each of the bedrooms have a range of helpful amenities (including a direct dial phone and baby-listening) and there are lots of leisure attractions for the exclusive use of guests, including a seasonally heated outdoor pool, an indoor pool with spa and swim jet, a sauna and a games room; family rooms, cots and high-chairs are also available. Packed lunches, hot and cold midday snacks and children's teas can also be ordered. Hinton Firs is conveniently situated for those travelling by road or rail, and is within easy reach of the town centre.

Open all year. No smoking in dining room or TV lounge. Vegetarian & other diets by arrangement. Licensed. Wheelchair access. Children. En suite, TV & tea-making in rooms. Access, Visa. D., B. & B. from £39.50.

Kingsley Hotel, 20 Glen Rd, Boscombe, Bournemouth, BH5 1HR (0202) 398683

The Kingsley is a small, 11-bedroomed hotel which, under the supervision of the resident proprietors, Janet and Martin Smith, offers personal service and a warm, friendly atmosphere. It is situated on a quiet road, away from passing traffic, yet is only 5 minutes from the cliff top gardens, glorious sandy beaches, shopping centre and coach pick up points; all the attractions of Bournemouth are just a short distance away. The bedrooms are bright and well-furnished and have (with the exception of the single rooms) en suite facilities and a hairdryer; there is a comfortable lounge and a separate lounge bar in which you can also enjoy snacks and bedtime drinks. Out of season visitors in Spring and Autumn can also enjoy special bargain breaks - as can senior citizens staying for a week or more. Boscombe is an ideal touring centre for visiting many other places of interest including the New Forest, Poole Harbour, Christchurch and Beaulieu.

Open Mar. - Oct. No smoking throughout. Licensed. Children welcome. En suite in most rooms. TV & tea/coffee-making in all bedrooms. Access, Visa. D., B. & B. from £144 - 174 p.w.

Marven Hotel, 5 Watkin Rd, Boscombe, Bournemouth, BH5 1HP (0202) 397099

Small, friendly hotel with a homely atmosphere; very comfortable rooms; generous fare. Parking.
Open Mar. to Oct. No smoking in the house. Vegetarian & other diets on request. Licensed. Children welcome. En suite in most rooms. Tea-making & Satellite T.V. in all rooms. ETB 3 Crowns. D. B. &. B. from £132. weekly.

St. Antoine Guest House, 2 Guildhill Rd, Southbourne, Bournemouth, BH6 3EY (0202) 433043

The St Antoine Guest House is a friendly family-run establishment in Bournemouth. It has the best of several worlds, being close to the river, sea and forest, in addition, of course, to the amenities of Bournemouth. Your hostess, Kathrin Mackie, offers a very warm welcome to guests: bedrooms are comfortable and inviting and there are two en suite family rooms. The food is particularly delicious: everything is home-cooked from fresh ingredients - including home-grown vegetables when in season - and vegetarians are also very welcome as Kathrin is able to create some imaginative meat-free options.

Open Mar. to Nov. No smoking in the house. Vegetarian & other diets by arrangement. Children welcome. En suite & tea/coffee-making in bedrooms. TV lounge. B. & B. from £13, H.B. £16.

BRIDPORT

Britmead House, 154 West Bay Road, Bridport, DT6 4EG (0308) 22941

Britmead House is located just a short, level walk from both the historic town of Bridport, Chesil Beach, the Dorset Coastal Path and the quaint little harbour of West Bay, with its beaches, golf course and walks. A friendly personal service is offered by the proprietors, Ann and Dan Walker. The 7 spacious individually decorated bedrooms (one of which is on the ground floor) have en suite bathrooms and a range of welcoming amenities, including a mini bar, hairdrier, etc., and all are centrally heated. There is a comfortable south-facing lounge and dining room both of which overlook the garden to the countryside beyond. The food is excellent; meals are prepared from fresh, local produce wherever possible, and the dinner menu changes daily.

Open all year. No smoking in dining room. Vegetarian & other diets by arrangement. Licensed. Some disabled access. Children & your dog (by arrangement) welcome. En suite in 6 rooms, 1 with private facilities. Tea/coffee-making & T.V. in all bedrooms. Credit cards. Car parking. B. & B. from £17-£32. D. £11.50. Bargain breaks available. ETB 3 Crown Commended.

The Mill House, East Rd, Bridport, Dorset, DT6 4AG (0308) 25147

Converted Georgian Corn Mill with pictureque garden, own stream and meadows. Acclaimed English breakfasts. Within easy reach of shops and beach.

Open Mar. - Oct. inc. No smoking in the house. Vegetarian & other diets by arrangement. Children: over 8s only. En suite in one double room. TV in all rooms. Tea/coffee-making in room/on request. B. & B. from £13.50.

BUCKLAND NEWTON

Annette Mc Carthy, Rew Cottage, Buckland Newton, DT2 7DH (03005) 467

Comfortable & peaceful cottage deep in green farming country. Breathtaking views on all sides. Within easy reach of Sherborne, Dorchester & the sea. Lovely walks. Golf & tennis nearby.

Open all year ex. Xmas & New Year. No smoking in dining room & bedrooms. Children: over 4s. Pets by arrangement. TV & tea/coffee-making in bedrooms. B. & B. from £17.

CHARMOUTH

Newlands House, Stonebarrow Lane, Charmouth, West Dorset, DT6 6RA (0297) 60212

This former 16th C. farmhouse is set in 2 acres of gardens and orchard on the fringe of the pretty village of Charmouth. It is comfortably furnished and in the dining room, with its exposed stone walls, excellent food is served. A typical dinner menu features Mushrooms with Soy Sauce, Salmon Steaks with White Wine Sauce and a home-produced dessert such as Apricot Streudl with cream. Charmouth is an ideal centre for walking and touring and is situated in an area of outstanding natural beauty. It is also famous for the fossil cliffs and beaches of Lyme Bay. Special breaks.

Open Mar. to Oct. No smoking ex. in bar lounge. Vegetarian by arrangement. Licensed. Children: over 6s only. Pets by arrangement. En suite , TV & tea/coffee-making & T.V. in all bedrooms. D, B. & B. from £31.60.

DORCHESTER

"Badgers Sett", Cross Lanes, Melcombe Bingham, Nr Dorchester, DT2 7NY (0258) 880697

Mellow 17th C. flint and brick cottage carefully modernised to retain such original features as oak beams and inglenook fireplaces; all bedrooms are sunny and light.

Open all year. No smoking in dining room & sitting room. Vegetarian & other diets by arrangement. Children. Pets by arrangement (garden facilities). En suite, TV, radio & tea-making in bedrooms. B. & B. from £16.50.

The Creek, Ringstead, Dorchester, DT2 8NG (0305) 852251

White-washed house in a beautiful garden overlooking Portland Bill on the Heritage Coast.

Open all year. No smoking in the house. Vegetarian & other diets by arrangement. Children welcome. Tea/coffee-making in bedrooms. T.V. in lounge. B. & B. from £13.50.

Forge Cottage, Duck St, Cerne Abbas, Dorchester, DT2 7LA

17th C. thatched forge, once a private school, in centre of large village with tea shops, dress shops, art gallery & 3 fine pubs.

Open Jan. - Nov. No smoking in the house. Vegetarian & other diets on request. Children welcome. En suite, TV & tea/coffee making in bedrooms. B. & B. from £18.

The Manor Hotel, West Bexington, Dorchester, DT2 9DF Tel: (0308) 897616 Fax: (0308) 897035

The Manor Hotel, the ancient Manor House of West Bexington, snuggles in a pocket of tree and garden on a gentle slope just a saunter from the sea at Chesil Bank; an old stone building, mellowed by nine centuries of sea and sun, the Manor Hotel has, nonetheless, every modern comfort you could wish for together with a few welcome traditional values of hospitality and service (crisp bed linen, warming log fires, real ales served in the stone-lined cellar bar); most bedrooms have uninterrupted sea views. The food is prepared with integrity and flair from fresh, local and seasonal ingredients (lobster, game, seafood, etc.), and there is a good childrens' menu (younger guests will also enjoy playing on the swings and slides in the garden). Its a wonderful place to come for those in search of safe sandy beaches (Weymouth, Charmouth & Lyme Regis are within easy reach), & historic towns, houses & gardens abound.

Open all year. No smoking in conservatory. Vegetarian & other diets by arrangement. Wheelchair access to restaurant. Licensed. Children welcome. En suite, TV & tea/coffee in rooms. B. & B. from £37.50, D. B. & B. from £56.

LYME REGIS

Coverdale Guest House, Woodmead Rd, Lyme Regis, DT7 3AB (0297) 442882

Coverdale is situated in a quiet residential area of Lyme Regis overlooking Woodland Trustland to the rear, and sea views to the front; the centre of this historically important and picturesque little town is just a few minutes walk away. The accommodation at Coverdale is comfortable and well-appointed - all bedrooms have tea and coffee-making facilities - and the food is served in an attractive dining room (organically home-grown vegetables and herbs are used in cooking when they are available); there is a comfortable lounge with a colour TV. There is much to see and do in Lyme; in addition to the many attractions of the town itself, there is exceptionally safe bathing. Boating, yachting and fishing can all be enjoyed at the COBB harbour. The South Coast path passes through Lyme and those wishing to venture further afield will find Coverdale an ideal touring base for exploring Dorset, Somerset and Devon. Car parking available.

Open Mar. - Oct. inc. No smoking in dining room & bedrooms. Special diets by arrangement. Children welcome. Pets by arrangement. En suite available. tea/coffee-making in rooms. TV lounge. B. & B. from £10.

Kersbrook Hotel, Pound Road, Lyme Regis (02974) 42596

Thatched, 18th C. listed building in 1 acre of picturesque gardens overlooking Lyme Bay.

Open Feb. to Dec. No smoking in dining room & bedrooms. Vegetarian & other diets by arrangement. Licensed. Pets by arrangement. En suite, tea/coffee-making & T.V. in all bedrooms. Credit cards.

Pitt White, Mill Lane, Uplyme, Lyme Regis (0297) 442094

Pitt White is a large Victorian house standing amidst superb countryside on the Devon-Dorset border, just a mile from the sea at Lyme Regis. It is surrounded by an acre and a half of garden, with trees and shrubs and (believe it or not), the most comprehensive selection of bamboos in Europe; adding to its charms, the River Lym winds its way through the garden enhancing the sense of tranquillity. The peaceful ambience pervades the house: each of the guest bedrooms has been comfortably furnished and there is a large, pleasant lounge, with garden views, which has been equipped with TV, stereo and video. The food is wholesome and delicious: everything is home-cooked from fresh ingredients (including locally produced meats and free-range eggs) and there is a strong wholefood emphasis - vegetarian food is a speciality.

Open all year. No smoking in the house. Vegetarian standard. Other diets by arrangement. Children & pets welcome. En suite, TV & tea/coffee-making in bedrooms. B. & B. £18 - 23.

POOLE

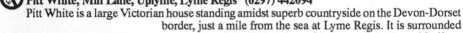 Gull Cottage, 50 Twemlow Avenue, Lower Parkstone, Poole, BH14 8AN (0202) 721277

Large family house overlooking Poole Park and close to harbour.

No smoking in the house. Vegetarian by arrangement. Children welcome. En suite rooms. B. & B. from £16.

SHAFTESBURY

Sunridge Hotel, Bleke St, Shaftesbury, Dorset (0747) 53130

The Sunridge Hotel is a listed 19th C. building in the centre of Shaftesbury, a thriving market town with an extensive history. The hotel has been comfortably furnished and tastefully decorated throughout, and has many leisure amenities for guests, including a sauna and a heated indoor swimming pool in addition to an elegant Victorian bar and restaurant. The food is imaginative and delicious: main dishes are served with a selection of fresh, locally grown vegetables, and a typical evening meal would feature deep-fried Camembert followed by Lemon Chicken, and a tempting dessert. Shaftesbury is town of great character and charm: standing on a hilltop overlooking the Blackmore Vale, it dates its origins from Saxon times and its many notable features include its abbey ruins and Gold Hill (the steep cobbled street featured in the Hovis ads!). A little further afield, visitors will find themselves within easy reach of Stonehenge, Avebury and the beautiful cathedrals of Salisbury and Wells.

Open all year. No smoking in dining room & 50% of bedrooms. Vegetarian & other diets by arrangement. Children welcome. Licensed. En suite, TV & tea/coffee-making in bedrooms. Credit cards. B. & B. from £26.

SHERBORNE

Half Moon Hotel, Half Moon Street, Sherborne (0935) 812017

Open all year. 50% no smoking dining room & some bedrooms. Vegetarian by arrangement. Licensed. Disabled access. Children. En suite, coffee-making & T.V. in bedrooms. Credit cards. B. & B. from £24.

Middle Piccadily Natural Healing Centre, Holwell, Sherborne (096323) 468

Beautifully furnished 17th C. farmhouse; therapists offering a range of holistic healing therapies. *Open all year ex. Xmas. No smoking throughout. Vegetarian standard. Other diets by arrangement. Tea/Coffee-making. Full board from £46.*

WEYMOUTH

The Beehive, Osmington, Nr Weymouth, DT3 6EL (0305) 834095

Lovely little thatched Georgian cottage in the picturesque village of Osmington. Real food! *Open Feb. to Dec. No smoking in the house. Vegetarian & other diets by arrangement. Children: over 5s only. Pets by arrangement. En suite 1 room. Tea/Coffee-making in bedrooms. T.V. in sitting room. B. & B. from £14.*

Fairlight, 50 Littlemoor Rd, Preston, Weymouth, Dorset, DT3 6AA (0305) 832293

Family-run establishment in rural situation 3 miles from Weymouth & ½ mile from beautiful Boleaze Cove. Excellent area for walkers and water sports. Family, double and single room avail. *Open all year. No smoking in the house. Own keys. Vegetarians welcome. Children: over 4s only. CTV, handbasins & refreshment trays in bedrooms. E.M., B. & B. from £18. Car parking.*

Restaurants

BOURNEMOUTH

Intermission Restaurant, Debenhams, The Square, Bournemouth, BH2 5LY (0202) 22177

Intermission is a friendly self-service family restaurant serving popular snacks, hot lunches and a wide range of hot and cold drinks. *Open store hours. No smoking throughout. Vegetarian meals. Disabled access. Children very welcome. Credit & debit cards.*

The Salad Centre, 22 Post Office Road, Bournemouth (0202) 21720

Vegetarian restaurant serving a wide range of dishes which varies daily. *Open 10 - 4, Mon. to Sat; 6 - 9, Thurs. to Sat. No smoking. Vegetarian, vegan & wholefood exclusively.*

CERNE ABBAS

Old Market House, 25 Long St, Cerne Abbas (03003) 680

Tasteful Georgian building serving lunches and cakes. *Open Mar. - Oct., daily, 10 - 5. No smoking throughout.*

LYME REGIS

Pilot Boat Inn, Bridge Street, Lyme Regis, DT7 3QA (02974) 43157

Historically interesting pub cum restaurant serving an imaginative range of freshly prepared dishes. Superb function room. *Open 11 - 2.30, 7 - 11, winter; 11 - 3, 6 - 11, summer. D. from around £10. No smoking in restaurant. Vegetarian meals a speciality. Licensed. Disabled access. Children welcome. Access, Visa.*

LYTCHETT MINSTER

Slepe Cottage Tea Rooms, Dorchester Road, Lytchett Minster (092 945) 281

Open 9.30 - 5.30. L. from £3.50. No smoking throughout. Licensed. Children welcome.

POOLE
The Clipper Restaurant, 100 Dolphin Centre, Poole, BH15 1SS (0202) 683334
Counter-service restaurant in shopping centre specialising in home-made dishes and cakes.
Open 9.30 to 5. Smoking banned in 75% of restaurant. Separate vegetarian counter. Licensed. Disabled access. Children welcome.

SHERBORNE
The Three Wishes, 78 Cheap Street, Sherborne (0935) 812164
180 seats. Open 9 - 5, Sun 11 - 4. L. from £4. Smoking banned in 50% of restaurant. Vegetarian standard. Limited disabled access. Children welcome. No credit cards.

WEYMOUTH
Milton Arms, 21 St. Alban's Street, Weymouth (0305) 782767
Open 9.30 - 2, 6.30 - 10. L. from £2.95. D. from £10. Separate area for smokers. Vegetarian standard. Licensed. Children welcome. Access, Visa.

Pubs & Wine Bars

ABBOTSBURY
Ilchester Arms Hotel, 9 Market Street, Abbotsbury, DT3 4JR (0305) 871243
Stone-built hotel in the centre of the lovely village of Abbotsbury; beamed ceilings and open fires in the bar; large attractive no-smoking conservatory.
Open 11 - 11. No smoking in conservaatory. Vegetarian available. Children welcome in conservatory and eating area of bar.

DORCHESTER
The Brace of Pheasants, Plush, Dorchester, DT2 7RQ (03004) 357
16th C. thatched building with restaurant, bar and separate family room.
Open 11.30 - 2.30, 6 - 11 (7 - 11 winter). L. around £8, D. around £12. Serving food 12 - 2, 7 - 10. No smoking in one room. Vegetarian available. Some wheelchair access. Children welcome.

Somerset
Accommodation

BRIDGWATER
Waterpitts Farm, Broomfield, Quantock Hills, Nr Bridgwater, TA5 1AT (082345) 1679
   A 5 acre small-holding with sheep, chickens, geese, ducks, cats & dogs in a secluded part of the Quantock Hills. Ideal for walking, cycling, fishing, riding & golf. Stables available for guests' horses. Pub with excellent food nearby. 6 miles from M5, Taunton & Bridgwater. B. & B.
Open all year. No smoking in the house. Vegetarian & other diets with notice. Children welcome. Pets by arrangement. TV in 1 bedroom. Tea/coffee on arrival & in bedroom on request. B. & B. £13.50-14.50.

DUNSTER
Burnells Farm, Knowle Lane, Dunster, Somerset, TA24 6UU (0643) 821841
   Comfortable modern farmhouse in lovely Avill Valley. Double, twin & single bedrooms & spacious lounge. Centrally heated & with electric blankets. Good centre for exploring Exmoor.
Open all year. No smoking in the house. Vegetarian & other diets "within reason". Children: over 8s only. Pets by arrangement. TV in lounge. B. & B. from £15.

Exmoor House Hotel, 12 West St. Dunster, TA24 6SN (0643) 821268
   Grade II Georgian listed building. Farm-fresh produce is used wherever possible in cooking.
Open Feb. to Nov. No smoking throughout. Vegetarian by arrangement. Licensed. Disabled access: 1 ground floor bedroom. Dogs by arrangement. En suite, tea/coffee-making & T.V. in all rooms. B. & B. from £25,

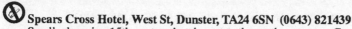

Spears Cross Hotel, West St, Dunster, TA24 6SN (0643) 821439
Small, charming 15th century hotel, next to the castle entrance. Car parking.
Open Mar. to Dec. No smoking in the house. Vegetarian by arrangement. Licensed. Children: over 12s welcome.
Pets by arrangement. En suite, TV & tea/coffee-making in all rooms. B. & B. from £19.50. D. from £11.

EAST BRENT

Knoll Lodge, Church Rd, East Brent, Somerset, TA9 4HZ (0278) 760294
19th C. listed house in a quiet village on the edge of the Somerset Levels. All 3 en suite
bedrooms are furnished with antique pine & hand-made American patchwork quilts. 2½ m M5
(J22).
Open all year. No smoking in the house. Vegetarian & other diets by arrangement. Children welcome. En suite,
TV & tea/coffee-making in bedrooms. B. & B. £18, D. £9.50.

FROME

Old Ford House, Old Ford, Frome, Somerset, BA11 2NF (0373) 462142
Old Ford House is a lovely period building with a Regency front and a 16th C. back! It stands
amidst a beautiful large garden in wonderful countryside just 1½ miles from Frome. Your hosts
take just one party of guests at any one time and there is a twin room (with en suite bathroom), a
double room (with a private bathroom) and one single room. Good home-cooking is the order of
the day: everything is prepared from fresh ingredients - some garden-grown vegetables are used -
and guests may choose either a pot-luck supper at the kitchen table or a rather grander candlelit
4-course evening meal in the dining room. Old Ford House is within easy reach of a number of
interesting places including Bath and the Cathedral city of Wells; additionally Oxford and London
are just 2 hours drive away.
Open all year. No smoking in the house. Vegetarian & most other diets by arrangement. Bring your own wine.
Children by arrangement. En suite/private bath & tea/coffee-making in each bedroom. TV in drawing room.
B. & B. £16

GLASTONBURY

Greinton House, Greinton, Nr Glastonbury, TA7 9BW (0458) 210307
Lovely house standing on the southern slopes of the Polden Hills amidst delightful gardens, with
tennis court, croquet lawn and heated swimming pool. Near Quaker burial ground.
Open all year. No smoking in the house. Children by arrangement. En suite in some bedrooms. Tea/coffee
making in all rooms. B. & B. from £15.

MINEHEAD

Hillside, Higher Allerford, Nr Minehead, TA24 8HS Tel & Fax: (0643) 862831
Hillside is a lovely West Country thatched cottage which stands amidst its own peaceful sunny
garden in the foothills of Exmoor; the location is outstanding

(the cottage is owned by the National Trust although run by
Kathy Bickerstaff) and there are wonderful views of vale,
moor and sea; the sunsets are breathtaking. This is the place
to come if you are in search of unspoilt countryside and
unspoilt villages! Allerford is also owned by the National
Trust and has retained its ancient pack-horse bridge and
blacksmith's shop; Hillside, which overlooks the village, has
many walks which literally begin from the doorstep. The
accommodation therein is comfortable and homely and guests
can look forward to a delicious breakfast of free-range eggs,
home-made bread, preserves and garden produce.

Open all year. No smoking in the dining room. Vegetarian & other diets by arrangement. Children & pets welcome. Tea/coffee-making facilities. TV in lounge & bedrooms on request. B. & B. from £14.50.

🚭 **Montrose, 14 Tregonwell Rd, Minehead, TA24 5DW (0643) 705136**
The Montrose is a friendly family-run hotel which is centrally situated on level ground within two minutes' walk of the sea front and shopping centre of Minehead. The two en suite guest bedrooms have been comfortably furnished and appointed and one is located on the ground floor, making it a good choice for guests who find stairs difficult; there is a centrally heated and pleasantly furnished T.V. lounge for guests' use. Breakfast and evening meal menus offer a good choice of dishes (which are served in generous portions) and meals are taken in a light, spacious dining room; refreshments may be requested between 9 and 10 p.m. each evening. Out of season bargain breaks are available and mid-week bookings are accepted. ETB Two Crowns.
Open Mar. to Oct. No smoking in the house. Vegetarian & other diets by arrangement. Children: over 3s only. 2 rooms en suite, 1 ground floor. Tea/coffee-making in all rooms. T.V. lounge. B. & B. from £14-£17.

MONTACUTE
Milk House Restaurant (with accommodation), The Borough, TA15 6XB (0935) 823823
Open all year ex. Xmas Day. No smoking in dining room, lounge & bedrooms; separate smoking room. Vegetarian & vegan standard. Licensed. Children: over 12s only. En suite in 2 rooms. T.V. D. from £19.80

PORLOCK
Porlock Vale House & Riding Centre, Porlock Weir, TA24 8NY (0643) 862338
Elegant and spacious Edwardian country house set in 25 acres of beautiful grounds sweeping down to the sea. Stables, riding school, show jumps and schooling paddocks; riding holidays a speciality.
Open all year. No smoking in dining room & 1 lounge. Vegetarian standard. Other diets by arrangement. Licensed. En suite in 70% rooms. Tea/coffee-making & T.V. in all bedrooms. B. & B. from £20.

SHAFTESBURY
Quiet Corner Farm, Henstridge, Templecombe, BA8 0RA (0963) 63045
Spacious farmhouse set in pretty garden with orchard and paddock with Shetland ponies on the edge of Henstridge village with stunning views. ETB 2 Crowns Commended.
Open all year. No smoking in dining room, bedrooms & sitting room. Vegetarian standard. Other diets by arrangement. Children welcome. 1 en suite. Tea/coffee-making. T.V. lounge. B. & B. from £16-£18.50.

SHEPTON MALLET
The Long House Hotel, Pilton, Shepton Mallet, BA4 4BP (0749) 890701
An 18th C. house with lots of character and a relaxed atmosphere in a picturesque village setting.
Open all year. No smoking in dining room & some bedrooms. Vegetarian & wholefood standard. Licensed. Children welcome. En suite all rooms. Coffee-making & T.V. Credit cards. B. & B. from £17. D. from £9.

TAUNTON
RoadChef Taunton Deane, Motorway Service Area M5 South & Northbound, Trull, Taunton, BS26 2US (0823) 271111
Conveniently located on the Somerset/Devon border, RoadChef Taunton Deane was the site for  the first 39 bedroom motorway lodge in England, and is an ideal place for holiday-makers to break a journey to the South West. Each of the 39 bedrooms in its Lodge have been comfortably furnished and well-appointed with a trouser press, hairdryer and tea and coffee making facilities. The self-service Orchards restaurants have excellent smoke-free areas and serve a wide selection of popular meals. There is always a vegetarian option on the menu and baby foods are also available (there is a changing room). Additionally travellers will be pleased to find a helpful range of other facilities including modern well-stocked shops and an auto-bank.
Open all year except Xmas day. No smoking in most of restaurant & some bedrooms. Disabled access. Children welcome. En suite, TV (plus Sky) & tea/coffee-making in bedrooms. Credit cards. B. & B. from £29.

Slimbridge Station Farm, Bishops Lydeard, Taunton, TA4 3BX (0823) 432223
A village farm of 140 acres offering accommodation in an attractive Victorian farmhouse.
Open all year ex. Xmas. No smoking in the house. Vegetarian & other diets by arrangement. Children welcome. Pets by arrangement. Tea/coffee-making & T.V. in all bedrooms. B. & B. from £15.

WEDMORE

Nut Tree Farm, Soughton Cross, Wedmore, BS28 4QP (0934) 712404
Lovely 16th C. farmhouse; 1 mile from the attractive and historic village of Wedmore; traditional and wholefood breakast offered; also self-catering holiday cottage to let.
Open all year. No smoking in the house. Vegetarian & other diets by arrangement. En suite in 2 rooms. Tea/coffee-making in all bedrooms. T.V. lounge. Access, Visa. B. & B. from £15.

WELLS

Bekynton House, 7 St. Thomas St, Wells, BA5 2UU (0749) 672222
Well-maintained period house, well-equipped and furnished, situated close to Cathedral.
Open all year. No smoking in dining room and bedrooms. Vegetarian & other diets by arrangement. Children: over 5s only. 6 rooms en suite. Tea/coffee-making & T.V. in all 8 rooms. Access, Visa. B. & B. from £20.

Worth House Hotel, Worth, Wells, BA5 1LW (0749) 672041
15th C. farmhouse and restaurant with exposed beams and open fireplaces.
Open all year. No smoking in dining room & T.V. lounge. Special diets by arrangement. Licensed. Children welcome. En suite & tea/coffee-making in all rooms. T.V. lounge. B. & B. from £28. D. £15.

WINSFORD (EXMOOR)

Karslake House Hotel, Winsford, Minehead, TA24 7JE (064385) 242

 Karslake House Hotel is a 500-year-old Grade II listed building which was originally a brewer's malt house and stands in a secluded garden in the very pretty village of Winsford (there is a charming thatched inn nearby). The building has been extensively renovated and, although many of the original features have been retained, the alterations have made of Karslake House a most comfortable hotel with all modern amenities. The imaginative menu features some unusual international - as well as more traditional English - dishes, and a typical evening meal selection would feature Quail's Egg in Paté followed by Steak and Kidney Pie (with fresh vegetables) and a tempting dessert, such as Raspberry and Almond Flan. Winsford is situated right in the heart of Exmoor and horse-riding, birdwatching, walking and fishing may all be enjoyed.
Open Easter to Oct. inc. No smoking in the house. Vegetarian & other diets by arrangement. Licensed. Children welcome. Pets by arrangement. En suite 4 rooms. Tea/coffee-making & T.V. in bedrooms. B. & B. from £24.50.

Restaurants

BRIDGWATER

The Hood Arms, Kilve, Bridgwater, Somerset, TA5 7EA (0278) 74210
17th C. coaching inn set amidst the outstanding scenery of the Quantocks.
Open all year. No smoking in restaurant. Vegetarian available.

CASTLE CARY

The Old Bakehouse Restaurant, High St, Castle Cary, BA9 7AW (0963) 50067
Wholefood shop and restaurant specialising in local produce and home cooking.
L. around £6. No smoking in restaurant. Exclusively vegetarian. Licensed. Disabled access. Children.

DULVERTON

Rock House Inn, Jury Rd, Dulverton, TA22 9DU (0398) 23558
Small country pub on the edge of the town, set in Exmoor National Park. Traditional English fare.
No smoking in restaurant. Vegetarian standard. Licensed. Disabled access. Children welcome.

DUNSTER

 The Tea Shoppe, Dunster, TA24 6SF (0643) 821304
15th C. cottage tea rooms; traditional, home-made English dishes using local, fresh produce.
Open L. 12 - 4. L. from £6. No smoking throughout. Vegetarian Licensed. Children welcome.

GLASTONBURY

 Rainbows End Café 17 High St, Glastonbury (0458) 33896
Warm, friendly atmosphere, counter service & pine tables. Vegetarian wholefood.
Open L. 12 - 3. L. around £2-£3. No smoking throughout. Vegetarian standard. Vegan and gluten-free items sometimes on menu. Licensed. Children welcome.

MONTACUTE

 Milk House, The Borough, Montacute, TA15 6XB (0935) 823823
The Milk House Natural Food Restaurant offers deliciously healthy food in an elegant setting.
30 seats. Open 12.30 - 2, 7.30 - 9.30. D. from £19.80. No smoking throughout. Vegetarian & vegan standard. Licensed. Children: over 12s only. Access, Visa.

King's Arms Inn, Montacute, TA15 GUU (0935) 822513
Pub specialising in home cooking and baking; traditional food prepared from fresh produce.
Open 12 - 2, 7.30 - 9. No smoking requested at lunch time when food is served.

TAUNTON

 Pavilion Coffee Shop, Debenhams, 19-26 North St, Taunton, TA1 1LL (0823) 272626
Pavilion is a friendly self-service coffee shop serving poular light lunches, snacks and a wide range of hot and cold drinks.
Open store hours. Smoking banned thoughout. Vegetarian meals. Disabled access. Children very welcome. Credit and debit cards accepted.

The Falcon Hotel, Henlade, Taunton, TA3 5DH (0823) 442502
Country house hotel in 2 acres of mature, landscaped gardens just a minute from the M5 (J25).
Open 7 - 9 (last orders). No smoking in restaurant. Vegetarian. Licensed. Disabled access. Children welcome.

WELLS

 The Good Earth Restaurant, 4 Priory Rd, Wells BA5 1SY (0749) 678600
Licensed vegetarian/wholefood restaurant sharing premises with a wholefood shop.
Open 9.30 - 5.30. Mon. L. from 12. L. around £6. No smoking. Licensed. Disabled access. Children.

The Worth House Hotel and Tylers Restaurant, Worth, Wells, BA5 1LW (0749) 72041
15th C. farmhouse with exposed beams and open fireplaces; traditional fare with a difference.
25 seats. Open 7 - 9. No smoking in restaurant. Licensed.

Pubs & Wine Bars

MONTACUTE

King's Arms Inn, Montacute, TA15 GUU (0935) 822513
Pub specialising in home cooking & baking; traditional English food prepared from fresh, sometimes organic, produce.
18 seats. Open 12 - 2, 7.30 - 9. No smoking requested in bar area where food is served at lunchtime. Licensed. Children welcome. Credit cards.

Wiltshire Accommodation

AVEBURY

Windmill House, Winterbourne Monkton, Nr Avebury, SN4 9NN (06723) 446
Beautifully renovated miller's house set amidst stunning scenery; 1m from Avebury stone circle; comfortably furnished; excellent cuisine with home-baked bread & home-grown veg.
Open all year. No smoking in dining room & discouraged throughout. Vegetarian, diabetic and other special diets by arrangement. Children welcome. B. & B. from £14.

BRADFORD ON AVON

Bradford Old Windmill, 4 Masons Lane, Bradford on Avon, BA15 1QN (0225) 866842

Standing high above the ancient wool town of Bradford-on-Avon, the stump of its former windmill, which was used commercially as such for just 11 years of its life, has now been beautifully restored by its current owners, Priscilla and Peter Roberts, who have reinstated the timber sail gallery, renovated the whole of the 4 storey Cotswold stone tower (and added a new 2 storey extension) and have charmingly decorated and furnished all the new rooms (which naturally enough come in all sorts of shapes and sizes) with lots of stripped pine and 'the flotsam and jetsam of beachcombing trips around the world'. A holiday destination of a highly unusual - yet thoroughly charming - variety. The food is as imaginatively prepared and eclectic in style as the building: menus vary from provincial French (Cruditées followed by Duck Egg Quiche and real Creme Caramel) to Indian Thali.
Open all year. No smoking in the house. Vegetarian standard. Vegan & other diets by arrangement. Children: over 6s only. En suite in some rooms. Tea/coffee-making in all bedrooms. T.V. on request. B. & B. from £24.50.

EAST KNOYLE

Milton House, East Knoyle, Salisbury, SP3 6BG (0747) 830397
Charming old house in peaceful hamlet; farm-fresh eggs, fresh fruit juice, wholemeal bread.
Open all year. No smoking in the house. Vegetarian & other diets by arrangement. Children welcome. Pets by arrangement. Private bathroom, T.V. & tea/coffee making facilities. B. & B. from £19-£22.

MARLBOROUGH

Laurel Cottage, Southend, Ogbourne St George, Marlborough, SN8 1SG (0672) 84288
Exquisite 16th C. thatched cottage with gardens; oak-beams, inglenook fireplace, etc.
Open March to Oct. No smoking in the house. Vegetarian standard. Other diets by arrangement. Children welcome. En suite in some rooms. Tea/coffee-making & T.V. in all rooms. B. & B. from £15.

'Westerly', Mildenhall, Marlborough, SN8 2LR (0672) 514254
Open Apr. to Feb. No smoking in the house. Vegetarian & other diets by arrangement. Children: over 8s.

MELKSHAM

'Josel', 117 Semington Rd, Melksham, SN12 6DP (0225) 709490
Josel is a small, modern, detached private house which is conveniently situated near the M4 between Melksham and Trowbridge. A very friendly welcome is offered to guests and the proprietor, Mrs Selina Wesley, will do all she can to make your stay happy and memorable. At Josel you are perfectly placed for visiting a range of tourist attractions including the stone circles at Avebury & Stonehenge, & the National Trust village, Lacock; Bath & Salisbury are nearby.
Open all year. No smoking in the house. Low-cal. & low-fat standard. Vegetarian & other diets by arrangement. Children welcome. Tea/coffee-making & T.V. in all rooms. B. & B. from £12-£13.

Shurnhold House, Shurnhold, Melksham, SN12 8DG (0225) 790555
Jacobean Manor House in 1 acre of mature gardens 1m from Melksham. 4-poster beds.
Open all year. No smoking in dining room, lounge & bedrooms. Licensed. Children welcome. Pets by arrangement. En suite, tea/coffee making, T.V. & phone in all rooms. Credit cards. B. & B. from £40.

SALISBURY

The Coach and Horses, Winchester St, Salisbury, SP1 1HG (0722) 336254

The Coach and Horses is Salisbury's oldest Inn and there are records showing it to be trading as early as 1482! Some five centuries later Martin and Angie Cooper, its present owners, completely renovated the building - gutting the bar, restaurant and kitchen - till now, beautifully refurbished (and still retaining some period features, such as timbered walls), the Coach and Horses has become one of the city's most popular eating and drinking establishments and has a well-deserved reputation for food and wine. Its menu is based around the inn's history as being one of the staging posts on the old A30 London to Penzance route: appetiser, main course, fish course and dessert are each named after other staging posts (Bagshot...Andover...Exeter, etc.) until the Penzance section entitles you, appropriately enough, at the end of your meal to enjoy a 'Smugglers' (coffee laced with liqueur).
Open all year. No smoking in restaurant & bedrooms. Vegetarian standard. Other diets by arrangement. Licensed. Children welcome. En suite, TV & tea-making in rooms. Credit cards. B. & B. from £38.

The Gallery, 36 Wyndham Rd, Salisbury, Wilts, SP1 3AB (0722) 324586
The Gallery is a small family-run bed and breakfast situated just 10 minutes' walk from the city centre and its cathedral, museums, leisure centre and swimming pool. Your hosts, David and Rina Musselwhite aim to give real 'home from home' service and do everything they can to make your stay a happy and memorable one. Each of the bedrooms has private facilities and after a comfortable night's sleep you can look forward to a delicious home-cooked breakfast with lots of choices including smoked mackerel and creamed mushrooms as alternatives to the usual English breakfast platter; fruit and herb teas are also available as well as the usual beverages. Salisbury has so much to commend it as a destination in itself: the city and cathedral draw visitors from all over the world; you are also ideally placed for visiting Avebury and Stonehenge stone circles.
Open all year. No smoking in the house. Vegetarian & other diets by arrangement. Children: over 12s only. En suite, TV & tea/coffee-making in bedrooms. B. & B. £28 - 34.

Glen Lyn Guest House, 6 Bellamy Lane, Milford Hill, SP1 2SP (0722) 327880
Large, elegant Victorian house in a quiet lane just a few minutes' easy walk from the city centre; several rooms overlook beautiful gardens. Ample parking.
Open all year. No smoking in the house. Children: over 12s only. En suite in some rooms. Tea/coffee-making & T.V. in all rooms. B. & B. from £19. ETB 2 Crowns. RAC & AA Acclaimed.

Holmhurst Guest House, Downtown Rd, Salisbury, SP2 8AR (0722) 323164
Well-appointed guest house just a short walk from the Cathedral, city centre and country walks. Easy access to coastal resorts and New Forest.
Open March to Oct. No smoking in dining room, lounge & some bedrooms. Children: over 5s only. En suite in most rooms. Tea/coffee served on request. T.V. in lounge. B. & B. from £16.

The New Inn at Salisbury, 41-43 New St, Salisbury, SP1 2PH (0722) 327679
Charming 15th C. timbered building in the old part of the city adjoining the cathedral close.
Open all year. No smoking throughout. Vegetarian standard. Licensed. Disabled access. Children welcome. En suite, tea/coffee-making & T.V. in all rooms. Credit cards. B. & B. from £39-£55.

The Rose & Crown, Harnham Rd, Harnham, SP2 8JQ Tel: (0722) 327908 Fax: (0722) 339816
13th C. inn with oak beams set in pretty rose gardens on the banks of the Avon; beautifully appointed & with spacious conservatory/restaurant; fresh produce used in cooking.
Open all year. No smoking in 50% of dining room & 1 bedrooms. Vegetarian & other diets by arrangement. Licensed. Children welcome. Pets by arrangement. Tea-making & T.V. in all rooms. Access, Visa, Amex, Diner's.

Ⓝ **Scotland Lodge, Winterbourne Stoke, Nr Salisbury, SP3 4TF (0980) 620943**
Beautiful old house offering exeptionally comfortable accommodation; breakfast only.
Open all year. No smoking throughout. Vegetarian standard. Children welcome. En suite, tea/coffee-making &
T.V. in all rooms. B. & B. from £17.50-£25.

Ⓝ **Stratford Lodge, 4 Park Lane Castle Rd, SP1 3NP Tel: (0722) 325177 Fax: (0722) 412699**

Stratford Lodge is an elegant Victorian house which stands in a quiet lane overlooking Victoria Park. Your host, Jill Bayly, offers a special brand of gracious hospitality: the complementary sherry before dinner speaks volumes - and is a welcome herald to a first-rate meal prepared by Jill from fresh ingredients, some home-grown. It is always advisable to book for dinner lest you miss such delights as Baked Roquefort Pears followed by Salmon Steak with Herb Butter and a selection of home-made desserts, all served by candlelight on beautiful china. Each of the bedrooms has en suite facilities and has been decorated and furnished with flair - one room has a brass Victorian bed; the house has been furnished throughout with antiques and there is a lovely garden with flowering shrubs. Salisbury is a beautiful city - not the less appealing because of its proximity to so much unspoilt countryside and historically interesting towns and villages.
Open 22 Jan - 23 Dec. No smoking in the house. Vegetarian & other diets by arrangement. Children: over 8s
welcome. Licensed. En suite, TV & tea/coffee-making in bedrooms. Credit cards.

Ⓝ **Yew Tree Cottage, Grove Lane, Redlynch, Salisbury, SP5 2NR (0725) 21730**
Attractive, comfortable 'Guest Home' standing in a lovely large garden & smallholding in pretty village of Redlynch 1m from New Forest. Traditional, wholefood, vegetarian or vegan b'fasts.
Open all year. No smoking throughout. Vegetarian & vegan standard. Other special diets by arrangement. No
disabled access. Children welcome. Tea/coffee on request. T.V. in lounge. B. & B. from £14.

SWINDON
Lower Shaw Farm, Old Shaw Lane, Shaw, Nr Swindon, SN5 9PJ (0793) 771080
Converted farm now a meeting place for w/e & week-long courses. Childrens' play barn. Substantial organic herb, fruit & vegetable garden & also goats, bees & hens producing milk, eggs and honey.
No smoking in the dining room. Children welcome. Pets by arrangement. Tariff depends on course.

ZEALS
Ⓝ **Cornerways Cottage, Longcross, Zeals, BA12 6LL (0747) 840477**
18th C. house of great character; very comfortably furnished. Breakfast is a generous feast including fresh croissants & muffins; alternative b'fast menus avail. for those on special diets.
Open all year. No smoking in the house. Vegetarian & other diets by arrangement. Children welcome. Pets
(small dogs) by arrangement. En suite in 2 rooms. Tea/coffee making. T.V. in lounge. B. & B. from £14 - 16.

Ⓝ **Stag Cottage, Fantley Lane, Zeals, BA12 6NA (0747) 840458**
17th C. thatched cottage in pretty gardens; 4-poster bed. B'fast & clotted cream teas.
Open all year. No smoking in the house. Vegetarian & other diets by arrangement. Children welcome -
baby sitting service available. Tea/coffee-making in all rooms. T.V. in dining room. B. & B. from £13.

Restaurants

AMESBURY
New Trawlerman, 7 Flower Lane, Amesbury, SP4 7HE (0980) 624438
Open 11 - 11. 50% no-moking. Vegetarian. Licensed. Children welcome.

AVEBURY
Stones Restaurant, Avebury, Marlborough, SN8 1RE (06723) 514
Excellent vegetarian restaurant serving fine cuisine prepared from fresh, local produce.
Open 10 - 6. 70% no-smoking. Licensed. Disabled access: good. Children welcome.

BRADFORD ON AVON

 The Bridge Tea Rooms, 24a Bridge St, Bradford on Avon (02216) 5537
Open 10 - 6. No smoking. Vegetarian available. Wheelchair access.

MARLBOROUGH

The Polly Tea Room, 27 High Street, Marlborough (0672) 512146
Award-winning tea rooms serving extensive selection of home-made cakes, pastries & snacks.
Open 8.30 (Sun. 9) - 6.30 daily. 60% no-smoking. Vegetarian. Licensed. Disabled access. Children.

SALISBURY

The Barford Inn, Barford St Martin, Salisbury, SP3 4AB   Proprietors: Marcelle and Phil Stansfield. Tel: (0722) 742242

The Barford Inn is a traditional 'Old World'English inn in which there is no pool, no darts and no fruit machines - but just quiet, unobstrusive background music, and great food and ale! The proprietors offer a wide range of excellent, freshly prepared meals (the vegetarian options are tasty and imaginative), and traditional cask ales, chilled lagers and a wide range of wines and non-alcoholic beverages are also served. Although the Barford Inn is in every sense a traditional English pub, the proprietors have made one important consession to contemporary public opinion: there is a bar reserved for non-smokers!

No smoking in 1 room. Vegetarian always available. Children welcome throughout the pub.

 Hob Nob Coffee Shop, The King's House, 65 The Close, Salisbury, SP1 2EN (0722) 332151
Museum coffee shop serving home-made snacks and hot dishes; good vegetarian options.
Open 10.30 - 4.30. No smoking throughout. Vegetarian. Disabled access. Children welcome.

SWINDON

 Oasis Leisure Centre, North Star Avenue, Swindon, SN2 1EP (0793) 533404/5
Restaurant/café within leisure centre, serving both wholefood and fast food.
Open 11.30 - 2, 6 - 9/ 10 - 7 W/ends. No smoking throughout. Disabled access. Children welcome.

WARMINSTER

 Jenners, 45 Market Place, Warminster, BA12 9AZ (0985) 213385
Home-made meals prepared daily from fresh produce.
No smoking throughout. Licensed. Disabled access: 'one small step - double front doors and wide toilet doors.'

Pubs & Wine Bars

SALISBURY

The Barford Inn, Barford St Martin, Salisbury, SP3 4AB (0722) 742242
For further details please see entry in the restaurant section.

The New Inn at Salisbury, 41-43 New St, Salisbury, SP1 2PH (0722) 327679
For further details please see the entry in the accommodation section.

The South of England

Hampshire
Accommodation

ALTON

The Grange Hotel, London Road, Alton, GU34 4EG (0420) 86565
Charming small hotel standing in 2 acres of gardens; beautifully appointed bedrooms; excellent cuisine in 'Truffles' restaurant; good conference facilities.
Open all year ex. Xmas - Dec. 30. No smoking in dining room & 2 bedrooms. Vegetarian. Licensed. Disabled access. Children: over 4s. En suite, tea/coffee-making & T.V. in all bedrooms. Credit cards. B & B from £25.

8 Goslings Croft, Selbourne, Nr Alton, GU34 3HZ (042 050) 285
Family home standing on the edge of historic village, adjacent to National Trust land. Ideal base for touring & walking. Roman Museum & Gilbert White Museum (18th C. naturalist) nearby.
Open all year. No smoking in the house. Vegetarian by arrangement. Children welcome (facilities for babies). 1 en suite. TV & tea/coffee-making in bedrooms. Credit cards. B. & B. from £14.75, single £19.50.

ANDOVER

Abbotts Law, Abbotts Ann, Andover, SP11 7DW (0264) 710350
Beautiful house in 3 acres of attractive gardens & woodland overlooking water meadows.
Open April to Oct. No smoking in the house. Vegetarian & other diets by arrangement. Children: over 10s welcome. En suite, tea/coffee-making & T.V. in all bedrooms. B. & B. from £21.

BASINGSTOKE

Oaklea Guest House, London Rd, Hook, Nr Basingstoke, RG27 9LA (0256) 762673

Oaklea is a fine Victorian house standing in an acre of walled gardens just a mile from junction 5 of the M3. It has been quite beautifully furnished throughout and offers first-class accommodation and food to guests. The food is basically of the good-old-fashioned home-cooking variety - but everything is beautifully presented and has been prepared from fresh ingredients wherever possible. Breakfast is a hearty feast - smoked haddock or manx kippers feature in the otherwise traditional meal - and the 4-course dinner menu would typically feature Chicken and Sweetcorn Soup followed by Roast Lamb with all the trimmings and a delicious home-made dessert, such as Gooseberry Upside-down Cake; a good cheese board, and coffee, would complete the meal. Oaklea is ideally situated for Heathrow (35 mins), Basingstoke, Farnborough, Camberley and Reading, and additionally there is a half-hourly train service to Waterloo from Hook.
Open all year. No smoking in dining room & some bedrooms. Vegetarian & other diets by arrangement. Licensed. Children welcome. En suite, tea-making & TV in some rooms. T.V. lounge. B. & B. from £17.

BEAULIEU

Coolderry Cottage, Masseys Lane, East Boldre, Beaulieu, SO42 7WE (0590) 612428
Coolderry is a small, recently extended cottage in a quiet lane on the edge of East Boldre; interestingly, there is a small Baptist meeting house in the garden which is now used by Brian, the proprietor, for furniture-making. Accommodation is in comfortable rooms - each overlooking fields at the back of the cottage - and breakfast is served in a charming dining room which is used as a music room at other times of the day; both traditional and Continental breakfast options are available. East Boldre is just one mile from Beaulieu, the site of the famous Abbey and of the National Motor Museum; additionally you are well-placed for visiting Bucklers Hard, Exbury Gardens, the Butterfly Farm and the beautiful Hampshire Coast.

Open all year ex. Xmas. No smoking in the house. Vegetarian by arrangement. Children welcome. Well-behaved dogs accepted. Tea/coffee-making in all bedrooms. T.V. available. B. & B. £14-16.

BURLEY

Ⓝ Mrs A Clarkson, The Vicarage, Church Lane, Burley, BH24 4AP (0425) 402303
     The Vicarage is a peaceful house set in its own well-kept grounds just three minutes' pleasant walk from the centre of the village of Burley. It is a comfortable family home set in the heart of the New Forest - in fact the forest ponies graze right up to the front gate! Although the village is surrounded by the New Forest countryside, Burley has a range of amenities, including a 9-hole golf course, pony-riding, Wagonette rides and a good selection of shops. In addition to the charms of its location, The Vicarage is easily accessible from the A31 or A35 and is within easy reach of the sea, the cathedrals of Salisbury and Winchester, and the houses at Broadlands and Beaulieu.
Open all year. No smoking in the house. Vegetarian breakfast by arrangement. Children welcome. Dogs by arrangement. Tea/coffee-making in all bedrooms. T.V. in dining room. B. & B. from £15.

Ⓝ Forest Tea House, Restaurant & B. & B., Pound Ln, Burley, BH24 4ED (04253 2305)
Classic New Forest style cottage just 250 yards from Burley next door to Cider Farm (free tastings).
Open all year. No smoking in the house & restaurant. Disabled access to tearoom. Children welcomed in tearoom (not B. & B.). En suite, tea/coffee-making, colour T.V. in all bedrooms. B. & B. from £18

CHANDLERS FORD

Ⓝ St Lucia, 68 Shaftesbury Avenue, Chandlers Ford, Eastleigh SO5 3BP (0703) 262995
     St Lucia is a 1920's detached home standing in a third of an acre of mature and well-maintained gardens in a quiet residential area of Chandlers Ford. The bedrooms are all comfortable and centrally heated and each has a range of helpful amenities, including T.V. and tea and coffee-making facilities. A traditional or Continental breakfast option is served to guests (in your room, if you wish!), and the evening meal consists of either a choice of snacks or lighter meals, which can be prepared at short notice, or a full 4-course menu which can be offered if a few hours' notice is given. A typical 4-course evening meal would feature home-made Spring Soup (lettuce and Spring Onion), followed by home-made Steak and Kidney Pie (with home-grown vegetables), and a traditional dessert, such as Lemon Meringue Pie; tea or coffee would complete the meal. Local facilities include a sports centre and 18-hole golf course, and you are close to M3 and M27.
Open all year. No smoking in the house. Vegetarian & other diets by arrangement. Children: over 10s only. H & C, tea/coffee-making & T.V. in all bedrooms. Parking for 5. B. & B. from £14.

FORDINGBRIDGE

Ⓝ Hillbury, 2 Fir Tree Hill, Alderholt, Fordingbridge, SP6 3AY (0425) 652582
Large bungalow in peaceful surroundings. Easy access M27. Large garden & patio. Ideal touring base New Forest & South Coast. Riding, swimming, golf nearby. Varied breakfast menus.
Open all year. No smoking in the house. Vegetarian & other diets by arrangement. Children welcome. 1 room en suite. TV & tea/coffee-making bedrooms. B. & B. from £15-17. (children over 3 yrs ½ price).

KILMESTON

Ⓝ Dean Farm, Kilmeston, Nr Alresford, SO24 0NL (0962) 771 286
     This welcoming 18th C. farmhouse in the picturesque village of Kilmeston forms part of a working mixed farm on the edge of the Hampshire Downs. The comfortable accommodation consists of two double bedrooms and one family room (all with lovely views), and the large sitting room and separate dining room each have log fires and a relaxing atmosphere. Situated on the Wayfarers Walk and approximately one and a half miles from the South Downs Way, the farm is an ideal stopping-off point for walkers and horse-riders alike (there is stabling and grazing for horses and superb riding over 170 acres of farmland). Several nearby pubs serve good food and real ale, and you are within easy reach of Winchester (8 m) and the New Forest (35 mins by car).

Open Jan. to Dec. No smoking in the house. Vegetarians standard. Diabetic & low-fat by arrangement. Children: over 5s welcome. Tea/coffee on request at any time. T.V. in sitting room. B. & B. from £15. ETB listed.

LYMINGTON

Albany House, 3 Highfield, Lymington, SO41 9GB (0590) 671900
Elegant Regency house built around 1840 on the western edge of Lymington. Sea views from most bedrooms. Log fires in winter. Afternoon tea served in sitting room overlooking walled garden.
Open seasonally. No smoking in dining room & actively discouraged elsewhere. Vegetarian by arrangement. Pets by arrangement. 3 en suites. Tea/coffee-making in all rooms. T.V. available. B. & B. from £18.

Candleford House, Middle Rd, Tiptoe, Lymington, SO41 6FX (0590) 682069
Modern, detached Georgian-style house standing in secluded garden surrounded by woods & fields. Bournemouth, Lymington & harbour, riding, woodland walks & coast, nearby. B. & B.
Open most of the year. No smoking in the house. TV & tea/coffee-making in all bedrooms. B. & B. from £13.50.

Redwing Farm, Pitmore Lane, Sway, Lymington, SO41 6BW (0590) 683319
Open all year. No smoking in the house. Vegetarian. 2 bedrooms ground floor. B. & B. from £17

Wheatsheaf House, Gosport Street, Lymington, SO41 9BG (0590) 679208
17th C. Grade II listed coaching inn. Self-catering accommodation also available. B'fast only.
Open all year. No smoking in the house. Children welcome. Pets by arrangement. En suite in some rooms. T.V. in sitting room. B. & B. from £18.

LYNDHURST, NEW FOREST

Little Hayes, Romsey Rd, Lyndhurst, New Forest, Hants, SO43 7AR (0703) 283000
Little Hayes is a lovely, late-Victorian house standing in Lyndhurst village in the New Forest. Recently restored by its owners, April and John Robinson, it has been comfortably furnished and appointed with elegance and style - and there is a friendly, relaxed atmosphere. Breakfast is sumptuous, with enough traditional and continental choices to satisfy the heartiest - or healthiest - of appetites, and there are several excellent local pubs and restaurants where you may enjoy an evening meal. You are ideally situated in Lyndhurst to enjoy all the charms of the New Forest, with its famous wild ponies, deer, cattle and donkeys, and you are also within easy reach of Beaulieu, Broadlands, Bournemouth and Southampton.
Open Spring - Autumn inc. No smoking in the house. Vegetarian & other diets by arrangement. Children: over 5s only. 1 private bathroom. TV & tea/coffee-making in bedrooms. B. & B. from £14.

PETERSFIELD

Mizzards Farm, Rogate, Petersfield, GU31 5HS (0730) 821656
Open all year ex. Xmas. No smoking in the house. Vegetarian by arrangement. Licensed. Children: over 6s only. En suite, TV & tea/coffee-making in all bedrooms. B. & B. from £20.

Trotton Farm, Rogate, Petersfield, GU31 5EN (0730) 813618
Lovely farmhouse situated in an area of outstanding natural beauty with many attractions within 1 hour's drive; many walks and fishing may be enjoyed within the environs of the farm.
Open all year. No smoking in the house. Vegetarian standard. Children welcome. En suite & tea/coffee-making in all bedrooms. T.V. in sitting/games room.

PORTSMOUTH

Holiday Inn, North Harbour, Portsmouth, PO6 4SH (0705) 383151
Open all year. No smoking in 40% of dining room & some bedrooms. Vegetarian & other diets by arrangement. Licensed. Disabled access. Children & pets welcome. En suite, TV & tea/coffee-making in all bedrooms.

RINGWOOD

Moortown Lodge, 244 Christchurch Road, Ringwood, BH24 3AS (0425) 471404
Country house hotel & restaurant situated just outside Ringwood on the edge of the New Forest.
Open all year. No smoking in dining room. Vegetarian & other diets by arrangement. Licensed. Children welcome. En suite in double/twin rooms. Tea/coffee-making & T.V. all rooms. Credit cards. B. & B. from £26.

ROMSEY

 Spursholt House, Salisbury Rd, Romsey, SO51 6DJ Tel: (0794) 512229 Fax: (0794) 523142

Spursholt House was originally built for one of Cromwells' generals; it later came into the hands of the Palmerston family who lived at Broadlands and, in the 1830s, was extended for occupation by Lord and Lady Cowper. The result of these additions is the charming country house you see today; surrounded by a magnificent garden in which paved terraces with urns of geraniums overlook a lawn, impressive topiary and a view of Romsey Abbey, and beyond the flowerbeds. Yew hedges enclose a succession of further pleasures - one garden leading into another, a parterre followed by apple trees, a lily pool and a dovecote with fan tails! The interior of the house has been furnished in keeping with its character: one bedroom is oak-panelled and all contain antiques, extra large beds, elegant sofas and have garden views. Downstairs the dining room has been handsomely furnished in Victorian style, and there is a spectacular sitting room with a Knole sofa, a love seat and carved fireplace.Breakfast and light suppers (advance order for the latter, please!) are the only meals to be served at Spursholt House but there are a number of good local inns in addition to the nearby Manor House restaurant where you may enjoy an evening meal.

Open all year. No smoking in the house. Vegetarian & other diets by arrangement. Children & pets welcome. En suite 1 room. Tea/coffee-making in bedrooms. TV in lounge. B. & B. £15-20.

SOUTHAMPTON

RoadChef Rownhams Motorway Service Area, M27 South & Northbound (0703) 734480

Tourists and business travellers heading for the Southern ferries or the New Forest will find RoadChef Rownhams near Southampton an ideal stop. Each of the 39 bedrooms in its Lodge have been comfortably furnished and well-appointed with a trouser press, hairdryer and tea and coffee making facilities. The self-service Orchards restaurants have excellent smoke-free areas (200 of 350 seats are smoke-free), and serve a wide selection of popular meals such as Golden Scampi Platter or Horseshoe Gammon Steak, served with chips and peas; there is always a vegetarian option on the menu and baby foods are also available (there is a changing room). Rownhams won the coveted Best Cup of Tea Award for 1991: the only service area in the country to win it twice.

Open all year ex. Xmas day. No smoking in most of restaurant & some bedrooms. Vegetarian standard. Disabled facilities. Children welcome. En suite, coffee-making & T.V. plus Sky in rooms. Credit cards. B. & B. from £32.

SOUTH WARNBOROUGH

Street Farmhouse, Alton Rd, South Warnborough, Hants, RG25 1RS (0256) 862225

Street Farmhouse dates from Jacobean times at which time it was two separate cottages which formed part of the 2,300 acre South Warnborough estate; the parish of Warnborough incidentally is referred to in mediaeval documents as Warnebourne or Warnburn and probably derives its name from the bourne or stream which has its source in the north of the parish. Over the centuries the farmhouse, which is a listed building, has been extended by its succession of owners but this has been carefully carried out and the house still retains many original features; the present owners have been particularly sympathetic in the restoration of such original details as the beamed ceilings, large inglenook

fireplace and vaulted kitchen ceiling. The guest accommodation is very well-appointed - all bedrooms have central heating and wash basins in addition to other helpful amenities - and there is an outdoor heated swimming pool in season plus ample parking. Street Farmhouse adjoins open farmland - and as such is ideal for country lovers - but it is also within easy reach of J5 on the M3 and accordingly affords visitors easy access to Guildford and London.
Open all year. No smoking in dining room & bedrooms. Vegetarian by arrangement. Children welcome. Pets by arrangement. En suite in 2 rooms. TV & tea/coffee-making in bedrooms. Amex. B. & B. £30 (per twin room).

SUTTON SCOTNEY

 'Dever View', 17 Upper Bullington, Sutton Scotney, SO21 3RB (0962) 760566

Dever View is an attractive guest house set in the peaceful rural village of Bullington: a tiny place with a population of just 23 people who live in the handful of houses which are surrounded by miles and miles of open countryside. Accommodation is in very comfortable rooms which have a helpful range of amenities and there is a pretty garden and comfortable lounge for guests' use. The breakfast is first-rate: your hostess, Mrs Somerton, offers a variety of delicious options including some healthy alternatives (low-fat, etc.) as well as more traditional fare. Bullington is just ½ mile from where the A34 crosses the A3039 and 9 miles from Winchester; there are numerous walks to be enjoyed in the locality and you are within easy reach of Stonehenge, Romsey & the New Forest.
Open all year. No smoking in the house. Vegetarian & diabetic diets by arrangement. Children welcome. Pets by arrangement. Tea/coffee-making in rooms. T.V. lounge. B. & B. from £15-18. ETB 2 Crowns Commended.

SWAY

 Arnewood Corner, Linnies Lane, Sway, SO41 6ES (0590) 683690
Country house in 2 acres of pretty garden with outdoor pool, and self-contained apartment.
Open all year. No smoking in the house. Children welcome. T.V. in all bedrooms. B. & B. from £18.

WINCHESTER

Mrs Cooke, B. & B., 3 Berc Close (Off Stockbridge Rd), Winchester (0962) 864292
Modern detached house with driveway in pleasant road. Less than 1 mile from station.
Open most of the year. No smoking in dining room & bedrooms. Children: over 5s only. B. & B. £13.50.

Brambles, Northbrook Avenue, Winchester, SO23 8JW (0962) 856387
Open all year. No smoking in the house. Vegetarian. Children welcome. T.V. B. & B. from £17.

Camellias, 24 Ranelagh Rd, Winchester (0962) 864129
Open all year. No smoking in the house. Vegetarian. Children. En suite. B. & B. from £15-£18.

The Wykeham Arms, 75 Kingsgate Street, Winchester, SO23 9PE (0962) 853834

Tucked away in the back streets of the oldest part of the city, the 250-year old Wykeham Arms is one of the more established institutions in Winchester. Anthony Trollope considered it a very "third-rate hostelry", but the subsequent 150 years have seen more improvements than he would have been able to imagine, and present day travellers can look forward to a night's comfortable repose in beautifully furnished bedrooms which have been luxuriously appointed in a manner which does not detract from their character. Observance of this priority prevails throughout the Wykeham Arms: log fires and candle light all add to the sense of history and the efficient service is likewise redolent of a different age. It is the food, however, of which the

proprietors are, perhaps the most proud - and with justification: the wine list alone has earned them the accolade of "Wine Pub of the Year 1991" (all items are available by the glass, incidentally); the food, prepared entirely from fresh, local produce, is outstanding, and the daily changing menu has earned them another award - that of Pub Caterer of the Year.
Open all year. No smoking in 2 of 4 eating areas & b'fast room. Vegetarian standard. Licensed. Disabled access. Children: over 14s only. Pets welcome. En suite , TV & tea/coffee-making in rooms. B. & B. from £32.50.

Restaurants

ALRESFORD

The Old School House Restaurant, 60 West Street, Alresford, SO24 9AU (0962) 732134
No smoking in restaurant. Vegetarian & other diets. Licensed.

CHAWTON

Cassandra's Cup, The Hollies, Chawton, Nr Alton, GU34 1SB (0420) 83144
    Charming restaurant opposite Jane Austen's house at Chawton; cosy atmosphere. Morning coffee, light lunches. Home-made scones, cakes & gateaux. Afternoon cream teas.
L. around £3. No smoking in the restaurant. Vegetarian standard. Licensed. Children welcome.

HAVANT

Nutmeg Restaurant, Old Town Hall, East St, Havant (0705) 472700
Vegetarian/wholefood restaurant situated in the old town hall; good home-made snacks and teas.
Open 9.30 - 4.30. No smoking in the restaurant. Vegetarian exclusively. Licensed. Disabled access. Children.

SOUTHAMPTON

Springles Restaurant, Debenhams, Queens Buildings, Queensway, SO9 7BJ (0703) 223888
Friendly self-service restaurant serving snacks, hot lunches & a wide range of hot and cold drinks.
Open store hours. No smoking. Vegetarian. Disabled access. Children very welcome. Credit & debit cards.

The Town House Restaurant, 59 Oxford Street, Southampton, SO1 1DL (0703) 220498
Open all year. No smoking. Licensed. Disabled access. Credit cards.

SOUTHSEA

Springles Restaurant, Debenhams, 44-66 Palmerston Rd, PO5 3QG (0705) 822401
    Friendly self-service restaurant serving snacks, hot lunches & a range of hot and cold drinks.
Open store hours. No smoking. Vegetarian. Disabled access. Children very welcome. Credit & debit cards.

WINCHESTER

Pavilion Coffee Shop, C & H Fabrics, 8 High St, Winchester, S23 9LA (0962) 841696
Friendly self-service coffee shop serving snacks, lunches & a wide range of hot & cold drinks.
Open store hours. No smoking. Vegetarian. Disabled access. Children welcome. Credit & debit cards.

Pubs & Wine Bars

ROMSEY

Star Inn, East Tytherley, Nr Romsey, SO51 0LW (0794) 40225
Attractive pub serving very good food.
No smoking in dining room & 1 bar. Vegetarian standard. Licensed. Disabled access. Children welcome.

WINCHESTER

The Wykeham Arms, 75 Kingsgate Street, SO23 9PE (0962) 853834
No smoking in 'Bishops Bar' and 'Watchmakers' dining area.

Isle of Wight Accommodation

COWES

 14 Milton Rd, Cowes, PO31 7PX (0983) 295723
B & B. near bus route and cycle track. Cycles available for hire nearby.

Open all year. No smoking in the house. Vegetarian, vegan, diabetic by arrangement. Children: over 6s only. En suite in 1 twin room. Tea/coffee making. T.V. available in rooms. B. & B. from £13. ETB listed.

FRESHWATER

Brookside Forge Hotel, Brookside Rd, Freshwater, PO40 9ER (0983) 754644

Beautiful hotel, with attractive terraced gardens, standing in a pleasant tree-lined road close to the centre of Freshwater; tastefully furnished; Guided Walk Holidays available.

Open all year. No smoking in dining room & bedrooms. Vegetarian, vegan & diabetic standard. Licensed. Children welcome. Most room en suite. Tea/coffee-making. T.V. Access, Visa. B. & B. from £18.50.

RYDE

Holmsdale Guest House, 13 Dover St, Ryde, PO33 2AQ (0983) 614805

Small, comfortable Edwardian guest house taking up to 12 guests; very convenient for ferries, buses and the shops; sea views from 2 rooms.

Open all year. Smoking banned in dining room and public areas. Vegetarian by arrangement. Children: over 3s only. Pets by arrangement. En suite in all rooms. B. & B. from £14.

Hotel Ryde Castle, The Esplanade, Ryde, PO33 1JA Tel: (0983) 63755 Fax: (0983) 68925

This imposing building is a magnificent, creeper-clad castle with unparalleled views of the Solent and Straight; this is where the Marie Rose, Henry VIII's flagship, was raised, and the castle was built on the orders of the king to defend the island and its surrounding waters from invasion. With such perils happily past, Ryde Castle's more peaceably-motivated guests may now enjoy magnificent views of the Solent from this beautiful hotel which, under the direction of its proprietors, has recently undergone careful restoration and retains many beautiful period features (open fires, moulded ceilings) while offering every modern facility to guests. Food is first-rate: freshly caught fish features highly on the menu and all dishes have been home-cooked from fresh island ingredients; a typical evening meal would feature Avocado Vinaigrette followed by Golden Apricot Chicken (breast of chicken poached in Rose Wine with Apricot and Cointreau), and a truly delectable dessert such as Chocolate Roulade.

Open all year. No smoking in part of dining room, some bedrooms, & bar areas. Vegetarian standard. Vegan, diabetic, low-fat & other special diets on request. Licensed. Children welcome. Pets by arrangement. En suite, T. V. & tea/coffee-making in all rooms. Access, Visa, Amex, Diners. B. & B. from £39.50.

SEAVIEW

Seaview Hotel and Restaurant, High St, Seaview, PO34 5EX (0983) 612711

Exquisite hotel in the small Victorian seaside resort of Seaview; beautifully furnished with antiques and designer fabrics; excellent cuisine prepared from fresh local produce. Mid-week breaks £39.50.

Open all year. Smoking only allowed in dining room at other guest's discretion. Vegetarian & other diets by arrangement. Licensed. Children welcome. En suite & T.V. Credit cards. B. & B. from £36.50.

SHANKLIN

 Edgecliffe Hotel, Clarence Gardens, Shanklin, PO37 6HA (0983) 866199
Charming, family-run hotel in peaceful, tree-lined residential road close to cliff top walk.
Open Feb. to Nov. No smoking in the hotel. Vegetarian & other diets by arrangement. Licensed. Children: over 3s only. Many rooms private bath. Tea/coffee making & T.V. in all rooms. Credit cards. B. & B. from £15.

VENTNOR

Hotel Picardie, Esplanade, Ventnor, PO38 1JX (0983) 852647

 Hotel Picardie is an attractive villa-type hotel situated on the Esplanade just across the road from the sandy beach at Ventnor. The bedrooms have all been very tastefully furnished and comfortably appointed, and some family rooms are available with bunk beds for children and cots for babies (one room can accommodate up to three youngsters); there is a stair-lift for those who find stairs a difficulty. The food is excellent: the generous breakfast - with its varied options - should keep you going till mid-afternoon, and the home-cooked evening meal, prepared wherever possible from fresh ingredients, features both imaginative and traditional dishes such as Mushrooms in Garlic Butter, followed by Honey-Orange Lamb Chops and a tempting dessert, such as Blackberry and Apple Meringue; the vegetarian options are imaginative and tasty. Ventnor is a resort of character and charm: situated on the south coast, it has a sunny and warm climate, as is testified to by the many sub-tropical plants which flourish in almost every garden.
Open March to Oct. No smoking ex. bar area. Vegetarian & other diets on request. Licensed. Children welcome. En suite, TV & coffee making in all rooms. Credit cards. B. & B. from £17.25. B., B. & E. M. £25.

Pine Ridge Country House, Niton, The Undercliff, Ventnor (0983) 730802
Beautiful country house standing in extensive grounds; all rooms have sea or country views; imaginative menu prepared from fresh, local produce.
Open all year. Smoking banned in one dining room and one bedroom. Vegetarian and most other special diets by arrangment. Licensed. Disabled access. Children welcome. Pets by arrangement. En suite in most rooms. Tea/coffee-making in all rooms. T.V. in all rooms. Credit cards accepted. B. & B. from £25.50.

WOOTTON BRIDGE

Bridge House, Kite Hill, Wootton Bridge, PO33 4LA (0983) 884163
Listed Georgian residence of great character in a beautiful garden on the water's edge.
Open all year. No smoking throughout. Vegetarian & other diets by arrangement. Children by arrangement. Pets by arrangment. En suite in some rooms. Tea/coffee making in all rooms. T.V. on request. B. & B. from £15.

WOOTTON CREEK

Ashlake Farmhouse, Ashlake Farm Lane, Wootton Creek, PO33 4LF (0983) 882124
Lovely 17th C. farmhouse on water's edge at Wootton Creek near Fishbourne ferry. Happy calm atmosphere. Delicious food.
Open all year. No smoking in the house. Vegetarian & other diets by arrangement. En suite & tea/coffee-making in bedrooms. B. & B. from £12.50 - 18.

West Sussex Accommodation

ARUNDEL

Burpham Country Hotel and Restaurant, Burpham, Arundel, BN18 9RJ (0903) 882160
Charming country house with mature garden and superb views over the South Downs.
Open all year. No smoking in dining room. Vegetarian & other diets by arrangement. Licensed. En suite, TV & tea/coffee-making in all bedrooms. Credit cards. B. & B. from £29.

Marsh Acres, South Lane, Houghton, Amberley, Arundel, BN18 9LN (0798) 831854
Small country house with glorious views. B'fast only.
Open all year ex. Xmas. No smoking in the house. Vegetarian & other diets by arrangement. Children: over 4s only. En suite in 1 room. Tea/coffee-making in all bedrooms. T.V. lounge. B. & B. from £17.

BOGNOR REGIS

Merryvale, Wessex Avenue, Bognor Regis, PO21 2QW (0243) 864001
Open all year ex. Xmas. No smoking in the house. Vegetarian & other diets by arrangement. Disabled: bedrooms on ground floor. Children welcome. En suite, TV & tea/coffee-making bedrooms. B. & B. from £16.

CHICHESTER

Crouchers Bottom Country Hotel, Birdham Rd, Apuldram, PO20 7EH (0243) 784 995
Country hotel set amidst fields with fine view of Chichester Cathedral.
Open all year. No smoking in dining room & bedrooms. Vegetarian by arrangement. Licensed. 4 ground floor rooms, 1 specifically for the disabled. Children. En suite, tea/coffee-making & T.V. B. & B. from £29.

COPTHORNE

Broad Oak, West Park, Rd, Copthorne, W. Sussex, RH10 3EX (0342) 714882
Country house in 3 acre garden opposite 9-hole golf course just 10 mins drive from Gatwick airport. Ideal for early flights! Courtesy service to airport. Good pubs nearby with smoke-free areas.
Open all year. No smoking in the house. Vegetarian & other diets by arrangement. Children welcome. Pets by arrangement. Tea/coffee-making available. TV in lounge. B. & B. £19.50 per person, single £23.

CRAWLEY

School Cottages Guest House, 2 School Cottages, Rusper Rd, Ifield Green, Crawley, RH11 0HL Tel: (0293) 518813 Fax: (0293) 565153

School Cottages was originally the teacher's house to the 11th C. village of Ifield and is now the home of Gareth and Joy Flemington who specialise in providing reasonably priced accommodation for the Gatwick-bound traveller. Travellers from overseas - and those from our shores bound for (hopefully) sunnier climes - have made a stay at School Cottages a feature of their holiday arrangements rather than a travel impediment to be overcome as quickly as possible: the Flemingtons will provide transport to and from the airport, for instance, and can arrange long-term parking with a local company. The charms of this part of the world have long been upstaged by the modern, but doubtless necessary, intrusion of the airport: one wonders what the first editor of Punch magazine (who is buried in Ifield churchyard) would have made of the incongruous juxtaposition of this Domesday listed village so close to the hi-tech "village" of Gatwick airport. No matter - Ifield itself still has much to commend it (the Ifield Barn Theatre, for instance) to divert those awaiting air, rail or bus transport elsewhere. The Flemingtons will make the transition as painless and smooth as possible!
Open all year. No smoking in the house. Vegetarian & other diets by arrangement. Children welcome. Tea/coffee-making & TV in bedrooms. Credit cards. B. & B. around £20, single £30.

White Lodge Guest House, 10 Langley Ln., Ifield, Crawley, RH11 0NA Tel: (0293) 546222 Fax: (0293) 518813

White Lodge is a 200 year-old house situated down a private lane just 10 minutes' drive from Gatwick airport. Privately owned and run by Art and Dawn Jameson, it is the ideal place for those wishing to make an early departure to the airport: your hosts offer a courtesy transport service to and from Gatwick from 8 a.m. to 10.30 p.m. If your journey to Gatwick has involved the use of train or bus, you will be glad to know that White Lodge is within walking distance of both stations. The house has been very attractively furnished and decorated: bedrooms have been individually styled and have beverage-making trays, colour TV and magazines.

Open all year ex. Xmas. No smoking in the house. Vegetarian & other diets by arrangement. Children: over 6s welcome. TV & tea/coffee-making in all bedrooms. Credit cards. B. & B. from £17.50.

EAST GRINSTEAD

'Toads Croak House', 30 Copthorne Road, Felbridge, RH1 2NS (0342) 328524

Charming 1920's Sussex-style house set in beautiful gardens, easy access to Gatwick airport.

Open all year. No smoking in the house. Vegetarian & other special diets by arrangement. Children welcome. En suite, tea/coffee-making & T.V. in all bedrooms. B. & B. from £15.

HAYWARDS HEATH

Mattagami, 61 Franklynn Rd, Haywards Heath, RH16 4DS (0444) 453506

Family home with parking for guests near centre of the town on the A272. Full central heating.

Open all year. No smoking in the house. Vegetarian & other diets by request. Children welcome. Tea/coffee-making facilities if requested. T.V. in each bedroom. B. & B. from £17.

HENFIELD

Little Oreham Farm, Nr Woodsmill, Henfield, BN5 9SB (0273) 492931

Charming, listed farmhouse - complete with wisteria and dovecot! - in quiet rural area.

Open all year. No smoking in the house. Vegetarian & other diets by request. En suite, tea/coffee-making facilities & T.V. in both bedrooms. B. & B. from £17.50.

The Tithe Barn, Brighton Rd, Woodmancote, Henfield, BN5 9ST (0273) 492267

Converted Sussex barn overlooking the South Downs & within easy reach of Brighton & Gatwick. B'fast is served in either the sunny conservatory or the beamed dining room with log fire.

Open all year. ex. Xmas. No smoking in the house. Vegetarian & other diets by arrangement. Children welcome. TV & tea/coffee-making in bedrooms. B. & B. from £15.

LITTLEHAMPTON

Bracken Lodge Guest House, 43 Church St, Littlehampton, BN17 5PU (0903) 723174

Bracken Lodge Guest House is a large detached house of great character which stands amidst lovely prize-winning gardens in the quiet seaside town of Littlehampton. It has been beautifully furnished throughout and the well-appointed guest bedrooms each have en suite facilities and a range of helpful amenities including drink-making facilities, a hair-dryer and a trouser press. The atmosphere is relaxed and friendly and your hosts offer a standard of service and attention usually associated with a small hotel: business meetings and seminars can be accommodated on the premises and secretarial and business services can be provided if a day's notice is given. An excellent cooked breakfast is offered to guests (there is an English, Continental or Scots option), and evening meals - with a light meal option - may also be taken (there are some good children's choices). *ETB 3 Crown Highly Commended.*

Open all year. No smoking in the house. Vegetarian & other diets by arrangement. Licensed. 1 ground floor bedroom. Children: over 2s only. All bedrooms en suite. Tea/coffee-making facilities, T.V., trouser press, iron, hairdryer and radio alarm in all bedrooms. Acess, Visa. B. & B. from £22.50.

Pindars, Lyminster, Littlehampton, BN17 7QF (0903) 882628
Country house standing amidst beautiful gardens in the small village of Lyminster.
Open April to Oct. Smoking banned in dining room and bedrooms. Vegetarian breakfast by arrangement. Children: over 10s only. Tea/coffee-making & T.V. in all bedrooms. B. & B. from £30.

PULBOROUGH

The Barn Owls Restaurant and Guestel, London Rd, Coldwaltham, RH20 1LR (07982) 2498
Early Victorian farmhouse in half an acre of grounds.
Open all year. No smoking in dining room. Vegetarian. Licensed. Pets by arrangement. En suite & tea/coffee-making in bedrooms. T.V. lounge. Access, Visa. B. & B. from £22. D. £15.

STEYNING

 Nash Hotel, Horsham Rd, Steyning (0903) 814988
Beautiful 16th C. country house with lawns, paddocks and pond.
Open all year. No smoking in the house. Vegetarian & other diets by arrangement. Licensed. Children welcome. Pets by arrangement. En suite in 2 rooms. Tea/coffee-making & T.V. in all bedrooms. B. & B. from £21.

Restaurants

CHICHESTER

 Dolphin & Anchor Hotel, West St., Chichester, O19 1QE (0243) 785121
No smoking in the restaurant. Vegetarian. Licensed. Children welcome. Credit cards.

CRAWLEY

The George Hotel, High St, Crawley, RH10 1BS (0293) 524215
16th century hotel in the centre of Crawley; table d'hôte, à la carte and snacks.
Coffee shop open 9 - 9. Restaurant 12 - 2, 7 - 9.45. Smoking banned in restaurant. Licensed. Children.

HOVE

 Windmill Room, Forfars Bakers, 123 Church Rd, Hove (0273) 727922
Comfortable coffee room on first floor.
Open 9.30 - 4.30. No smoking throughout. Children welcome.

JEVINGTON

 The Hungry Monk Restaurant, Jevington (03212) 2178
Open 12 - 2, 10 - 7.30. L. & D. £17.95. Smoking banned throughout. Vegetarian. Licensed.

PLAISTOW

Clements Vegetarian Restaurant, Rickman's Lane, Plaistow, RH14 0NT (040388) 246
 Open Wed - Sat 12 - 2, 7 - 11 (last orders 9.30), Sunday 12 - 2. Vegetarian & vegan. No smoking.

RUDGWICK

Queen's Head Pub, Bucks Green, Rudgwick, RH12 3JF (Rudgwick) 2202
Large food dining pub famous for home-cooked food and real award winning ales.
30 seats. Smoking banned in restaurant. Vegetarian on request. Licensed. Children welcome.

WORTHING

 Pavilion Coffee Shop, Debenhams, 14-20 South St, Worthing, BN11 3AA (0903) 34321
Friendly self-service coffee shop serving popular light lunches, snacks, and a wide range of hot and cold drinks.
Open store hours. Smoking banned throughout. Vegetarian available. Disabled access. Children very welcome. Credit and debit cards accepted.

South East England

East Sussex
Accommodation

ARLINGTON

Ⓝ Bates Green, Arlington, Polegate, E. Sussex (0323) 482039

Bates Green was originally an 18th C. game-keeper's cottage which has been restored and enlarged since 1922 and stands amidst a large tranquil garden, developed with enthusiasm since the 1970s: there is a rock garden, pond and a secluded area - in fact the garden is open under the National Garden Scheme and "garden chat is always welcomed" by your hostess, Carolyn McCutchan. Your host, John McCutchan, works the 130 acre sheep and turkey farm and was a past winner of the Country Life Farming and Wildlife Trophy. In addition to gardening and conservation farming, the McCutchans are warm and welcoming hosts: there is home-made cake and tea to greet you on arrival, and a log fire blazes in the sitting room grate in cooler weather; bedrooms are comfortable and well-equipped, and farmhouse cooking is the order of the day (there are also a number of good pubs and restaurants nearby). There is much to enjoy at Bates Green: in addition to the hard tennis court in the garden there are many lovely walks nearby and you are within easy reach of the South Downs, Eastbourne and Glyndebourne. *Open all year ex. Xmas & New Year. No smoking in the house. Vegetarian & other diets by arrangement. En suite & tea/coffee-making in bedrooms. TV in 1 of 2 lounges. B. & B. from £20.*

BEXHILL-ON-SEA

Ⓝ 'Helensholme', Heatherdune Rd., Bexhill-on-Sea, TN39 4HB (0424) 223545

Helensholme is a delightful chalet home which is peacefully situated on the outskirts of Bexhill overlooking the Downs. The house has been lovingly furnished throughout and guests are made to feel very welcome and at home. Your host specialises in vegetarian cuisine and imaginative and tasty meals are prepared from fresh, local produce wherever possible. With its easy access to numerous scenic walks and proximity to the sea, 'Helensholme' is the perfect place to come for a stress-free, relaxing and revitalising away-from-it-all break. *Open all year. Smoking banned throughout the house. Exclusively vegetarian. All special diets with good notice. Children: over 10s welcome. Vanity units in 2 rooms. Tea/coffee making facilities. T.V. lounge. B. & B. £17.*

BRIGHTON

Ⓝ Dudley House, 10 Madeira Place, Brighton BN2 1TN (0273) 676794

Dudley House is a spacious Victorian guest house conveniently situated near the sea front and the centre of Brighton. Your hosts, Mr and Mrs Lacey, offer a very friendly welcome and will do all they can to make you feel comfortable and at home. The house has great charm and has retained many of the original Victorian features, but there is every modern comfort and many of the tastefully decorated bedrooms have en suite facilities and sea views. Brighton is an elegant and culturally lively town with much to offer the tourist and holiday-maker: there are shops, theatres and excellent leisure facilities - and of course the splendid Royal Pavilion and Marina are well worth a visit. *Open all year. No smoking in the house. Vegetarian, diabetic & most other special diets by arrangement. Children welcome. En suite rooms available. T.V. in all rooms. B. & B. from £16.*

Ⓝ Rozanne Mendick, 14 Chatsworth Rd., Brighton, BN1 5DB (0273) 556584

Large, comfortable family home. *Open all year. No smoking in the house. Vegetarian & vegan standard. Other diets by arrangement. Children welcome. Tea/coffee making. T.V. B. & B. from £14.*

COODEN

 Beam Ends. 175 Cooden Drive, Cooden Beach, Cooden, E. Sussex, TN39 3AQ (04243) 3880
Very comfortable family house 200 feet from the sea. Close to site of 1066 invasion. Easy access to station and to London.
Open all year. No smoking in the house. Vegetarian & other diets by arrangement. Children: over 8s only. TV in drawing room. Tea/coffee-making in bedrooms. B. & B. from £20.

EASTBOURNE

 Arden Hotel, 17 Burlington Place, Eastbourne, BN21 4AR (0323) 639639
Friendly, family run hotel, established for non-smokers only. Ideal for relaxing in Victorian elegance or being active in the Sussex sea air. Some rooms have sea views and the hotel is close to all amenities - only a couple of minutes from Eastbourne's splendid Promenade.
Open mid Jan. - end Nov. No smoking throughout. Vegetarian & other diets by arrangement. Licensed. Children welcome. En suite 9 rooms. Tea/coffee on request. T.V. in lounge & in room. Credit cards. B. & B. from £20.

Cuckmere House, 20 South Cliff Avenue, Eastbourne, BN20 7AH (0323) 20492
Pleasant well-furnished guest house in a peaceful tree-lined avenue one minute from the sea front and close to theatres, etc. Centrally heated in all bedrooms.
Open all year. Smoking banned everywhere except lounge. Vegetarian & other diets by arrangement. Licensed. Children: over 10s only. En suite, tea/coffee-making, TV, radio in all rooms. B. & B. from £17. D. £7.

The Oakwood Hotel, 28 Jevington Gardens, Eastbourne, East Sussex, BN21 4HN (0323) 721900
Open all year. No smoking in the dining room. Vegetarian & other diets by arrangement. En suite, TV & tea/coffee-making most bedrooms. Children & pets welcome. B. & B. from £20.

HARTFIELD

 Bolebroke Watermill, Edenbridge Rd, Hartfield, TN7 4JP (0892) 770425
Magical watermill in secluded woodland. Quaint, rustic rooms in miller's barn include romantic honeymooners' hayloft. '91 Winner *Best Breakfast in Britain & Int. Fairy Story Hotel.*
Open 1 March - 20 Dec. No smoking. Vegetarian by arrangement. Children: over 7s only. En suite, TV & tea/coffee in rooms. Visa, Amex. B. & B. from £24. ETB Highly Commended. RAC Highly Acclaimed.

HASTINGS

Norton Villa, Hill St., Old Town, Hastings (0424) 428168
Delightful house built in 1847 set on cliffs overlooking the Channel, Old town and harbour. 4-poster room available in B. & B. Self-catering cottage available for summer let.
Open all year. No smoking in dining room & most bedrooms. Children: over 8s. En suite in 3 rooms. Tea/coffee making facilities. T.V. Overnight car parking. B. & B. from £16.

 'Risingholme', High St., Heathfield, TN21 8LS (0435) 864645
Open all year. No smoking in the house. Vegetarian & other diets by arrangement. Children: Over 10s. En suite rooms. Tea/coffee making. T.V. in all rooms. B. & B. from £17.50.

LEWES

 Crink House (B & B) & Trust Cottage (S/C), Barcombe Mills, BN8 5BJ (0273) 400625

Crink House was originally a Victorian farmhouse and stands, surrounded on three sides by fields and breathtaking views of the South Downs, near the popular beauty spot of Barcombe Mills. It is the home of the Gaydon family who offer a warm welome and very comfortable B. & B. accommodation to guests (there is a 4-poster bed in one room and twin beds in the other); breakfast is a generous meal and there is a choice of a traditional English or lighter Continental option. In the same location - and with similarly wonderful views - the Gaydons offer self-catering accommodation at Trust Cottage: this beautifully appointed cottage is heated by a wood-burning stove, and has two

bedrooms (one twin and one double) and a comprehensive range of facilities including a microwave, a fridge-freezer, a dishwasher and washer/dryer in addition to a private coin-operated phone; the adjacent games room has facilities for table tennis, darts and snooker. You are in excellent walking country at Crink house yet just 4 miles from the historic town of Lewes.
Open all year ex. Xmas. No smoking throughout. Special diets by arrangement. Children welcome. En suite in both rooms. Tea/coffee making. T.V. in dining room. B. & B. from £21.

 Millers, 134 High St, Lewes, BN7 1XS   (0273) 475631

 This 16th C. timber framed house has many historic associations including links with the Bloomsbury Group. Furnished and decorated in harmony with its unique character, all Millers' rooms have antique double beds. The architecture of the ancient county town of Lewes is well documented and its many interesting shops include those specialising in crafts and antiques. The town is an excellent centre for walking in the Downs, while Brighton, Newhaven and Glyndebourne are just a short drive away.
Open all year ex. Xmas & New Year. No smoking in house. Vegetarian b'fast on request. En suite 2 rooms. Tea/coffee making & T.V. in rooms. B. & B. from £18.

Berkeley House Hotel, 2 Albion St, Lewes, E. Sussex, BN7 2ND   (0273) 476057
Elegant Georgian town house in quiet conservation area in the historic county town. South-facing roof terrace. Candle-lit smoke-free restaurant.
Open all year. No smoking in the restaurant. Vegetarian & other diets by arrangement. En suite, TV & tea/coffee-making in bedrooms. Children welcome. Licensed. Credit cards. B. & B. £25 - 48.

PEVENSEY

 Montana B. & B., The Promenade, Pevensey Bay, Pevensey   (0323) 764651
Quiet house in a convenient situation close to village shops, pubs and the beach.
Open all year ex. Xmas and part of Oct. No smoking in the house. Any diet on request. Children welcome. Tea/coffee making in all rooms. T.V. lounge and in 1 bedroom. B. & B. from £13.

RYE

 **Green Hedges, Hillyfields, Rye Hill, Rye, TN31 7NH   (0797) 222185**
Green Hedges is a large Edwardian country house superbly situated on rising ground, with wonderful views of the ancient town of Rye and the sea beyond. It is a comfortable family home and stands in a beautiful landscaped garden, just a short walk from the town; during the summer months the heated outdoor swimming pool is available for guests' use. Breakfast is prepared from seasonal garden produce, home-made preserves and free range eggs. You can explore the cobbled streets of mediaeval Rye and are within easy reach of Royal Tunbridge Wells, the beautiful Cathedral city of Canterbury and many National Trust properties. There is ample parking in the private road directly beside the house.
Open all year ex. Xmas. No smoking throughout. Vegetarian standard. Any other special diet by arrangement. Children: over 12s only. En suite, tea/coffee making & T.V. in all rooms. B. & B. from £22.50.

Jeake's House, Mermaid St, Rye, TN31 7ET   (0797) 222828   Fax (0797) 222623
Beautiful listed building, oak-beamed & wood-panelled, on a picturesque cobbled street.
Open all year. No smoking in dining room. Vegetarian. Licensed. Children welcome. Pets by arrangement. En suite. Tea/coffee-making & T.V. in all bedrooms. B. & B. from £19.50.

The Old Vicarage Guest House, 66 Church Square, Rye, TN31 7HF   (0797) 222119
Listed 16th C. building delightfully situated in the quiet and picturesque Church Square.
Open all year ex. Xmas. No smoking in dining room and bedrooms. Vegetarian standard. Other diets by arrangement. Children: over 12s only. En suite. Tea/coffee making & T.V. in rooms. B. & B. from £17.50.

ST LEONARDS ON SEA

 'Merryfield House', 3 St Matthews Gardens, St Leonards, TN38 OTS (0424) 424953
Large Victorian house overlooking private gardens 1m from sea & Hastings town centre.
Open all year ex. Xmas. No smoking in the house. Exclusively vegetarian. Children and well behaved dogs welcome. Tea/coffee-making & T.V. in all bedrooms. B. & B. from £14.50. D. £8.50.

WADHURST

Cheviots, Cousley Wood, Wadhurst, TN5 6HD (0892) 782952
Modern, centrally heated detached house built of brick and hanging tiles in 2 acre garden.
Open mid-March - mid-Nov. No smoking in the house. Special diets by arrangement. Children welcome. No pets. En suite in 2 rooms. Tea/coffee-making. T.V. in all bedrooms. B. & B. from £17. D. £13.

New Barn, Wards Lane, Wadhurst, E. Sussex, TN5 6HP (0892) 782042
New Barn is a beautiful 18th C. farmhouse overlooking Bewl Water and Trout Fishery and standing amidst magnificent and peaceful countryside near Wadhurst. The house is beamed throughout and is warm and comfortable: logs fires blaze in the sitting room inglenook and bedrooms are light and spacious with lovely views. Breakfast is the only meal to be served at New Barn, but it is a hearty feast of home-made jams, marmalades and preserves with local home-baked bread and free range eggs; there are plenty of good pubs and restaurants nearby where you may enjoy an evening meal. In spite of its rural setting, you are just 55 minutes train journey from Charing Cross and 30 minutes' drive from the South Coast; many other attractions are within easy reach including Vita Sackville-West's garden at Sissinghurst, Hever Castle and Canterbury (just 1½ hours away).
Open all year. Smoking only allowed in 1 lounge. Vegetarian & other diets by arrangement. Children welcome. Pets by arrangement. En suite & TV in bedrooms. Tea/coffee-making downstairs. B. & B. £19-24, Single £21.

Restaurants

BRIGHTON

Debenhams, 94-99 Western Rd, Brighton, BN1 2LB (0273) 26531
Friendly self service cafe serving snacks, hot lunches & a wide range of hot and cold drinks.
Open store hours. No smoking throughout. Vegetarian. Disabled access. Children welcome. Credit/debit cards.

Flavour of Life, 17 Regent Arcade, East St, Brighton   (0273) 28236
Small sandwich shop with two tables and counter space.
No smoking throughout. Vegetarian.

Food for Friends, 17a-18 Prince Albert St., The Lanes, Brighton BN1 1HF Tel: (0273) 202310 Fax: (0273) 202001
Food for Friends is a licensed vegetarian wholefood restaurant, informal and friendly, in the heart of the Lanes area of Brighton. Everything on the menu (which changes daily) has been prepared from additive-free ingredients (some organic), and in addition to the counter service offered in the restaurant, there is also an excellent takeaway and home-delivery menu; the latter is exceptionally well-organised and Food for Friends will cater for all *your* friends as well - parties of up to 120 guests can be catered for for as little as £4 a head. The menu is too extensive to reproduce here, but it regularly includes such delights as Lasagna con Spinacci, Tijuana Tortilla and some scrumptious desserts, such as Ginger Fruit Slice or Guinness Cake (the famous ale plus muscovado sugar plus fruit cake!). Children are very welcome (highchairs are provided).
55 seats. Open 9 - 10. 50% no smoking. Licensed. Disabled access. Children very welcome.

Pavilion Coffee Shop, C & H Fabrics Ltd, 180 Western Rd, BN1 2BA (0273) 28906
Friendly self service cafe serving snacks, hot lunches & a wide range of hot and cold drinks.
Open store hours. No smoking. Vegetarian. Disabled access. Children welcome. Credit/debit cards.

Slims Healthfood Restaurant, 92 Churchill Square, Brighton, BN1 2EP (0273) 24582
Friendly health food restaurant established 16 years ago, offering a range of savoury dishes,

cakes, pastries & fresh salads. Competitively priced vegetarian outside catering service.
Open 9.30 - 5.30. 50% smoke-free. Vegetarian exclusively. Vegan, diabetic and gluten free diets by arrangement. Licensed. Disabled access. Children welcome.

EASTBOURNE

Ⓝ **Pavilion Coffee Shop, C & H Fabrics Ltd, 82-86 Terminus Rd, BN21 3LX (0323) 649301**
Friendly self service café serving popular snacks, hot lunches & a wide range of hot and cold drinks.
Open store hours. No smoking throughout. Vegetarian. Disabled access. Children welcome. Credit/debit cards.

HAILSHAM

Ⓝ **The Homely Maid Restaurant and Pie Shop, 2 High St, BN27 1BJ (0323) 841650**
       Cosy 13th century cottage with inglenook, oak beams, good home cooking & friendly service.
Traditional home-baked tea shop fare catering for most tastes including vegetarian, low-fat, etc.
Open Mon - Fri. 9 - 5, Sat. 9 - 1.30. No smoking. Vegetarian & low-fat. Children welcome.

HASTINGS

Ⓝ **Springles Restaurant, Debenhams, 1-3 Robertson St, Hastings (0424) 422601**
Friendly self service restaurant serving snacks, hot lunches & a wide range of hot & cold drinks.
Open store hours. No smoking throughout. Vegetarian. Disabled access. Children welcome. Credit/debit cards.

HOVE

Ⓝ **Inglenook Restaurant, 68 Portland Rd, Hove, BN3 5DL (0273) 821335**
Fine food, a friendly atmosphere, & crafts by local people for sale. Traditional English fare.
No smoking. Licensed. Disabled access. Children welcome.

LEWES

The Runaway, Lewes Railway Station, Lewes, BN7 2UP (02273) 473919
Privatised cafe-bar on Lewes railway station commended as one of the best station cafes.
36 seats. Open Mon - Fri 6.30 - 6.30, Sat. 8 - 5.30. No smoking in 30% of restaurant (separate room).

White Hart Hotel, 55 High St., Lewes, BN7 1XE (0273) 476695
16th century coaching inn with a reputation for good food; carvery and à la carte.
No smoking in part of dining room. Vegetarian. Licensed. Disabled access. Children welcome.

NEWHAVEN

Healthibody Wholefood and Body Care Specialists, 52 High St, BN9 9PD (0273) 512957
Cosy restaurant with varied menu of light and main meals.
Open Mon - Sat., 9 - 5. No smoking in 60% of restaurant. Vegetarian & vegan standard. Children welcome.

Pubs & Wine Bars

SEAFORD

The Golden Galleon, Exceat Bridge, Seaford, BN25 4AB (0323) 892247
The Golden Galleon is a highly acclaimed free-hold pub (featured in the Good Pub Guide and
nominated Daily Telegraph Best Waterside Inn) situated in an area of outstanding beauty, complete
with landscaped gardens, patio and grass area. It has an attractive beamed room with coal fire and
inglenook fireplace. There are always four cask conditioned beers in stock including Harvey's
Armada, Fuller's Chiswick and Shepherd & Neame's 'Bishop's Finger'(a fourth cask is changed
regularly) and, as the proprietors are commited non-smokers, half the pub is smoke-free. The food
is excellent: the blackboard choices include lasagne and other pasta dishes in addition to local pies
and steaks and a range of snacks (ploughman's lunches, etc.). Excellent choice of ales
notwithstanding, there are over 40 reasonably priced wines to choose from and - thumbs up for
health awareness - decaffeinated coffee and skimmed milk are also available as beverage choices.
50% no-smoking. Vegetarian & low-cholesterol meals avail. Disabled access: 'a few steps - help given.'

Kent
Accommodation

ASHFORD

 Birchley, Fosten Green Lane, Biddenden, Ashford, TN27 8DZ (0580) 291413

Birchley is an early 17th C. timber-framed listed house standing in a peacefully secluded six acre garden complete with covered heated swimming pool and, for the pleasure of more eccentric visitors, a miniature railway. It has been beautifully furnished and appointed: the bedrooms are large and decorated in Laura Ashley style, while the oak-panelled sitting room has a welcoming log fire. A 'very full' English breakfast is served on an ancient refectory table in a large, oak-beamed dining room with a magnificent carved oak inglenook. A delicious 4-course evening meal can be served by arrangement although there are many excellent pubs and restaurants within a few minutes drive. Biddenden is fortunate in being exceptionally well located centrally for visiting all the places of interest in the South east. A typical Birchley evening meal would feature Crab Creams followed by Chicken Marengo with fresh vegetables and a dessert, such as Lemon Meringue Pie; cheese and coffee would complete the meal. Birchley won 'Highly Commended' in the ETB's 1991 *England for Excellence* Awards as England's Bed & Breakfast of the Year 1991'.

Open all year ex. Xmas. No smoking throughout. Vegetarian & other diets by arrangement. Not licensed, but own wine welcome. Children: over 10s only. En suite, T.V. & tea/coffee making in all rooms. Credit cards. B. & B. from £25-£30, with reductions for longer stays.

AYLESFORD

 Wickham Lodge, 73 High St, Aylesford, Kent, ME20 7AY (0622) 717267

Wickham Lodge stands on the river bank at Aylesford village and was originally two Tudor Lodges which were later converted into a Georigan house. Accommodation is in three guest rooms: the Georgian "Gate Room", a double/twin room, which overlooks the river and has en suite facilities, and the Tudor "Garden Room", a double room with wash basin, which overlooks the rear walled garden. Both these rooms are joined by double connecting doors, allowing them to be easily converted into a family suite, and each has a "galley" cupboard, allowing tea and coffee-making facilities to be conveniently available - but out of sight (fresh coffee and various teas are provided, incidentally). There is another single room, the "Blue Room" in the eaves which has its own staircase; a large drawing room is available for guests' use. Breakfast is as hearty or as healthy as you wish: there is a buffet of fresh fruits, yoghurts and cereals, and a cooked breakfast with copious quantities of coffee and toast; suppers by arrangement.

Open all year. No smoking in the house. Vegetarian & other diets by arrangement. Children welcome. 1 en suite. TV & tea/coffee-making in bedrooms. B. & B. £17.50 (£20 en suite). Private parking.

BECKENHAM

 123 Park Rd, Beckenham, Kent, BR3 1QJ (081) 650 1281
Open all year. No smoking in the house. En suite & TV in bedrooms. Children & pets. B. & B. £15.

BENENDEN

Crit Hall, Cranbrook Rd, Benenden, TN17 4EU Tel: (0580) 240609 Fax: (0580) 241743
Elegant Georgian country house standing in peaceful countryside with panoramic views.
Open mid Jan. - mid Dec. No smoking in dining room & bedrooms. Vegetarian & other diets by arrangement. Licensed. Children: over 12s. En suite/private bath, TV & tea-making in rooms. B. & B. from £22.50, D. £15.

CANTERBURY

Magnolia House, 36 St Dunstan's Terr., Canterbury, CT2 8AX Tel & Fax: (0227) 765121

Magnolia House is a charming detached late Georgian house situated in a quiet residential street near to the city centre and just 2 minutes' drive, or twenty minutes' walk, from the university. The house itself has much of architectural interest to commend it and has been decorated sympathetically with each bedroom being individually designed and coordinated in a light, bright decor (lots of Laura Ashley fabrics and wallcoverings); there is a walled garden with fishpond, terraces and shrubberies (the perfect place to relax in after a day's sightseeing). Ann Davies, the proprietor, tells me, "because we only take 10 guests, each one is special", and guests are aware of this special treatment from the moment they arrive, when a welcome tray is offered. Breakfast is a generous meal with a wide range of options; special diets are treated sympathetically.

Open all year. No smoking ex. lounge. Vegetarian & other diets by arrangement. Children welcome. En suite, TV & tea/coffee-making in all bedrooms. Credit cards. B. & B. from £22.50.

⊗ Walnut Tree Farm, Lynsore Bottom, Upper Hardres CT4 6EG (0227) 87375

14th C. thatched farmhouse in 6 acres. Home-made bread, preserves & new laid eggs.

Open Feb. to Nov. No smoking in the house. Vegetarian & other diets by arrangement. Children welcome. En suite, radio & tea/coffee-making in all rooms. B. & B. from £16-£18. Reduction for children under 13.

CRANBROOK

⊗ Hancocks Farmhouse, Tilsden Lane, Cranbrook, TN17 3PH (0580) 714645

The earliest mention of Hancocks is in a will of 1520 in which the house was left by a clothier,

Thomas Sheaffe, to his son Gervase. Today this fine well-preserved timber-framed building is a family home which also takes guests. Hancocks has been decorated and furnished with antiques, in keeping with its period origins and there is a large inglenook fireplace with log fires for cooler evenings. Set in a lovely garden and surrounded by farmland and beautiful views, Hancocks is the perfect place to come for those in search of peace and tranquillity. The food is first-rate: dinner is by prior arrangement and there is a complimentary afternoon tea served daily in addition to a very generous breakfast; organic and wholefood ingredients are used in cooking whenever availability permits. A typical evening menu would feature garlic stuffed mushrooms with home-made brown rolls, followed by fresh white fish cooked with leeks and ginger, and a tempting dessert such as crème brulée or fresh lime tart.

Open all year. No smoking in the house. Vegetarian & other diets by arrangement. Children: over 9s welcome. Pets by arrangement. En suite & TV in some rooms. Tea/coffee-making in all rooms. B. & B. from £18.

Hartley Mount Country House Hotel, Hartley Rd, Cranbrook, TN17 3QX (0580) 712230

Hartley Mount Hotel is a fine old Edwardian country manor house set in 2 acres of gardens overlooking the glorious views of Cranbrook and the Weald of Kent. It has been sympathetically refurbished - all the grace and elegance of the Edwardian era have been retained in the decor and furnishings - yet has all the modern conveniences of a luxury hotel: breakfast is served in an Edwardian conservatory and the bedrooms are decorated in keeping with the period, with a heavily draped four-poster bed and 'old-time' bathroom en-suite. Meals are served in an elegant dining room and a typical evening meal would feature Scotch Woodcock followed by Blanquette of Lamb and a selection of home-made desserts. There is a good vegetarian menu and an extensive wine list and all food is prepared from fresh, local ingredients.

Open all year. No smoking ex. in conservatory. Vegetarian standard. Other diets by arrangement. Licensed. Children welcome. En suite, tea-making & T.V. in all rooms. Access, Visa. B. & B. from £35 (inc. VAT & service).

DOVER

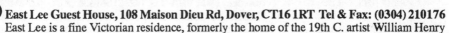

Castle House, 10 Castle Hill Rd, Dover, CT16 1QW Tel: (0304) 201656 Fax: (0304) 210197
Family-run B. & B. 2 mins from town centre, docks, Dover Castle & restaurants.
Open all year. No smoking. Children: over 12s only. En suite, TV & tea/coffee-making. B. & B. from £16.

East Lee Guest House, 108 Maison Dieu Rd, Dover, CT16 1RT Tel & Fax: (0304) 210176
East Lee is a fine Victorian residence, formerly the home of the 19th C. artist William Henry

East, which has been beautifully restored and tastefully decorated in period style throughout; it stands just 10 minutes walk down the famous White Cliffs from Dover Castle which historic fort has been continually garrisoned since Norman times. Your hosts, Patricia and Michael Knight, offer a very warm welcome to guests and the friendly atmosphere of this family house makes visitors feel very relaxed and at home. Bedrooms have been individually furnished in sympathetic style, and all rooms are well-appointed and have en suite facilities.
East Lee is ideally suited for those seeking an early morning getaway to the continent via the nearby Hoverport and Ferry Services across the channel; accordingly your hosts will gladly serve a continental breakfast option in your room on request, while later risers can look forward to a generous English breakfast. Although most visitors to Dover tend to pass through it en route to other destinations, the town has much of interest to commend it: a crucial part of England's Maritime heritage, the town is near to Canterbury and Sandwich. RAC Highly Commended.
Open all year. No smoking in the house. Vegetarian & other diets by arrangement (b'fast only). Children welcome. En suite, tea/coffee-making & T.V in all bedrooms. Credit cards. B. & B. from £18.

Sunshine Cottage, The Green, Shepherdswell, Nr Dover, CT15 7LQ (0304) 831359
Open all year. No smoking in dining room & bedrooms. Vegetarian & other diets by arrangement. Children welcome. En suite in some rooms. Tea/coffee-making in all rooms. T.V. in lounge. B. & B. from £16. D. £12.

EAST MALLING

Blacklands House, Blacklands, East Malling, ME19 6DS (0732) 844274
Open all year. No smoking in dining room & bedrooms. Vegetarian & other diets by arrangement. Children welcome. Pets by arrangement. En suite & tea/coffee making. T.V. lounge. Car parking. B. & B. from £17.

MAIDSTONE

Homestead, Greenhill, Otham, Nr Maidstone, ME15 8RR (0622) 862234
16th C. beamed farmhouse set in ½ acre of cottage gardens in the peaceful village of Otham.
Open Apr. to Oct. No smoking in the house. Children welcome. Pets by arrangement. En suite in some rooms. Tea/coffee making in all rooms. T.V. in lounge. B.& B. from £14.

SEVENOAKS

The Gables, 36 Dartford Rd, Sevenoaks, TN13 3TQ (0732) 456708
Built in 1870, The Gables is a friendly, comfortable and spacious Victorian house conveniently situated on the A225 just a short distance from Sevenoaks town and its railway station with frequent services to London and the coast. Bedrooms are comfortably furnished and decorated and each is equipped with a colour T.V. and beverage-making facilities. Sheila Castle offers a warm welome to guests - and a full English breakfast. There are lots of lovely walks in the locality and you are within easy reach of the many beautiful country houses and castles of Kent, including Knole, Hever, Ightham Mote and Chartwell.
Open all year ex. Xmas. Exclusively for non-smokers. Vegetarian & other diets by arrangement (breakfast only). Private bathroom & shower room. Tea/coffee-making & T.V. in all bedrooms. B. & B. from £16.50.

TENTERDEN

Brattle House, Cranbrook Rd, Tenterden, TN30 6UL (05806) 3565

Open all year. No smoking in the house. Vegetarian & other diets by arrangement. Children: over 12s only. En suite & Tea/coffee-making in all rooms. B. & B. from £26.

TONBRIDGE

Goldhill Mill, Golden Green, Tonbridge, TN11 0BA Tel: (0232) 851626 Fax: (0232) 851881

Picturesque Goldhill Mill was mentioned in the Domesday Book and was a working watermill for at least 850 years; peacefully standing in its own 20 acres, this beautiful old mill has been lovingly restored by its present owners and now offers accommodation of the very highest standard to guests. Three luxury double bedroom suites are available: two have jacuzzis and the third has a fourposter and gas/coal fire; additionally there is a cottage in the grounds offering the ultimate in luxury self-catering accommodation (crayfish and organic vegetables are available to guests staying therein). Breakfast is served in the splendid farmhouse kitchen with its Tudor beams (the mill machinery is on display behind glass) and anything from full English to Continental fare can be ordered. Goldhill Mill is an ideal touring base: Leeds Castle, Bodiam, Sissinghurst, Hever Castle and Chartwell are among the many places of interest which may be comfortably visited in a day's drive, and those wishing to spend a day *in situ* can enjoy the lovely garden & flood-lit tennis court.

Open 1 Jan. - 15 July; 1 Sept. - 31 Dec. No smoking in the house. Vegetarian & other diets by arrangement. Children by arrangement. En suite, TV, D.D. phone & tea/coffee in bedrooms. Credit cards. B. & B. £55-65.

TUNBRIDGE WELLS

Danehurst House Hotel, 41 Lower Green Rd, Rusthall, TN4 8TW (0892) 527739

Danehurst is a charming gabled guest house standing in a lovely rural setting in the heart of Kent; accommodation is in tastefully decorated rooms - all of which have private bathrooms and beverage-making facilities. The food is excellent: everything has been home-prepared from fresh, seasonal ingredients, and a typical evening menu would feature Carrot and Orange Soup followed by Chicken in Cream and Tarragon (with a selection of five seasonal vegetables and baby new potatoes), and a tempting dessert, such as Strawberry and Kiwi Fruit Shortcake with Cream; an English Cheeseboard, coffee and mints would complete the meal. You are just a short distance from Royal Tunbridge Wells and the gracious country houses of Kent are easily reached.

Open all year. No smoking ex. in lounge. Vegetarian & other diets by arrangement. Licensed. Children welcome. En suite in some rooms. Tea/coffee-making & T.V. in all bedrooms. Credit cards. B. & B. from £21.50.

WEST MALLING

Scott House, High St, West Malling, ME19 6QH (0732) 841380 /870025

Scott House is a Grade II listed Georgian town house situated opposite the library in the lower part of West Malling High Street. It is a family home from which the owners, the Smiths, also run an antique business and is therefore, unsurprisingly enough, quite beautifully decorated in keeping with its period origins; all bedrooms are furnished with taste and style. Only breakfast is offered at Scott House but there are lots of healthy options on the menu including muesli, yoghurt and porridge as well as the usual 'Full English' fare. The Smiths assure me that there are several good restaurants in West Malling which has, in addition to this, several other features to commend it to the touring visitor including an 11th C. abbey, a craft centre and a lakeside country park with numerous delightful walks.

Open all year ex. Xmas. No smoking in the house. Vegetarian & other diets by arrangement. En suite, TV & tea/coffee-making in all rooms. Access, Visa, Mastercard, JCB. B. & B. from £25.

Restaurants, Pubs & Wine Bars

ASHFORD

Cornerstone Wholefood Restaurant, 25A High St, Ashford, TN24 8TH (0233) 642874
No smoking throughout. Vegetarian. Disabled access: 'good for wheelchairs'. Children welcome.

BIDDENDEN

Claris's, 1 - 3 High St, Biddenden, Nr Ashford, TN27 8AL (0580) 291025

Claris's is a Grade I listed black and white timber framed building which forms part of a long row of houses in the High Street of the charming village of Biddenden. The proprietors have worked in harmony with the building to create an atmosphere of cosy intimacy: the inglenook fireplaces, oak beams and casement windows combine happily with the table settings of white lace and china. The fare is 'afternoon tea' and 'lunchtime snack' - but with a plus! Home-made creamed mushrooms on toast with fresh mushrooms and cream compete for attention with a plate of hand-made Smoked Salmon Paté served with toast and salad or home-made soup with thick buttered toast; the cakes are delectable (for example Claris's Cointreau Cake with pure orange juice, liqueur and fresh local cream).
Open 10.30 - 5.30 (closed Mondays). L. around £4. No smoking throughout, including garden. Vegetarian standard. Disabled access. Children welcome.

BROMLEY

Chinwags Coffee Shop, Debenhams, 44 High St, Bromley, BR1 1EJ (081460) 9977
Friendly self service coffee shop serving snacks, hot lunches & a range of hot and cold drinks.
Open store hours. No smoking. Vegetarian available. Children very welcome. Credit/debit cards.

Pavilion Coffee Shop, Debenhams, The Glades Shopping Centre, Bromley
Friendly self service coffee shop serving snacks, hot lunches & a range of hot and cold drinks.
Open store hours. No smoking. Vegetarian available. Children very welcome. Credit/debit cards.

CANTERBURY

Food for Living Eats, 116 High St, Chatham, ME4 4BY (0634) 409291
No smoking throughout. Disabled access. Children welcome. Access, Visa.

FOLKESTONE

Springles Restaurant, Debenhams, 48-66 Sandgate Rd, Folkestone (0303) 850171
Open store hours. No smoking. Vegetarian available. Children very welcome. Credit/debit cards.

Holland & Barrett Restaurant, 80 Sandgate Rd, CT20 2AA (0303) 243646
No smoking throughout. Children welcome.

MARDEN

Butcher's Mere, Collier St Village, Marden, TN12 9RR. Collier Street 495
12 seats. Open 10 - 7.30. L. around £2. No smoking. Vegetarian. Disabled access. Children.

SMARDEN

The Bell, Bell Lane, Smarden (023 377) 283
Historic inn, built during the reign of Henry VIII, originally a farm which became a 'registered Ale House' in 1630. Oak beams & inglenooks. Good food, reasonable prices, real ales & local wines.
Open 11.30 - 2.30, 6 - 11. Serving food 12 - 2, 6.30 - 10. No smoking in 1 room. Children welcome in family area.

Surrey
Accommodation

CAMBERLEY

⊗ Tekels Park Guest House, Camberley, GU15 2LF (0276) 23159
Open all year. No smoking in the house. Vegetarian & vegan exclusively.

DORKING

⊗ Danesmore, Pilgrims Way, West Humble, Dorking, Surrey, RH5 6AP (0306) 882734
Quietly situated chalet in private road with lovely views in area of Oustanding Natural Beauty. London 45 mins by rail. Easy access Gatwick & Heathrow.
Open all year. No smoking in the house. Vegetarian & other diets by arrangement. Pets 'possibly, by arrangement'. En suite (spa bath), TV & tea/coffee-making in bedrooms. B. & B. from £16.25, single £23.

GATWICK

⊗ The Lawn Guest House, 30 Massetts Road, Horley, RH6 7DE (0293) 775751

The Lawn Guest House. run by Ken and Janet Stocks, is a converted Victorian school house and stands in a pleasant rural location despite its being just over a mile from Gatwick airport! A cooked breakfast of bacon, egg and tomato is included in the price, with an optional light breakfast of fruit juice, fresh fruit, yoghurt, cereals and toast also being available. Horley town centre, with its excellent restaurants, shops and pubs, is just two minutes away and from its mainline railway station services run regularly to London and the South Coast. The Lawn is also ideal for those using Gatwick Airport. AA & RAC listed. ETB 2 Crowns Highly Acclaimed.
Open all year ex. Xmas. No smoking throughout. Disabled access. Children welcome. Pets by arrangement. En suite most rooms. Tea/coffee-making. T.V. in all bedrooms. Access, Visa, Amex, Diners. B. & B. from £17.50.

GUILDFORD

⊗ Beevers Farm, Chinthurst Lne, Bramley, Guildford, GU5 0DR (0483) 898764
Modern farmhouse in 5 acres of natural garden with abundant wildlife; peaceful rural setting.
Open March to Oct. No smoking in the house. Continental or English Breakfast. Children welcome. Pets by arrangement. En suite in 1 room. Tea/coffee-making & T.V. in all bedrooms. B. & B. from £13.

Weybrook House, 113 Stoke Road, Guildford, GU1 1ET (0483) 302394/36625
Open all year. No smoking in dining room & all public areas. Vegetarian. Children welcome. B. & B. from £14.

HORLEY

⊗ Woodlands Guest House, 42 Massetts Rd, Horley, RH6 7DS (0293) 782994/776358
The Woodlands Guest House is conveniently situated just a mile from Gatwick airport - and as such is ideal for early morning departures or late night return flights. It is also close to the M25 and is just five minutes from Horley railway station with its fast London connections. The house has full central heating and double glazing throughout and all bedrooms are furnished and equipped to a high standard. You are assured of a friendly, personal service by the Moore family and safe car parking facilities are available at £10 per week if you wish to leave your car whilst holidaying abroad; a courtesy car to the airport is available by arrangement.
Open all year ex. Xmas. No smoking in the house. Children: over 4s only. En suite, tea/coffee-making & T.V. in all rooms. B. & B. from £25 (single), £35 (double).

LEATHERHEAD

Ⓐ **Hazelgrove, Epsom Rd, West Horsley, Near Leatherhead, KT24 6AP (04865) 4467**
Friendly informal family home in pleasant gardens. Convenient Gatwick & Heathrow..
Open Mar. to Oct. No smoking in the house. Children: over 6s only. No en suite:- wash basins and shaver points in all rooms. Tea/coffee-making in all bedrooms. T.V. lounge. B. & B. from £15.

OXTED

Ⓐ **The New Bungalow, Old Hall Farm, Tandridge Lane, Nr Oxted, RH8 9NS (0342) 892508**
Spacious bungalow set in green fields 40 mins from London by rail. Close to Chartwell and Hever Castle. Easy access from M25. Relaxed family atmosphere.
Open Jan. to Nov. No smoking in the house. Wheelchair access. Children welcome. Pets by arrangement. TV & tea/coffee-making in bedrooms. B. & B. from £16.

Ⓐ **Rosehaven, 12 Hoskins Rd, Oxted, RH8 9HT (0883) 712700**
Open March to Nov. No smoking in the house. Vegetarian & other diets by arrangement. Children welcome. Tea/coffee making & T.V. B. & B. from £15.

WEST MOLESEY

Ⓐ **Alderton Guest House, 30 Cannon Way, West Molesey, KT8 2NB (081) 9791055**
Small, friendly guest house within easy reach of the Thames & Hampton Court Palace.
Open all year. No smoking in the house. Vegetarian & other diets by arrangement. Children: over 10s only. Tea/coffee making & T.V. in all bedrooms. B. & B. from £18. ETB Commended.

Restaurants

CROYDON

Ⓐ **Intermission Restaurant, Debenhams, 11-31 North End, Croydon (081) 688 4455**
Friendly family restaurant serving snacks, hot lunches & a wide range of hot and cold drinks.
Open store hours. No smoking. Vegetarian available. Disabled access. Children welcome. Credit/debit cards.

Ⓐ **Hockneys Vegetarian Restaurant, 96/98 High St, Croydon, CRO 1ND**
No smoking. Vegetarian exclusively. Children welcome. Access, Visa, Amex, Diners.

Selsdon Park Hotel, Sanderstead, South Croydon, CR2 8YA (081) 657 8811
No smoking in Phoenix Brasserie. Vegetarian. Licensed. Disabled access with prior notice. Children.

DORKING

Chaucer's Restaurant, The White Horse, High St, Dorking, RH4 1BE (0306) 881138
Open 12.30 - 2, 7 - 9.30. 60% no smoking. Vegetarian standard. Licensed. Children welcome. Credit cards.

Pizza Piazza, 77 South St, Dorking, RH4 2JU (0306) 889790
40% no-smoking. Vegetarian standard. Licensed. Children welcome. Access, Visa, Amex, Switch.

GUILDFORD

Ⓐ **Intermission Restaurant, Debenhams, Millbrook, Guildford, GU1 3UU (0483) 301300**
Friendly self-service family restaurant serving snacks, hot lunches & a range of hot & cold drinks.
Open store hours. No smoking throughout. Vegetarian. Disabled access. Children welcome. Credit/debit cards.

SUTTON

Ⓐ **Pavilion Coffee Shop, Unit 21-22, Times 2, High St, Sutton, SM1 1LF (081) 643 9519**
Friendly self-service coffee shop serving snacks, hot lunches & a range of hot & cold drinks.
Open store hours. No smoking throughout. Vegetarian. Disabled access. Children welcome. Credit/debit cards.

London and Middlesex

London
Accommodation

N1

Regent Palace Hotel, Piccadilly Circus, N1A 4BZ (071) 734 7000
Open all year. No smoking in part of restaurant & some bedrooms. Vegetarian. Licensed. Children.

N19

Parkland Walk Guest House, 12 Hornsey Rise Gardens, N19 3PR (071) 263 3228
Small, friendly B. & B. in a pretty, comfortable Victorian family house.
Open all year. No smoking in the house. Vegetarian & other diets on request. Children welcome. Tea/coffee making & T.V. in all rooms. B. & B. from £18.

NW3

Hampstead Village Guest House, 2 Kemplay Rd, NW3 1SY (071) 435 8679
Victorian house with original features; spacious rooms; pine floors & antique furniture.
Open all year. No smoking in the house. Vegetarian by arrangement. Children welcome. Tea/coffee making & T.V. in all rooms. B. & B. from £19.

NW4

18 Golders Rise, Hendon, London, NW4 2HR (081) 202 5321
Small, private guest house in a tree-lined crescent near Hampstead Heath. Parking.
Open all year ex. Xmas. No smoking in the house. Children welcome. T.V. lounge. B. & B. from £12.

NW8

London Regents Park Hilton, 18 Lodge Rd, St John's Wood, NW8 7JT (071) 722 7722
Open all year. No smoking in part of dining room. Vegetarian by arrangement. Licensed. Credit cards.

W1

The Cumberland Hotel, Marble Arch, W1A 4RF (071) 262 1234
Open all year. No smoking 50% of restaurant & some bedrooms. Vegetarian standard. Licensed. Disabled access. Children welcome. Pets by arrangement. En suite, TV & tea-making in rooms. B. & B. from £125.

The Hilton on Park Lane, 22 Park Lane, W1A 2HH (071) 493 8000
The Hilton on Park Lane is a magnificent 12-storey building which stands in a prestigious location overlooking Hyde Park. Luxuriously appointed it offers accommodation of an exceptionally high standard to business & tourist guests. Food is excellent & service is fast, efficient & friendly.
Open all year. No smoking in part of dining room & some bedrooms. Vegetarian & other diets standard. Licensed. Disabled access. Children welcome. En suite, tea/coffee-making & T.V. in all rooms. Credit cards.

The Mayfair Hotel, Stratton St, W1A 2AN (071) 629 1459
Open all year. No smoking in part of dining room. Vegetarian standard. Licensed. Disabled access. Children welcome. Pets by arrangement. En suite & T.V. in all rooms. Credit cards. B. & B. from £100.

Berners Park Plaza Hotel London, 10 Berners St, W1 (071) 636 1629
Splendid Edwardian hotel with classical ceilings and marble columns.
Open all year. No smoking in 50% of dining room & some bedrooms. Vegetarian standard. Licensed. Disabled: '10 rooms equipped for disabled guests'. Children welcome. En suite & T.V. in all rooms. Credit cards accepted.

WC1

Bloomsbury Crest Hotel, Coram St, WC1N 1HT (071) 837 1200
Open all year. No smoking in 66% of dining room & some bedrooms. Vegetarian & diabetic. Licensed. Disabled access. Children welcome. En suite, tea/coffee making & T.V. in all rooms. Credit cards. B. & B. from £120.

W2

The Parkway Hotel and Conference Centre, The Master's Hotel Group, 8 - 18 Inverness Terrace, Bayswater, W2 3HU Tel: (071) 229 9223 Fax: (071) 221 4802

The Parkway Hotel and Conference Centre is conveniently situated in Inverness Terrace close to its junction with Bayswater Road; it is just 200 yards from the nearest underground station which provides easy access to and from the West End and London's mainline stations; Heathrow is just 45 minutes'away and the busy bus routes on Bayswater Road give easy acess to all other parts of London. The Parkway Hotel is under Salvation Army Management and as such is an entirely smoke and alcohol-free establishment; it offers superb value for money in its 80 well-appointed bedrooms (there are single, twin, triple & family rooms as well as serviced, en suite apartments), and additionally there are conference and seminar facilities for between 10 and 100 people. A range of areas are available for exhibitions & trade shows, and the hotel is the perfect venue for private parties & functions. Bargain & w/e breaks. *Open all year, ex. Xmas & New Year. No smoking throughout. Vegetarian, diabetic & other diets on request. Children. En suite & TV some rooms. Tea/coffee making all rooms. Credit cards. B. & B. from £20-35.*

W4

Elliott Hotel, 62 Elliott Rd, Turnham Green, W4 1PE (081) 995 9794
2 lovely Victorian houses, joined & converted into very comfortable accommodation.
Open all year. No smoking in dining room and some bedrooms. Children: over 5s only. B. & B. from £20.

W9

Colonnade Hotel, 2 Warrington Crescent, W9 1ER (071) 286 1052

The Colonnade Hotel is an elegant, Grade II listed Victorian building which is situated in the fashionable residential area of Little Venice just 10 minutes' by bus or tube from London's West End. Beautifully refurbished in a manner in keeping with its original period features, the Colonnade Hotel offers an excellent choice of comfortably furnished en suite rooms to suit all tastes, including single, twin, double and four-poster bedded suites, each of which has been equipped with a helpful range of amenities including a hair dryer, trouser press and direct dial phone; foam pillows, featherless eiderdowns, cots and bed boards are all available on request. An excellent English breakfast is served daily and there is also the newly refurbished 'Cascades on the Crescent' restaurant and bar in which a full table d'hôte or light refreshment menu is served daily.
Open all year. No smoking in part of dining room & some bedrooms. Vegetarian standard. Licensed. Disabled access. Children welcome. Pets by arrangement. En suite, tea/coffee making & T.V. in all rooms.

SW1

Elizabeth Hotel & Apartments, 37 Eccleston Square, SW1V 1PB (071) 828 6812

The Elizabeth Hotel is an intimate privately owned hotel in a quiet location, overlooking the magnificent gardens of a stately residential square (circa 1835) on the fringe of Belgravia, yet it is situated only 750 yards from the Victoria travel network. It offers thoroughly clean and comfortable accommodation and a good English breakfast at moderate prices. Every effort has been made to retain the atmosphere of a mid-19th C. London house where guests can enjoy a "home away from home" which a hotel, after all, is really supposed to be! The hotel - which has 40 bedrooms and a lift in which smoking is banned - was a 1986 winner of the BTA's London B. & B. Award. Family rooms, luxury studios and 2-bedroom apartments (minimum rental period 3 months for the latter) are also available.
Open all year. No smoking in breakfast room. Children welcome. En suite in many rooms. B. &. B. from £27.50.

Vandon House Hotel and Conference Centre, The Master's Hotel Group, 1 Vandon St, (off Buckingham Gate), SW1 0AG Tel: (071) 799 6780 Fax: (071) 799 1464

Vandon House Hotel is conveniently situated right in the heart of London with Buckingham Palace, the Houses of Parliament and Westminster Abbey just a short walk away. It offers comfortable accommodation for up to 60 guests in en suite single, double, twin and family bedrooms which have each been furnished in a pleasant, modern style and some of which have en suite facilities. The Vandon House Hotel is under Salvation Army Management and as such is entirely smoke and alcohol-free; it offers exceptionally good value for money (lunch is available daily in the restaurant), and there are excellent facilities for hosting conferences and seminars. The Vandon House Hotel is close to Victoria Station (with its rapid link to Gatwick Airport) and the Coach Terminal; additionally you are just 3 minutes' walk from the St James' Park Underground Station which provides a link of just 45 mins with Heathrow Airport. Bargain & w/e breaks available.

Open all year, ex. Xmas & New Year. No smoking throughout. Vegetarian & other diets by arrangement. Children welcome. Some rooms en suite. Tea/coffee making & T.V. all rooms. Credit cards. B. & B. from £30-40,

SW7

 Aster House Hotel, 3 Sumner Place, SW7 (071) 581 5888
Early Victorian terrace in the heart of London on the borders of South Kensington & Knightsbridge.
Open all year. No smoking in restaurant and bedrooms. En suite & T.V. in rooms. B. & B. from £30.

SE10

Traditional Bed and Breakfast, 34 Devonshire Drive, Greenwich, SE10 8JZ (081) 691 1918
Victorian house near Cutty Sark, Thames & local antique markets; 25 mins to central London.
Open all year. No smoking in dining room. Vegetarian standard. Vegan, diabetic & other special diets by arrangement. Children welcome. T.V. & tea/coffee-making in all bedrooms. B. & B. from £16.

Restaurants

N1

Pizza Express, 820 High Rd, North Finchley, N12 (081) 445 7714
Open daily 11.30 - midnight. No smoking in part of restaurant. Vegetarian. Licensed. Disabled. Children.

W1

 Country Life Vegetarian Buffet, 1B Heddon St, W1 (071) 434 2922
Open 11.30 - 3 p.m. Mon. to Thurs., 11.30 - 2 p.m. Fri. No smoking throughout.

Debenhams Intermission Coffee Shop, 334-348 Oxford St, W1A 1DF (071) 580 3000
A friendly self-service coffee shop serving light lunches, snacks & a range of hot and cold drinks.
Open store hours. No smoking. Vegetarian. Disabled access. Children welcome. Credit/debit cards.

Mildred's Wholefood Cafe and Take-Away, 58 Greek St, W1V 5LR (071) 494 1634
Acclaimed vegetarian and wholefood restaurant serving very reasonably priced meals.
Open 12 noon - 11 p.m. No smoking. Vegetarian. Licensed. Children welcome.

Ming, 35-36 Greek St, W1V 5LN (071) 437 0292
A peaceful, friendly Chinese restaurant in Soho.
75 seats. Open 12 - 11.45. Smoking banned in part of restaurant, separate area. Vegetarian standard: large selection. Licensed. No disabled access. Children welcome. Credit cards accepted.

The Royal Academy Restaurant, Burlington House, Piccadilly, (071) 287 0752
Open 10 - 5.30 daily. Sunday Brunch a speciality 11.45 - 2.45. No smoking. Vegetarian. Licensed. Excellent disabled access.

WC1

Greenhouse Vegetarian Restaurant, 16 Chenies St, WC1E 7EX (071) 637 8038
Excellent and acclaimed vegetarian restaurant serving generous portions of imaginative food.
Open Mon. 10 - 6, Tues - Fri 10 - 10, Sat 1 - 8.30. No smoking. Vegetarian. Disabled: 'by prior arrangement'.

W2

Seasons Vegetarian Restaurant, 22 Harcourt St, W2 (071) 402 5925
No smoking in part of restaurant, upstairs. Vegetarian & vegan exclusively. Licensed.

WC2

The Canadian Muffin Co., 5 King St, Covent Garden, London, WC2E 8HN (071) 379 1525
Open every day. No smoking throughout.Vegetarian. Children welcome.

Brixtonian Backyard, 4 Neal's Yard, Covent Garden, WC2 9DP Tel: (071) 240 2769
35 seats. Open 7.30 - 11. No smoking throughout. Vegetarian standard. Licensed.

Food For Thought, 31 Neal St, WC2 (071) 836 0239

Food For Thought, situated in the heart of Covent Garden, is one of London's most popular vegetarian restaurants and has been serving excellent meat-free fare since 1974. It is a friendly family-run concern, serving food which is 'unadulteratedly good for you', and good for your wallet too (a 3-course meal costs under £10). The menu is relatively straightforward, offering a balanced choice of rich with more simply prepared dishes, and everything is freshly prepared daily on the premises with the minimum of 'processing', so that the nutritional value of the natural ingredients is retained. In order to extend their scope, the proprietors are now offering a special delivery/catering service to businesses in the central London area: menus may be faxed out in advance or designed to meet one-off requirements (conferences, business lunches, office parties).
Open 12 - 8. No smoking. Vegetarian & vegan exclusively. Some disabled access. Children welcome.

The National Gallery Restaurant, Trafalgar Square, WC2N 5DN (071) 389 1760
Open 10 - 5. 75% no-smoking (sep. room). Vegetarian standard. Licensed. Disabled access. Children.

Smollensky's On The Strand, 105 The Strand, WC2R 0AA (071) 497 2101
Smollensky's on the Strand is a large, bustling 'fun'restaurant situated right in the heart of central London. It is patronised by many faithful clientele who come to enjoy its terrific atmosphere (Americabilia bedeks the walls), dancing on Fridays and Saturdays and its excellent food. The something-for-everyone menu includes a range of steak options (tender beef in French bread, Steak Tartare, a choice of six accompanying sauces), imaginative vegetarian dishes (Tricolour Pasta Gateau, Wild Rice and Vine Leaf Risotto), special food for children and a range of daily changing specialities. Desserts are scrumptious (Very, Very Chocolate Fudge Cake (sic.), New York Toffee Cheesecake) and the wine list competes for attention with the exotic range of house cocktails (there is the usual Bloody Mary and Pina Colada, but also some less familiar choices such as Long Island Iced Tea: 4 heavy duty spirits, a dash of Coke and a strong sense of adventure).
Open Mon. - Thurs. 12 noon - midnight, Fri. & Sat. 12 noon - 12.30 a.m., Sun. 12 noon - 1.30 a.m. 50% no smoking. Vegetarian standard. Licensed. Children welcome. Credit cards accepted.

SW1

 Café Figaro, 6 Lower Regent St, London
No smoking throughout.

Wilkins Natural Food, 61 Marsham St, SW1 P3DP (071) 222 4038
Open weekdays. No smoking. Vegetarian and vegan exclusively. Disabled access. Children welcome.

The Wren at St James's, 35 Jermyn St, SW1Y 6JD (071) 437 9419
Open Mon. to Sat. 8 - 7, Sun. 10 - 4. No smoking. Vegetarian & vegan exclusively. Disabled access.

SW6

Windmill Wholefoods, 486 Fulham Rd, SW6 5NH (071) 385 1570
Open 12 - 11. No smoking. Vegetarian & vegan exclusively. Licensed. Disabled access. Children welcome.

SW7

Natural History Museum Restaurant, Cromwell Rd, SW7 5BD (071) 938 8149
Open 10-5. No smoking throughout. Vegetarian. Licensed. Disabled access. Children welcome.

New Restaurant, The Victoria and Albert Museum, Cromwell Rd, SW7 2RL
Open 12 noon - 2.45. 40% smoke-free. Vegetarian. Licensed. Disabled access. Children welcome.

Terrace Cafe Restaurant, Museum of London.
60% no-smoking. Vegetarian standard. Licensed. Disabled access. Children welcome.

SW9

Brixtonian, 11 Dorrell Place, Brixton, SW9 3PL (071) 978 8870
Open 7.30 - 11. No smoking. Vegetarian. Licensed. Disabled access to downstairs. Children welcome.

E2

Cherry Orchard Vegetarian Restaurant, 241 Globe Rd, E2 (081) 980 6678/981 3764
Open Tues - Fri. 12 - 3, 6.30 - 10.30, Sat. 3 - 6.30. No smoking. Vegetarian. Disabled access. Children.

Pubs & Wine Bars

SE1

The Anchor Tap, 20A HorseleyDown Lane (071) 403 4637
Open 7 days. Separate smoke-free rooms. Vegetarian menu. Children welcome.

The Lamb, 94 Lambs Conduit St, Bloomsbury, WC1
Smoking banned in part of pub.

Three Lords, The Minories, City, EC3
Smoking banned in part of pub.

Crown & Greyhound, 73 Dulwich Vilage, SE21 (081) 693 2466

Situated in the heart of South London, Dulwich Village is a haven of rural peace and has much of unique interest including the Dulwich Picture Gallery (the oldest in London) and a toll-gate (which is the only one in the city). Most significantly for our purposes is the tradition of hospitality which has prevailed at the Crown & Greyhound since the 18th C. and whose 19th C. customers included Charles Dickens and John Ruskin. There have, of course, been changes over the years - but these have not included the addition of wall-to-wall muzak and there is still a friendly, intimate atmosphere - despite the pub's obvious popularity. The food is good pub fare - reasonably priced and served in generous portions - and the room which served as a banqueting suite in the old building is now still a splendid venue for private parties or small conferences.
No smoking in the family room. Vegetarian options. Children welcome. Credit cards.

Middlesex
Accommodation

HEATHROW AIRPORT/WEST DRAYTON
Holiday Inn Crowne Plaza - London Heathrow, Stockley Rd, West Drayton, UB7 9NA (0895) 445555

The recently refurbished Holiday Inn Crowne Plaza is situated just 2 miles from Heathrow airport and now offers a superb choice of 380 bedrooms and suites - 50% of which are non-smoking. The upgraded hotel - now one of Holiday Inns' 4 star de luxe range of hotels - has two new restaurants: the informal Café Galleria (offering famous regional dishes, light snacks, buffet breakfasts and superb hot and cold tables) has a light summery atmosphere, while the more formal dining room, Marlowe's, offers superb food and sound wine in an elegant ambience. Thirty three new meeting rooms with extensive conference facilities and a purpose-built training centre are also available, and guests may additionally take advantage of the first-rate Health and Leisure Club with its indoor pool, steam room, sauna, plunge pool, whirlpool spa, sunbed, gym and beauty therapy room.

Open all year. Smoking banned in 50% of restaurant & bedrooms. Vegetarian and other special diets on request. Licensed. Disabled access. Children welcome. Pets by arrangement. En suite, tea/coffee making & T.V. in all rooms. Credit cards. B. & B. from £127.50.

Excelsior Hotel, Heathrow, Bath Rd, West Drayton, UB7 ODU (081) 759 6611
858-bedroom hotel opposite the airport; regular courtesy service to all terminals.
Open all year. No smoking in part of restaurant & in some bedrooms. Vegetarian standard. Licensed. Disabled access. Children welcome. En suite, TV & tea/coffee making in all rooms. B. & B. from £110.

Restaurants

HARROW

Ⓝ Debenhams, Station Rd, Harrow, HA1 1NA (081) 427 4300
Intermission, a friendly self-service restaurant serving lunches, snacks & range of hot & cold drinks.
Open store hours. No smoking throughout. Vegetarian. Disabled access. Children welcome. Credit/debit cards.

NORTH HARROW

Ⓝ Percy's Restaurant, 66-68 Station Rd, North Harrow, HA2 7SJ (081) 427 2021

Percy's is an elegant, award-winning restaurant offering quite exceptional food at very reasonable prices. The menu changes regularly and offers a very wide range of freshly prepared dishes from which you might choose Grilled Aubergine (lightly cooked in olive oil and lemon juice and served with yoghurt, mint and almond sauce), followed by Char-grilled Lamb with Redcurrant and Rosemary Sauce (there are some imaginative meat-free options, too), and some highly tantalising desserts, such as Steamed Chestnut Pudding and Spiced Profiteroles and a tempting choice of home-made ice creams and sorbets; a limitless supply of tea or coffee (3 different varieties of each), accompanied by chocolates and dried fruits, would complete the meal. The proprietors also provide a selection of 'healthy food' choices which have been prepared with minimum saturated fats, sugar and salt, and minimum cooking time.

Open Tues. - Fri., 12 - 3 & 6 - 12, Sat., 6 - 12, last orders 10.30. L. from £13. No smoking throughout. Vegetarian standard. Coeliac, vegan, gluten-free and other special diets by arrangement. Licensed. Disabled access. Children: over 10s welcome. Access, Visa, Amex.

Thames and Chilterns
Berkshire & Bedfordshire Accommodation

COOKHAM DEAN

Primrose Hill, Bradcutts Ln., Cookham Dean, Berks., SL6 9TL (0628) 528179
Large turn of the century house in rural location close to Windsor, Heathrow, Henley & Marlow. Easily accessible from M40 & M4.
Open all year ex. Xmas. No smoking in the house. Vegetarian by arrangement. TV B. & B. £15-17.50.

NEWBURY

11 Donnington Square, Newbury, Berks, RG13 1PJ (0672) 46771
Late Georgian house in quiet residential square 10 mins walk from town centre; twin & double rooms on top floor with private facilities.
No smoking in the house. B. & B. from £19.

The Bell at Boxford, Lambourn Road, Newbury, Berks, RG16 8DD (048838) 721
No-smoking dining room & some bedrooms. Vegetarian. Licensed. Children. B. & B. from £32.50.

Fishers Farm, Shefford Woodlands, Newbury, RG16 7AB (048838) 466
No smoking ex. sitting room. Vegetarian. Not licensed, but wine included. Children welcome. B. & B. from £20.

READING

The Berkeley Guest House, 32 Berkeley Avenue, RG1 6RE (0734) 595699/568296
Large, double-fronted, family-run guest house near the town centre; central heating.
Open all year. No smoking in the house. Vegetarian & other diets by arrangement. Children welcome. Pets by arrangement. Tea/coffee-making & T.V. in all rooms. Car parking space. B. & B. from £15.

Tudor House, Maidenhatch, Pangbourne, Reading, Berks, RG8 8HP (0734) 744482
Open all year. No smoking in the house. Vegetarian. Children welcome. B. & B. from £18.50.

SANDY

Highfield Farm, Tempsford Rd, Sandy, Beds, SG19 2AQ (0767) 682332

Set well back from the road and beautifullly situated in its own grounds and arable farm, Highfield Farm is a haven of peace and tranquillity - a rest for travellers although a deceptive 2½ miles from the A1's junction with the A428. Accommodation is in comfortable twin, double and family rooms - with bathroom en suite; two of the rooms are on the ground floor in the carefully converted stable block, with its original beams - lots of character, and an ideal choice for those who find stairs difficult. Your hostess, Margaret Codd, serves a delicious traditional English breakfast to guests (all special dietary needs can be accommodated by arrangement) before your day's sightseeing in Cambridge or Woburn Abbey.
Open all year. No smoking in the house. Vegetarian & other diets by arrangement. Children welcome. Pets with notice. Disabled: 2 ground floor rooms. En suite, TV & tea/coffee-making in bedrooms. B. & B. from £14.

WINDSOR

Bronwen Hughes, 62 Queen's Rd, Windsor, SL4 3BH Tel & Fax (0753) 866036
Deceptively spacious Victorian home in quiet town centre location just 10 minutes' walk from Windsor Castle and the railway station; good restaurants nearby; private parking.
Open all year. No smoking in the house. Vegetarian, fat-free on request. Ground floor bedroom but limited wheelchair access to bathroom. Children welcome. En suite, tea-making & T.V. in rooms. B. & B. from £15.

Restaurants

BEDFORD

Debenhams Springles Restaurant, 48 - 54 High St, Beds., MK40 1ST (0234) 42581
Friendly self-service family restaurant serving snacks, hot lunches & hot and cold drinks.
Open store hours. No smoking. Vegetarian meals. Disabled access. Children welcome. Credit/debit cards.

LUTON

Debenhams Pavilion Coffee Shop, 56 - 80 The Arndale Centre, LU1 2SZ (0582) 21201
A friendly self-service coffee shop serving snacks, hot lunches & hot and cold drinks.
Open store hours. No smoking. Vegetarian meals. Disabled access. Children welcome. Credit/debit cards.

NEWBURY

The Curious Cat, 5 Inch's Yard, Market St, Newbury, Berks. (0635) 35491
No smoking. Vegetarian & fresh fish a speciality. Licensed. Children welcome (high chair, feeder mugs)

Watermill Theatre & Restaurant, Bagnor, Newbury, Berks., RG16 8AE (0635) 46044
Open pre-show 6 - 7.15, post-show, 9.45. No smoking. Vegetarian. Licensed. Children welcome.

READING

Chez Fontana, 3 Queen's Walk, Reading (0734) 504513
Open 12 - 2.30, 7 - 11. Separate area for non-smokers. Vegetarian standard. Licensed. Children welcome.

Debenhams Intermission Restaurant, 125-133 Broad St, RG1 2BQ (0734) 588811
A friendly self-service family restaurant serving snacks, hot lunches & hot and cold drinks.
Open store hours. No smoking. Vegetarian. Disabled access. Children welcome. Credit/debit cards.

Pipers Island Restaurant, Pipers Island, Reading (0734) 391920
Open 6 - 10. Separate area for smokers. Vegetarian standard. Licensed. Children welcome. Credit cards.

Pizza Express, 56 St Mary's Butts (0734) 391920
Open daily, 12 noon till 12 midnight. Smoking banned in 26 seats in separate section. Vegetarian. Licensed.

THATCHAM

Garlands, Shop 3, 16 High St, Thatcham (0635) 61017
Open Mon. - Sat. No smoking throughout. Good facilities for children.

WINDSOR

Chaos Café, Windsor Arts Centre, St Leonards Road, Windsor (0753) 859421
Open Tue. - Sat. 11 - 2.30, Fri. - Sat. 7.30 - 9.50% no-smoking. Vegetarian standard. Children welcome.

Country Kitchen, 3 King Edward Court, Windsor (0753) 868681
Open 8 - 5. 50% no-smoking. Vegetarian standard. Licensed. Children welcome. Access, Visa.

Pubs & Wine Bars

FINCHINHAMPSTEAD

The Queen's Oak, Church Lane, Finchinhampstead, Nr Wokingham (0734) 734855
Pub serving great pizzas and real ales, with one smoke-free bar (oldest no-smoking bar in Berks.).
Smoking banned in one room.

TWYFORD

The Golden Cross, Twyford, (0734) 340180
Smoking banned in one area.

Buckinghamshire
Accommodation

AYLESBURY

Foxhill Farmhouse, Kingsey, Aylesbury, HP17 8LZ (0844) 291650
Peaceful 17th C. Grade II listed oak-beamed house set in a large garden with views to the Chiltern Hills. Breakfast only. Swimming pool available.
Open Feb. to Nov. No smoking in the house. Vegetarian on request. Children: over 5s only. En suite , TV & tea/coffee-making in bedrooms. B. & B. from £17.

Poletrees Farm, Brill, Ludgershall Road, Aylesbury, HP18 9TZ (0844) 238276
Friendly farmhouse accommodation.
Open all year. No smoking in the house. Vegetarian by arrangement. T.V. in lounge. B. & B. from £15.

BUCKINGHAM

Folly Farm, Padbury, Buckingham, MK18 2HS (0296) 712413
Comfortable well-appointed farmhouse situated on the A413, 3 miles from the market town of Buckingham. Close to Stowe Landscape Gardens and Silverstone Circuit.
Open all year ex. Xmas. No smoking in the house. Vegetarian & other diets by arrangement. Children welcome. 1 room en suite. Tea/coffee-making & TV in all bedrooms. B. & B. from £15. Single £16.

FARNHAM COMMON

The Oldfields Hotel, Beaconsfield Road, Farnham Common, SL2 3HP (0753) 643322
Beautiful detached mock tudor house which has been attractively decorated.
Open all year. No smoking in dining room and most bedrooms. Disabled access. Children welcome. Pets by arrangement. En suite some rooms. Tea/coffee-making & T.V. in all bedrooms. Credit cards. B. & B. from £20.

HIGH WYCOMBE

Belmont Guest House, 9 Priory Avenue, High Wycombe (0494) 27046
Splendid Victorian building in the centre of High Wycombe. Pizzas, salads and soft drinks can be ordered in the evening for serving in your room.
Open all year ex. Xmas. No smoking in dining room & some bedrooms. Vegetarian by arrangement. Disabled access. Children welcome. Some rooms en suite. Tea/coffee-making & T.V. in bedrooms. Credit cards.

The Chiltern Hotel, 181-183 West Wycombe Road, High Wycombe, HP12 3AF (0494) 452597
Popular hotel with very friendly staff. Good recommendations from previous guests.
Open all year. No smoking in dining room & some bedrooms. Vegetarian menu always available. Other special diets by arrangement. Licensed. Disabled access. Children welcome. Pets by arrangement. En suite in some rooms. Tea/Coffee-making, T.V. and phone in all bedrooms. Credit cards. B. & B. from £20-£28.60.

LITTLE MARLOW

Monkton Farm, Little Marlow, SL7 3RF (0494) 21082
Charming 14th C. 'cruck' farmhouse with 150 acre working dairy farm in the beautiful Chilterns. English breakfast served in the large farm kitchen.
Open all year. No smoking throughout the house. Vegetarian & other diets by arrangement. Children: over 5s welcome. Tea/coffee-making & T.V. in all bedrooms. B. & B. from £16.

MILTON KEYNES

Chantry Farm, Pindon End, Hanslope, Milton Keynes, MK19 7HL (0908) 510269
Old farmhouse built of Northamptonshire Stone with 500 acre mixed farm. Swimming pool and trout lake.
Open all year. No smoking in the house. Vegetarian standard. Most other special diets by arrangement. Disabled access. Children welcome. Pets by arrangement. Tea/coffee-making & T.V. in all bedrooms. B. & B. from £12.50.

Richmond Lodge, Mursley, Nr Milton Keynes, MK17 0LE (0296) 720275
Built as a hunting lodge at the turn of the century, Richmond Lodge is set in 3 acres of gardens and an orchard which has grazing sheep and lambs.
Open all year. No smoking in the house. Vegetarian & other diets by arrangement. Children: over 6s welcome. En suite in 2 rooms. Tea/coffee-making facilities. T.V. available. B. & B. from £18.

PRESTWOOD

 Wildridings, 3 Glebelands Close, Prestwood, Great Missenden, Bucks., HP16 0QP (02406) 3627
Traditionally-built family home in quiet situation overlooking farmland and meadows. One double en suite bedroom. Near to historic village of West Wycombe & N.T. houses. Simple suppers.
Open all year. No smoking in the house. En suite, TV & tea/coffee-making in bedroom. B. & B. £15, D. £5.50.

Restaurants

AMERSHAM-ON-THE-HILL

 Upper Crust Tea Room, 103 Sycamore Road, Amersham, HP6 5EJ (02406) 6919
Tea room above butcher's shop serving snacks and lunches.
27 seats. Open 9.30 - 4.30. No smoking throughout.Children welcome. Credit cards.

BEACONSFIELD

Georgian Coffee House, Wycombe End, Beaconsfield (0494) 678550
40 seats. Open 9.30 - 5. L. around £3.50. Separate area for smokers. Vegetarian standard. Children welcome.

The Kings Head, Oxford Road, Holtspur, Beaconsfield (0494) 673337
120 seats. Open 12 - 2.30, 5.30 - 11. L. & D. from around £6. 50% no-smoking. Vegetarian standard. Licensed. Children welcome. Credit cards accepted.

BOURNE END

The Spade Oak, Oldmoorholm Lane, Well End, Bourne End (06285) 20090
84 seats. Open 12 - 10.30. D. around £10. 50% no-smoking. Vegetarian standard. Licensed. Children welcome. Access, Visa.

HIGH WYCOMBE

Blacksmiths Arms, Old Marlow Road, High Wycombe (0494) 25323
120 seats. Open 12 - 2.30, 6 - 10.30. D. from £7. 50% no-smoking. Licensed. Disabled access. Children welcome. Credit cards.

Moni's Bistro, Booker Garden Centre, Clay Lane, Booker, High Wycombe (0494) 462182
100 seats. Open 10 - 6. L. from £5. Separate dining room for smokers. Vegetarian standard. Disabled access. Children welcome. Credit cards.

MIDDLE CLAYDON

 Claydon House, Middle Claydon, MK18 2EY (0296) 730349
Charming tea room within stately home owned by the National Trust.
90 seats. L. (only if booked) 12.30 - 1.30, Tea 2.30 - 5.30. Afternoon tea around £2.50. No smoking throughout. Vegetarian and other special diets by arrangement. Disabled access. Children welcome.

MILTON KEYNES

Fountain Harvester, London Road, Loughton, Milton Keynes, MK5 8AF (0908) 666203
80 seats. Open 12 - 2.30, 5.30 - 11; all day Sat. and Sun. 50% no-smoking. Vegetarian standard. Licensed. Disabled access. Children welcome. Credit cards.

Hertfordshire
Accommodation

BISHOP'S STORTFORD

The Cottage, 71 Birchanger Lane, Birchanger, CM23 5QA (0279) 812349
Open all year. No smoking. Vegetarian. Licensed. Disabled access. Children. B. &. B. from £22.50-£32.

HERTFORD

The Hall House, Broad Oak End, Off Bramfield Rd, Hertford, SG14 2JA (0992) 582807
Open all year. No smoking. Vegetarian b'fast. En suite. Tea-making & T.V. B. &. B. from £32.

RICKMANSWORTH

6 Swallow Close, Nightingale Road, Rickmansworth, WD3 2DZ (0923) 720069
B & B for the discerning traveller! A charming guest house, furnished throughout with antiques, & situated in a quiet cul-de-sac just ½ hr's tube ride from central London (the underground station is nearby). All food is home-cooked - including the bread and preserves - and there are home-grown vegetables and home-laid eggs! *Open all year. No smoking in the house. Vegetarian by arrangement. Children: over 5s only. B. &. B. from £17.*

ST ALBANS

The Squirrels, 74 Sandridge Rd, St Albans, AL1 4AR (0727) 40497
Edwardian terrace house within 10 mins walk of historic St Albans town centre & 20 mins to mainline station with frequent & all night trains to London. Imaginative breakfast options. *Open mid Jan. - mid Dec. No smoking in the house. Vegetarian & other diets by prior arrangement. En suite, TV & tea/coffee-making in bedrooms. B. & B. £12.50, single £15.*

25 Ridgmont Rd, St Albans, AL1 3AG (0727) 862755
Open all year. No smoking in the house. Vegetarian. Children. Tea-making & T.V. B. & B. from £14.

Restaurants

BERKHAMSTEAD

Cooks Delight, 360-364 High St, Berkhamstead, HP4 1HU (0442) 863584
No smoking. Vegetarian, vegan, macrobiotic standard. Licensed. Children welcome. Access, Visa.

HEMEL HEMPSTEAD

The Gallery Restaurant, The Old Town Hall, High St, HP1 3AE (0442) 232416
Open all day 7 days a week. No smoking throughout. Children welcome. Licensed. Credit cards.

ST ALBANS

Kingsbury Watermill Waffle House, St Michaels St, St Albans, AL3 4SJ (0727) 53502

Kingsbury Watermill is situated in one of the loveliest corners of St Albans on the River Ver. The building in which it is housed is scheduled for listing as it was used for the milling of flour until 1936 & still has the atmosphere of a bustling workplace plus the working machinery of the original corn crushing mill. The Millers Parlour & house is now converted into a Waffle House where freshly baked waffles are served with tasty toppings; many organic ingredients are used including organically-grown, stone-ground flour, free-range chicken & eggs, and meat from 'real meat' farms.
Open Tues. to Sat. 11 - 6, Sun. 12 - 6. Closes 5pm in winter. Vegetarian dishes daily. Children welcome.

Oxfordshire Accommodation

BANBURY

Pond Cottage, The Green, Warmington, Banbury, OX17 1BU Tel: (029589) 682
Old, stone-built cottage with honeysuckle & overlooking pond in peaceful Conservation Area just 6 miles from the M40 - midway between junction 11 (Banbury), and 12 (Gaydon)
Open April - Oct. inc. No smoking in the house. One room en suite, one with private bathroom. Tea/coffee making in both bedrooms. TV in sitting room. B. & B. £32 double, £16 single. D. £11.80.

Studleigh Farm, Wales St, Kings Sutton, Banbury, OX17 3RR (0295) 811979
17th C. renovated and modernised farmhouse on 8 acres of pastureland in picturesque village; several good village pubs nearby and fishing rights on the Cherwell are available.
Open all year. No smoking in the house. Vegetarian and most other special diets by arrangement. En suite & tea/coffee-making in all bedrooms. T.V. in lounge. B. & B. from £19.

Sugarswell Farm, Shenington, Banbury, OX15 6HW (0295) 680512

This lovely large stone-built farmhouse looks as though it has been part of the lush Oxfordshire countryside in which it stands, for centuries. In fact it has been built relatively recently and as such boasts all the modern conveniences you could wish for - but also has a standard of cosiness and character that you would only expect with much older buildings: there are log fires in the lounge and the prettily decorated bedrooms are furnished in a cottagey style. Food is of great importance at Sugarswell combining the best of British farmhouse fare with continental dishes. Your hostess is a Cordon Bleu cook - so you can be sure of an excellent meal (a house speciality is home-produced fillet of beef in port and cream). There is much to see and do in the area - Warwick, Woodstock, Oxford and Stratford are all within easy reach while Banbury has much of historic interest (including its cross) to commend it.
Open all year. No smoking in the house. En suite & tea-making in rooms. Amex. B. & B. from £20.

Wroxton House Hotel, Wroxton St Mary, Nr Banbury, OX15 6QB (0295) 730777
Three 17th C. village houses and a clocktower! Oak beams, inglenooks and carved oak recesses.
Open all year. No smoking in dining room & part of bar. Vegetarian by arrangement. Licensed. Children welcome. Pets by arrangement. En suite, tea/coffee-making & T.V. in all rooms. B. & B. from £45.

BICESTER

Newby Cottage, Weston on the Green, Bicester, OX6 8QL (0869) 50662
18th C. stone and brick thatched cottage overlooking farmland.
Open all year. No smoking in the house. Vegetarian by arrangement. Children welcome.T.V. B. & B. from £12.

CHIPPING NORTON

Southcombe Lodge Guest Hse, Southcombe, Chipping Norton, OX7 5JF (0608) 643068

Southcombe Guest House is an attractive modern bungalow standing in 3 acres of grounds overlooking Chipping Norton golf course. The ground floor arrangements make it an ideal choice for disabled guests as there are no stairs to negotiate and en suite facilties are also available. An entirely smoke-free establishment, Southcombe is an ideal choice for those touring the Cotswolds, Blenheim and Stratford. Evening meals are available and guests will be pleased to hear that everything is home-cooked (using low-fat cooking methods wherever possible); the traditional British menu would typically feature soup followed by a roast dinner with fresh vegetables and a choice of home-made desserts such as apple pie.

Open all year. No smoking in the house. Vegetarian & other diets by arrangement. Licensed. Disabled access.
Children welcome. En suite, TV & tea/coffee-making in some rooms. T.V. lounge. B. & B. from £16.

FARINGDON

Bowling Green Farm, Stanford Rd, SN7 8EZ Tel: (0367) 240229 Fax: (0367) 242568
Small, family-run farm 1 mile south of Faringdon; packed lunches available.
Open all year. No smoking in the house. Children. En suite, TV & tea-making in rooms. B. & B. £18.

OXFORD *train*

Combermere House, 11 Polstead Rd, Oxford, OX2 6TW (0865) 56971
Family-run guest house in quiet tree-lined road off Woodstock Road in residential N. Oxford.
#2 *No 12* *Open all year. No smoking in dining room. Vegetarian & other diets by arrangement. Disabled access:*
to ground floor including dining room'. Children welcome. Pets by arrangement. En suite, TV & tea/coffee-
making in all rooms. Visa, Mastercard. B. & B. from £22.

#3 **Cotswold House, 363 Banbury Rd, Oxford, OX2 7PL (0865) 310558**
Open all year. No smoking in the house. Vegetarian standard. Other diets by arrangement (breakfast only).
No *Children: over 6s only. En suite, TV & tea/coffee-making in all rooms. B. & B. from £23.*
cost train

The Dial House, 25 London Rd, Headington, Oxford, OX3 7RE (0865) 69944
#1 *no singles* This elegant half-timbered house, set in a beautiful garden just one and a half miles from

Oxford city centre (there is a bus service with routes both to London and the centre of Oxford just outside the front door), is the perfect choice for holiday-makers in search of clean, comfortable accommodation with all the modern conveniences of a well-appointed hotel - but with the personal service and attention of a small, friendly guest house. Your hosts, Tony and Julie Lamb, will do everything possible to make your stay a happy and comfortable one - and, while breakfast is the only meal available at Dial House, it is good and hearty (with vegetarian options on request), and there are literally scores of good restaurants in Oxford (your hosts will help you choose).
Open all year ex. Xmas. No smoking in dining room and bedrooms. Children: over 6s only. Pets by arrangement.
En suite/private, tea/coffee-making & T.V. in all bedrooms. B. & B. from £22.50 (£45 for 2 persons).

The Farmhouse Hotel & Restaurant, University Farm, Lew, Oxford, OX8 2AU (0993) 850297/851480
This beautiful 17th C. Cotswold stone farmhouse forms part of a working farm and has a herd

of black and white Friesian milking cows; it stands amidst rolling countryside just 12 miles west of Oxford in the tiny village of Lew. The farmhouse has been carefully and comfortably furnished - each of the pretty bedrooms has beamed ceilings and rural views (one ground floor room is specially designed to have wheelchair access) - and there is a comfortable, airy lounge with a massive inglenook fireplace (filled with flowers in summer and blazing logs in winter!). The cuisine has earned a very high reputation amongst the locals: the daily changing menu features a range of tasty options which have all been prepared from the finest of fresh ingredients; meals are served in either the cosy dining room with its beamed ceilings and stone walls, or in the light and airy Garden Room - which also forms the perfect venue for private functions.
Open all year ex. Xmas. No smoking in 75% dining room. Vegetarian & other diets by arrangement. Licensed.
Disabled access. Children: over 5s. En suite, TV & coffee-making in all rooms. Access, Visa. B. & B. from £25.

Morar Farm, Weald St, Bampton, Oxford, OX18 2HL (0993) 850162 Fax 0993 851738
Morar Farm is a spacious stone-built farm house which is pleasantly situated in the little village of Bampton which is famous for its beautiful 11th C. church and annual Spring festival of Morris dancing and wild flower garlands. Morar is the home of Janet and Terry Rouse - a lively couple who enjoy bell-ringing, barn dancing, Morris dancing and spinning! They also enjoy welcoming

guests to their home, and offer a special brand of helpful hospitality which has earned them a Highly Commended status from the English Tourist Board. The food is plentiful and excellent and features lots of wholesome items such as home-made preserves and home-baked bread. There are a wealth of things to enjoy and places to visit within the area: Cheltenham, Bath, Cirencester and Oxford are all easily visited (to add to the many attractions of the latter there is now the Oxford Story: an animated recreation of Oxford's history); garden lovers would enjoy visiting nearby Waterperry Gardens, and there is a wildlife park and rare breed farm within a short drive of Morar. Blenheim Palace, Avebury Stone Circle and Didcot Steam Railway Centre are all nearby, and for those seeking to relax in situ there are lovely well-marked walks to the Thames from the farmhouse.

Open Jan. to early Dec. No smoking in the house. Vegetarian & other diets by arrangement. Licensed. Children: over 6s only. 2 double rooms en suite, one twin room has private bathroom. Tea/coffee-making in all rooms. T.V. in lounge. Most credit cards. B. & B. from £16.

Mount Pleasant Hotel, 76 London Rd, Headington, Oxford, OX3 9AJ Tel & Fax: (0865) 62749

The Mount Pleasant Hotel is a small family-run hotel which stands in the shopping area of Headington but is within easy reach of the main shops and colleges of Oxford. Mr and Mrs Papamichael are especially welcoming hosts and will do all they can to make you feel at home: the food is excellent - Greek, English and Continental dishes are all home-cooked from fresh ingredients - and special diets can be catered for by arrangement. Accommodation is in comfortable bedrooms - each of which has en suite facilities - and there is a safe car park for guests'use.

Open all year. No smoking ex. in the bar. Vegetarian & other diets by arrangement. Licensed. Wheelchair access. Children welcome. En suite, TV & tea/coffee-making in rooms. Credit cards. B. & B. from £35.

The Old Farmhouse, Station Hill, Long Hanborough, OX7 2JZ (0993) 882097

16th C. house with inglenook fireplace, beamed ceilings & flag floors. 15 mins Oxford.

Open all year. No smoking. Vegetarian. Children: over 12s. En suite. Tea-making. T.V. B. & B. from £14.

Studley Farmhouse, Horton cum Studley, OX91BP Tel: (086735) 286 Fax: (086735) 631

16th C. farmhouse with flagstone floors and inglenook fireplace in peaceful rural setting 15 mins drive from Oxford and M40. 1 hr. from London & Cotswolds.

Open all year. No smoking in the house. Vegetarian & other diets by arrangement. En suite & TV in bedrooms. Tea/coffee-making in guests' kitchen. Credit cards. B. & B. from £20-25.

Westwood Country Hotel, Hinksey Hill Top, OX1 5BG Tel: (0865) 736408 Fax: (0865) 736536

The brochure of the Westwood Country Hotel shows, instead of the pleasing facade of this attractive small hotel, a badger standing near an oak tree; this is a significant emphasis - as the hotel, which is just 3 miles from Oxford, boasts an exceptional abundance of wildlife in its 3 acres of grounds: woodpeckers, nightingales, badgers, foxes and, if you are lucky, deer have all been spotted in and around the 400 acres of woodland which surround the hotel grounds - which is a testament to the peace and tranquillity to be found at Westwood. The bedrooms are exceptionally comfortable & well-appointed & the food (served on lace tablecloths in a beamed dining room) is exceedingly good; the cosy bar welcomes walkers from the footpaths that radiate from the front door.

Open all year ex. Xmas. No smoking in dining room & T.V. lounge. Vegetarian & other diets by arrangement. Licensed. Disabled access. Children welcome. En suite, tea-making & T.V. in rooms. All major credit cards. 2-night country breaks from £46, 7 nights £242. Winner of 1991 Daily Mail Award for Tourism for All.

Windrush Guest House, 11 Iffley Rd, Oxford (0865) 247933

Family-run guest house near Magdalen Bridge. Easy walk to shops, restaurants & all the places of interest. Healthy eating award. Non-smokers preferred. Coaches to and from London airport.

Open all year. No smoking in the dining room. Vegetarian by arrangement. Children welcome. TV & tea/coffee-making facilities. Credit cards. B. & B. from £11-21.

TOWERSEY

Upper Green Farm, Manor Rd, Towersey, OX9 3QR (084421) 2496
Open all year. No smoking. Vegetarian & other diets by arrangement. 2 ground floor bedrooms.

WOODSTOCK

Gorselands, Boddington Lane, Nr Long Hanborough, OX8 6PU (0993) 881202
Open Apr. to Nov. No smoking in the house. Vegetarian. Children welcome. En suite. B. & B. from £12.50.

Hamilton House, 43 Hill Rise, Old Woodstock, Oxford, OX7 1AB (0993) 812206
Open all year. No smoking. Pets by arrangement. En suite & tea-making. T.V. lounge. B. & B. £15.

The Laurels, Hensington Rd, Woodstock, Oxford. OX7 1JL (0993) 812583
Open all year. No smoking in the house. Vegetarian by arrangement. Children. B. & B. from £17.50.

Restaurants

ABINGDON

Poppies Tea Rooms, 37 Stert St, Abingdon, OX14 3JF (0235) 526660
No smoking in back room. Vegetarian. Disabled access: 'wide doorway & corridor for wheelchairs'. Children.

Thame Lane House, 1 Thame Lane, Culham, Abingdon, OX14 3DS (0235) 524177
No smoking. Vegetarian by arrangement before booking. Licensed. Children: over 3s.

BURFORD

Huffkins, High St, Burford (099382) 2126
Open Apr. to Nov., daily, 10 - 5. No smoking throughout.

CHIPPING NORTON

Nutters Healthy Lifestyle Centre, 10 New St, Chipping Norton, OX7 5LJ (0608) 641995
Wholefood restaurant in charming terrace. Excellent home-made food. Range of therapies
40 seats. Open 9 a.m. - 10 p.m. Prices 'reasonable'. No smoking throughout. Vegetarian standard, vegan, diabetic, coeliac and other special diets on request. Licensed. Children welcome.

The Old Bakehouse Restaurant & Tearoom, 50 West St, Chipping Norton (0608) 3441
Open daily, 10 - 6. Smoking banned throughout. Access, Visa.

OXFORD

Betjeman's at Betjeman & Barton Ltd, 90 High St, Oxford (0865) 241855
Open 10 - 4.30. L. from £3. No smoking throughout. Vegetarian standard. Children welcome.

Brown's, 5 - 11 Woodstock Rd, Oxford, OX2 6HA
Open all day. L. around £5.50. No smoking in part of restaurant. Vegetarian standard. Children welcome (highchairs available). Licensed. Wheelchair access. Credit cards.

Debenhams, Magdalen St, Oxford (0865) 243161
Intermission, a friendly self-service restaurant serving light lunches, snacks & hot and cold drinks.
Open store hours. No smoking. Vegetarian. Disabled access. Children welcome. Credit/debit cards.

Café MOMA, Museum of Modern Art, 30 Pembroke St, Oxford (0865) 722733
Café MOMA is a pleasant eating place which specialises in serving vegetarian food although meat dishes are also available. A recent winner of the Heartbeat Award, Cafe MOMA offers a wide selection of wholesome, home-made meals and snacks, such as freshly prepared salads, mouthwatering cakes, first-rate coffee from the Italian Cappuccino machine and a good selection of speciality teas, including some herbal varieties. Children and nursing mothers are very welcome (although childrens' portions are not available), and there is good access for disabled guests.

90 seats. Open Tues. - Sat. 10 a.m. to 5 p.m., late night opening Thurs., Sun. 2 to 5 p.m. Prices 'reasonable'.
Smoking banned throughout. 80% Vegetarian. Licensed. Disabled access. Children welcome.

 St Aldate's Coffee House, 94 St Aldate's, Oxford (0865) 245952

 St Aldate's Church Coffee House was opened in 1963 as 'a place of Christian Hospitality and Intellectual Refreshment for all who come within its walls'and as such - as its brochure reminds us - forms part of the coffee house tradition of this university city where 'many famous philosophers have argued their theories and dreams in such places.' For those of us less intent on contributing to the history of Western Civilisation and more focussed on finding tea, cakes and a jolly good selection of coffees - St Aldate's amply fits the bill. Here you will find delicious lunchtime treats with loosely ecclesiastical names such as Monk's Morsel, Parson's Plateful and Curate's Crumb; there are baked potatoes also, and a tempting selection of home-made cakes and biscuits.

60 seats. Open 12 - 2 for hot food, 10 - 5 for cold snacks. Prices: various. Smoking banned throughout. Vegetarian diets on request. Disabled access: 'yes, but toilets are difficult'. Children welcome.

The Nosebag, 6 - 8 St Michael's St, Oxford, OX1 2DU
Open 9.30 a.m. - 10 p.m. (Ex. Mon. close 5.30 p.m., Sun. 9 p.m.) No smoking throughout.

The Wykeham Coffee Shop, 15 Holywell St, Oxford (0865) 246916
Open 10.30 - 5.30. L./D. around £5-£6. No smoking throughout. Vegetarian standard. Children welcome.

 Annie's Tea Rooms, 79 High Street, Wallingford, OX10 0BX (0491) 36308

 If you are visiting the ancient and historic market town of Wallingford, just a few miles south of Oxford, be sure to pay a visit to these charming 17th C. tearooms. You will receive a friendly welcome from the waitresses who contribute to the relaxing atmosphere engendered by the soft pink decor. Morning coffee is followed at noon by light lunches which include soup, filled jacket potatoes and open sandwiches together with a traditional hot dish. Set afternoon teas include delicious scones, scrumptious tea cakes with home-made jam accompanied by a mouthwatering selection of cakes. Prices are exceptionally reasonable, particularly in view of the fact that almost everything is home-baked.

30 seats. Open 10. to 5. ex. Sun. & Wed. Sunday teas 2.30 - 5.30. (July - Sept.) No smoking throughout. Vegetarian standard. Children welcome.

THAME

    The Coffee House, 3 Buttermarket, Thame, OX9 3EW (084) 421 2266
Open 8.30 - 5. No smoking. Vegetarian standard. Licensed. Disabled access. Children welcome.

WOODSTOCK
The 1627 Coffee Room, 20 High St, Woodstock (0993) 811231

Pubs & Wine Bars

BICESTER
The Six Bells, Church St, Bicester (0869) 253578.
Serving food 12 - 2.30, 7 - 9. Smoking banned in one room.

OXFORD
Kings Arms, 40 Holywell St, Oxford (0865) 242369/247049
Smoking banned in one of three rooms. Vegetarian standard. Wheelchair access.

Central England

Gloucestershire
Accommodation

BLAKENEY

🏵 **Lower Viney Country Guest House, Viney Hill, Nr Blakeney, GL15 4LT (0594) 516000**

Open all year. No smoking in the house. Special diets by arrangement. Licensed. Children welcome. En suite, tea/coffee-making & T.V. in all rooms. Access, Visa. B. & B. from £17.50.

BOURTON ON THE WATER

🏵 **Coombe House, Rissington Rd, Bourton on the Water, GL54 2DT (0451) 821966**

Coombe House is a family-run concern quietly situated in pretty lawned gardens in Bourton on the Water. This delightful village is often dubbed The Venice of the Cotswolds on account of the River Windrush which gracefully wends its way through willow-draped banks on which delightful stone houses and cottages nestle. Coombe House interior is bright, fresh and airy with an overall feeling of relaxation (it has been awarded a Highly Commended status by the English Tourist Board and your hosts, Graham and Diana Ellis, will make you very welcome). Breakfast is the only meal available at Coombe House and it can be 'as healthy or as non-healthy as each guest wishes.' Accordingly yoghurt and Flora are available together with decaffeinated coffee & a continental alternative breakfast of a warm croissant with apricot jam.

Open all year. No smoking in the house. Vegetarian & other diets by arrangement. Licensed. Disabled access: '2 ground floor rooms'. Children welcome. En suite, TV & tea/coffee-making in all rooms. B. & B. from £24.50.

Dial House Hotel, Bourton on the Water, GL54 2AN (0451) 22244

Built in 1698, Dial House is a charming stone-built hotel beautifully situated in the centre of one of the Cotswolds' most attractive villages. With an acre of lovely secluded garden, complete with croquet lawn and ornamental pool, Dial House offers an exceptionally high standard of service to guests who are made to feel very welcome and at home. Guest rooms are furnished in a light, cheerful manner (some four-poster suites are available), and there is an open fire in the comfortable lounge with its lovely garden views. Your hosts, Lynn and Peter Boxhall, have 26 years of hotel experience and have a well-deserved reputation for serving first-class cuisine: meals are served in a charming dining room with oak beams and an inglenook, and there is an interesting selection of dishes complemented by a choice of good quality wines.

Open all year. No smoking in dining room & some bedrooms. Vegetarian & other diets by arrangement. Licensed. Disabled access. En suite, TV & tea/coffee-making in all rooms. Access, Visa. B. & B. from £32.50.

🏵 **Farncombe, Clapton, Bourton on the Water, GL54 2LG (0451) 20120**

Farncombe is a beautifully appointed Cotswold family house standing in 2 acres of gardens some 700 ft above sea-level in the tiny hamlet of Clapton on the Hill just 2 miles from Bourton on the Water. All bedrooms are prettily decorated and furnished and tea and coffee-making facilities are available in the guest lounge. Breakfast is the only meal available at Farncombe but there is a 'Full English' and 'Continental' choice for guests: the former consisting of generous platters of bacon with sausage, egg and tomato - while the latter offers a lighter meal of cheese, rolls and wholemeal bread; herbal teas can be taken as beverage alternatives. Clapton is situated in the centre of a triangle formed by Cheltenham, Stow on the Wold and Burford - and as such you are perfectly placed for touring all these beautiful Cotswold towns and cities.

Open all year. No smoking in the house. Vegetarian & other diets by arrangement (breakfast only). Children welcome. One double room with shower. Tea/coffee-making in dining room. T.V. in lounge. B. & B. from £15.50.

The Strathspey, Lansdown, Bourton on the Water, GL54 2AR (0451) 820694

Strathspey is a Cotswold-stone-built end of terrace family home which is delightfully situated in the charming village of Bourton on the Water; there is a pretty riverside walk to the centre of the village at the rear of the house. Your hosts, Sue and Andrew Firth, offer a very friendly welcome, and serve a delicious traditional English breakfast (special diets by arrangement) in the pleasant dining room. Bourton-on-the-Water is one of the prettiest Cotswold villages and accordingly has a deserved popularity; an additional attraction is that it is within easy reach of a number of other interesting places including Statford upon Avon, Cheltenham and Royal Leamington Spa.

Open all year. No smoking in the house. Vegetarian and most other special diets by arrangement. 1 ground floor bedroom. En suite in some rooms. Tea/coffee-making & T.V. in all bedrooms. B. & B. from £14.

Windrush Farm, Bourton on the Water, GL54 3BY (0451) 20419

Open all year. No smoking in the house. Vegetarian. En suite, TV & tea-making. B. & B. from £15.

CHELTENHAM

Charlton Kings Hotel, London Rd, Charlton Kings, Cheltenham, GL52 6UU (0242) 231061

Visitors to Cheltenham Spa or the Cotswolds could not do better than spend their stay at the recently refurbished Charlton Kings Hotel just 2 miles from the centre of Cheltenham. Situated in an area of Outstanding Natural Beauty, this elegant building stands in an acre of lawned gardens and features trees, the whole surrounded by the rolling Cotswold hills. Guests are accommodated in the 14 beautiful en suite bedrooms - each of which have views of the hills (one has a private balcony); in fact a gentle stroll from the hotel will take you to the hills (a footpath runs alongside the building) or you can see them by one of the Hot Air Balloon flights (lazy but romantic) which depart from the hotel lawn. There are plenty of good eating houses in the area, but a varied and interesting menu is served in the Bistro style restaurant; the charming reception lounge and welcoming conservatory (with its snug leather sofa by the fire) is open to both guests and non-residents for tea and coffee.

Open all year. No smoking in dining room & some bedrooms. Vegetarian standard. Licensed. Disabled access. Children & pets by arrangement. En suite, tea/coffee-making & T.V. in rooms. Credit cards. B. & B. from £29.

Hallery House Hotel, 48 Shurdington Rd, Cheltenham Spa, GL53 0JE (0242) 578450

This lovingly-restored Victorian building is a small, family-run hotel with a welcoming atmosphere. The sixteen light, airy bedrooms are each individually furnished and there is an elegant dining room and comfortable lounge; the pleasant patio provides a suntrap in clement weather. Hallery House food is fresh, healthy and simple, prepared from the best local produce to imaginative and tasty recipes; traditional or continental breakfasts are provided and the evening meal would typically feature Chicken and Vegetable Terrine followed by Poached Salmon with Hollandaise Sauce and Milk Chocolate and Raspberry Fool.

Open all year. No smoking in dining room & some bedrooms Vegetarian & other diets by arrangement. Licensed. Children & pets welcome. En suite most rooms. Tea/coffee-making, T.V. and satellite service in all bedrooms. Visa, Amex, Mastercard. B. & B. from £20.

Cleyne Hage, Southam Lane, Southam, Nr Cheltenham, GL52 3NY (0242) 518569
Situated in the heart of the Cotswolds between Cheltenham and Winchcombe this charming detached guest house offers very comfortable accommodation to guests. Parking.
Open all year. No smoking in the house. Children welcome. Pets by arrangement. Tea/coffee-making facilities.Credit cards. B. & B. from £12.50.

Katslyde, Church Lane, Toddington, Cheltenham, GL54 5DQ (0242) 621509
Open all year. No smoking in the house. Vegetarian and other special diets on request. Children welcome. En suite. Tea/coffee-making and T.V. in all bedrooms. B. & B. from £17.50.

New Barn Farmhouse, Temple Guiting, Cheltenham, GL54 5RW (0451) 850367
Open all year. No smoking ex. lounge. Vegetarian by arrangement.Children: over 8s only. B. & B. from £12.50.

Northfield B. & B., Cirencester Rd, Northleach, Cheltenham, GL54 3JL (0451) 860427
Northfield is a lovely detached family home set in large gardens overlooking open countryside. Although functioning principally as a bed and breakfast, packed lunches and evening meals can be taken at Northfield by arrangement and fresh, home-grown produce - including free-range eggs - are used wherever possible in cooking; in sunny weather meals may be enjoyed in the garden either on the lawn or relaxing by the pond. Northfield is conveniently situated just off the A429 a mile from the market town of Northleach, with its beautiful church and musical museum; its proximity to so many other lovely towns and villages in the Cotswolds makes it a perfect base from which to explore all the charms and delights of this lovely part of the world.
Open all year. No smoking in the house. Vegetarian & other diets by arrangement. Children welcome. En suite, TV & tea/coffee-making in all bedrooms. B. & B. from £30 double, single £20.

The Old School Cottage, School Lane, Southam, Cheltenham (0242) 518267
Open Mar. to Nov. No smoking in the house. Disabled access: ground floor. Children: over 9s only. En suite in one room. Tea/coffee-making & T.V. in all bedrooms. B. & B. from £11.50.

Old Vineyards, Charlton Hill, Cheltenham, GL53 9NE (0242) 582893
Open all year ex. Xmas & New Year. No smoking in the house. Special diets with notice. Children welcome. Tea/coffee-making in all rooms. B. & B. from £17. Short breaks at reduced rates available on request.

Stretton Lodge, Western Rd, Cheltenham, GL50 3RN (0242) 528724 or 570771
Open all year. No smoking in the house, ex. some bedrooms. Vegetarian by arrangement. Licensed. Children welcome. En suite, tea/coffee-making & T.V. in all bedrooms. Access, Visa. B. & B. from £25.

Turret House, Aldsworth, (between Burford & Bibury), GL54 3QZ (04514) 547
Open all year. No smoking in the house. Vegetarian & other diets by arrangement, (b'fasts only). Children: over 14s only. Tea/coffee-making & T.V. in all rooms. B. & B. from £12.50.

The Wynyards, Butts Lane, Woodmancote, Nr Cheltenham, GL52 4QH (0242) 673876
Open all year ex. Xmas. No smoking in the house. Special diets by arrangement. Children welcome. Tea/coffee-making available all day. T.V. in lounge. B. & B. from £12.50.

CHIPPING CAMPDEN

The Cotswold House Hotel, Chipping Campden, GL55 6AN (0386) 840330

17th C. Cotswold House is a beautiful country hotel which stands in pride of place on Chipping Campden's High Street. Originally built as the country home of a prosperous wool merchant (and with an interesting subsequent history), it has recently been painstakingly restored to its original splendour and the elegantly furnished rooms now have antiques and works of art which complement the period features. First-rate meals are served in the intimate dining room with its garden views, and the fifteen beautifully furnished bedrooms have each been individually decorated and styled. In winter open fires blaze invitingly in the lounge and sitting room, whilst in summer the willow-shaded coutryard is perfect for pre-dinner drinks or al fresco eating.
Open all year ex. Xmas. No smoking in dining room. Vegetarian & other diets by arrangement. Licensed. Children: over 8s welcome. En suite & TV in all rooms. Room service. Credit cards. B. & B. from £45.

Wyldlands, Broad Campden, Chipping Campden, GL55 6UR (0386) 840478
Wyldlands is a modern house which stands in the village of Broad Campden and has lovely views of the surrounding countryside. The proprietor, Mrs Wadey, is a keen gardener and guests may enjoy her lovely, large garden. Wyldlands is a totally smoke-free house which has been comfortably furnished and appointed (it has been awarded a Commended status by the English Tourist Board), and it is an ideal base from which to explore the many attractions of the Cotswolds: Hidcote Gardens and Batsford Arboretum are within easy reach and the Cotswold Way Walk begins just 1 mile away. Mrs Wadey is unable to accommodate pets because she has a dog of her own.
Open all year. No smoking in the house. Vegetarian by arrangement. Children welcome. En suite in one room. TV & tea/coffee-making in all bedrooms. B. & B. from £16, single £18.

CIRENCESTER

Wimborne House, 91 Victoria Rd, Cirencester, GL7 1ES (0285) 653890
Open all year ex. Xmas. No smoking in the house. Vegetarian and most other special diets by arrangement. Children: over 5s only. En suite, tea/coffee-making & T.V. in all bedrooms. B. & B. from £15.

DURSLEY

School Cottage, Coaley, Dursley, GL11 5ED (0453) 890459
Open all year. No smoking in the house. Children welcome. Pets: small dogs only. Tea/coffee-making in all rooms. T.V. in 1 bedroom. B. & B. from £10.

GLOUCESTER

The Red House, Cranham Woods, Gloucester, GL4 8HF (0452) 862616
Open all year. No smoking in the house. Vegetarian & other diets by arrangement. Children welcome. Pets by arrangement. T.V in all bedrooms. B. & B. from £12.50.

Severn Bank Guest House, Minsterworth, GL2 8JH (0452) 750357
Fine country house standing in 6 acres of grounds on the banks of the Severn just 4 miles west of Gloucester. Attractively decorated and furnished.
Open all year. No smoking in dining room, hall & bedrooms. Vegetarian & other diets by arrangement. Children welcome. En suite, TV & tea/coffee-making in all rooms. B. & B. from £17.50.

KILCOT

Orchard House, Aston Ingham Rd, Kilcot, Nr Newent, GL18 1NP (0989) 82417

Orchard House is a beautiful Tudor-style country home which stands amidst 5 acres of peaceful grounds (including well-tended lawns, paddocks and country walks) in a tranquil country setting close to the unspoilt Wye Valley and the Forest of Dean; the oldest parts of the house date from the 18th C. and many original beams are still to be seen - in, for example, the TV lounge with its log fires. Your hosts, Anne and Basil Thompson, have done everything they can to make their home as warmly welcoming as possible: the elegant and finely furnished rooms provide a very high standard of accommodation (Orchard House has been awarded a Highly Commended status by the ETB) but there is, nonetheless, a friendly relaxed feel about the place. Anne is an excellent cook and provides a wide selection of delicious and imaginative fare: only fresh produce - with local specialities - are ever used in cooking, and a typical evening menu would feature Green Pea and Mint Soup followed by Poached Salmon or Spinach Roulade with Cottage Cheese, and fresh fruit salad; coffee and mints would complete the meal. You are within easy reach of a number of interesting places including the Brecon Beacons, the Malverns, the Cotswolds and Ross-on-Wye.
Open all year. No smoking in the house. Vegetarian & other diets by arrangement. Licensed. Children: over 12s only. En suite & tea/coffee-making in bedrooms. Credit cards. B. & B. from £17.50, D. from £12.50.

MORETON-IN-MARSH

Blue Cedar House, Stow Rd, Moreton in Marsh, GL56 0DW (0608) 50299
Beautiful detached residence set in attractive gardens within easy reach of the centre of the picturesque town of Moreton in Marsh. All bedrooms comfortably appointed.
Open all year ex. Xmas. No smoking in the house ex. T.V. lounge. Vegetarian & other diets by arrangement. Disabled access: 'one ground floor suite'. Children welcome. En suite in some rooms. Tea/coffee-making & TV in all rooms. T.V. in lounge. B. & B. from £15, D. from £7.

ⓧ **Mr & Mrs Malin, 21 Station Rd, Blockley, GL56 9ED (0386) 700402**
Open all year. No smoking in the house. Vegetarian & other diets by arrangement. Children: 'depends on age'. Tea/coffee-making & T.V. in all bedrooms. B. & B. from £13.

ⓧ **Newlands Farmhouse, Aston Magna, Moreton in Marsh, GL56 9QQ (0608) 50964**

Newlands Farm is a Grade II listed Tudor farmhouse which was once a working farm; these days it has been tastefully restored and now offers bed and breakfast accommodation of a very high standard indeed. The two double and one twin-bedded rooms have each been very comfortably appointed and attractively decorated, and there is a T.V. lounge for guests' use. Breakfast is the only meal available at Newlands Farmhouse but there is a wide range of good eating places within a few minutes'drive. There is much to enjoy in the area: the surrounding countryside is beautiful and full of lots of lovely walks, and the gardens of Hidcote, Kiftsgate and Sezincote are all within a 5 mile radius.
Open all year ex. Xmas. No smoking. Tea/coffeeg on request. T.V lounge. B. & B. from £15 - less for 2 nights.

PAINSWICK

Upper Dorey's Mill, Edge, Nr Painswick, GL6 6NF (0452) 812459
ⓧ *Open all year. No smoking in the house. Vegetarian & other diets by arrangement (b'fast only). Children welcome. No pets. En suite & tea/coffee-making in all rooms. T.V. in lounge. B. & B. from £17.50.*

RUARDEAN

The Lawn, Ruardean, GL17 9US (0594) 543259
ⓧ *Open all year ex. Xmas. No smoking. Vegetarian & other diets by arrangement. Disabled access: 'limited, ground floor en suite bedroom available.'Children: over 8s only. Pets by arrangement. En suite in some rooms. Tea/coffee-making in all rooms. T.V. in lounge. B. & B. from £14.*

ST BRIAVELS

Cinderhill House, St Briavels, GL15 6RH (0594) 530393
14th C. building, complete with oak beams, inglenook fireplaces and bread oven, nestling in hillside below St Briavel's castle with breathtaking views.
Open all year. No smoking ex. in sitting room. Vegetarian & other diets by arrangement. Licensed. Children welcome. En suite & tea/coffee-making in all rooms. B. & B. from £21.

STROUD

ⓧ**Burleigh Cottage, Burleigh, Minchinhampton, Stroud, GL5 2PW (0453) 884703**
Charming cottage with splendid views of the surrounding countryside.
Open all year. No smoking in the house. Vegetarian and most other special diets by arrangement. Children accepted. En suite in 2 rooms. Tea/coffee-making & T.V. in all bedrooms.

TEWKSBURY

ⓧ **Lampitt House B. & B., Lampitt Ln., Bredon's Norton, GL20 7HB (0684) 72295**
Large home set in 1½ acres of gardens; all food home-cooked from fresh ingredients.
Open all year. No smoking. Vegetarian & other diets by arrangement. Disabled access: one ground floor room avail. but no wheelchair access. Children welcome. Pets by arrangement. En suite, tea/coffee-making & T.V. in all bedrooms. B. & B. from £16.

WOTTON UNDER EDGE

⊛ Coombe Lodge Vegetarian B. & B., Wotton under Edge, GL12 7NB (0453) 845057
Spacious Georgian house in an acre of gardens with mature trees.
Open all year ex. Xmas and New Year. No smoking in the house. Vegetarian standard. Other meat-free special diets by arrangement. Children: over 3s only. Tea-making & T.V. in bedrooms. B. & B. from £15.

Restaurants

CHELTENHAM

The Baytree, Regent Arcade, Cheltenham, GL50 1JZ (0242) 516229
Pleasantly furnished café in busy, modern Regent Arcade in the centre of Cheltenham. Vegetarian dishes always available & a wide range of beverages including speciality teas.
14 seats. Open 8.30 - 5.30. L. around £2. 50% no-smoking. Vegetarian. Disabled access. Children welcome.

CIRENCESTER

⊛ Rosamond de Marco, Shop 7, Swan Yard, West Market St, Cirencester (0285) 659683
Open daily, 9.30 - 6 (summer), 10 - 5 (winter). No smoking throughout.

GLOUCESTER

⊛ The Undercroft Restaurant, Church House, College Green, GL1 5ER (0452) 307164
This lovely restaurant and coffee shop was opened in 1988. It is situated just off the cloisters of the cathedral and above it are three historic, beamed rooms of differing sizes which are available for private bookings. The food is first-rate and features a selection of fine coffee and teas, lunches and afternoon teas. Everything is freshly prepared on the premises - including the delicious cakes - and there are some good vegetarian options.
80 seats. Open 10 - 5. L. around £2.50. Smoking banned in two dining rooms. Vegetarian standard. Licensed. Disabled access. Children welcome.

⊛ Debenhams, Kings Square, Gloucester (0452) 22121
Intermission, a friendly self-service restaurant serving lunches, snacks and hot and cold drinks.
Open store hours. No smoking. Vegetarian. Disabled accesS. Children very welcome.. Credit/debit cards.

LECHLADE

⊛ Katie's Tearoom & Gift Shop, Marlborough House, High St, Lechlade (0367) 52273
Open all year, daily, 9.30 - 6 (varies according to season). No smoking throughout.

MORETON-IN-MARSH

⊛ Cotswold Restaurant, Coffee House and Patisserie, High St, Moreton-in-Marsh
Open Apr. - Dec, daily except Wed. & Fri., 9.30 - 5. No smoking throughout.

STROUD

The Ragged Cot Inn, Hyde, Chalford, Nr Stroud, Gl6 8PE (0453) 884643/731333
16th C. 'olde worlde' inn, tastefully decorated, in the heart of the Cotswolds; friendly personal service, good home-made food in no-smoking area; 3 years holder of 'Fit to Eat' Award.
50 seats (restaurant). L./D. around £7-£10. Serving food 12 - 2.30, 7 - 11. No smoking in restaurant. Vegetarian standard. Licensed. Wheelchair access. Children: over 14s only. Credit cards accepted.

TEWKSBURY

⊛ The Abbey Tea Rooms, 59 Church St, Tewksbury, GL20 5RZ (0684) 292215
Pleasant 'old world' tea rooms located in 15th C. building offering range of snacks, lunches and afternoon teas. Home-cooked foods a speciality, including excellent home-made cakes.
28 seats. Open 10.30 - 5.30, Mar. to Nov. L. around £3.50. No smoking throughout. Vegetarian and Weight Watchers standard. Licensed. Disabled access. Children welcome.

Hereford
Accommodation

FELTON

Felton House, Felton, Herefordshire, HR1 3PH (0432) 820366

Felton House is an old, stone-built, former rectory standing in 3 acres of beautiful grounds and gardens adjacent to the parish church in the peaceful hamlet of Felton. The proprietors, Marjorie and Brian Roby, have furnished their lovely home in keeping with its period charm, and each of the centrally-heated, guest bedrooms have been decorated in original and distinctive style - some have four poster or half-tester beds. A wide choice of traditional or vegetarian options are offered at breakfast, and there are several good, local inns - one within walking distance - at which you may enjoy an evening meal. The countryside surrounding Felton House is unspoilt rural England at its finest: the 20th C. hardly seems to have touched the environs of the village but you are only 8 miles from the cathedral town of Hereford and there are numerous other towns, villages, stately homes and antique centres to be visited nearby.

Open Jan. to Nov. inc. No smoking in the dining room, bedrooms, bathrooms & 1 lounge. Vegetarian & standard English bfasts. Children & pets welcome. Tea/coffee-making in bedrooms. TV in lounge. B. & B. from £13.

HAY-ON-WYE

Kilvert Court Hotel, Bullring, Hay-on-Wye, HR3 5AG (0497) 821042

Open all year. No smoking throughout. Vegetarian & other diets by arrangement. Licensed. Disabled access to restaurant. Children. En suite, tea/coffee-making & T.V. in all bedrooms. B. & B. from £30.

The Haven, Hardwicke, Hay-on-Wye, HR3 5TA (04973) 254

The Haven is an early Victorian vicarage standing in 2 acres of mature gardens and paddocks set deep amidst beautiful Herefordshire countryside yet just 2 miles from the famous 'book town' of Hay on Wye. The comfortable bedrooms are named after the fine views they command and are exceptionally well-appointed (the Radnor has a four-poster and huge bathroom, for instance, while the ground floor room, the Clyro, is suitable for disabled guests); both sitting and dining rooms have open log fires and there are plenty of books, maps and guide books to help you plan your stay. The food is excellent: everything has been prepared from fresh, often home-grown, ingredients, and the traditional breakfast features a range of alternatives including kippers, haddock and kedgeree while the four-course evening meal is imaginative and tasty and would typically feature such dishes as Sorrel Soup, Pears in Tarragon Mayonnaise and Honeyed Chicken followed by Elderflower Sorbet or Spiced Plum Crumble. There is an open air swimming pool in the garden for refreshing dips on fine summer days.

Open Mar. to Nov. No smoking ex. in library. Vegetarian & other diets by prior arrangement. Licensed. Disabled access:1 ground floor en suite room.' Children welcome. Pets by arrangement. En suite in most rooms. Tea/coffee-making & T.V. in all rooms. Amex. B. & B. from £21.

Stoneleigh Guest House, Clifford, Nr Hay-on-Wye, HR3 5ER (04973) 361

Charming stone-built house situated on the quiet B4350 road half-way between Hay-on-Wye and the Whitney-on-Wye toll bridge. Good home-cooking. Family, twin and double rooms avail. *Open all year. No smoking in the house. Vegetarian and most other special diets by arrangement. Children welcome. Pets by arrangement. B. & B. from £12. Singles at same rate.*

York House, Victorian Guest House, Cusop, Hay on Wye, HR3 5QX (0497) 820705

York House is an elegant, late Victorian house which has been sympathetically refurbished by the present owners, Peter and Olwen Roberts, in period style to a very high standard while retaining many of the features of the original building. Each of the individually decorated bedrooms

have little personal touches (sewing kits, plants or dried flowers, biscuits and tissues), as well as the usual facilities; two en suite rooms have a single bed, a double bed and a sitting area. The evening menu features an imaginative selection of freshly prepared dishes such as home-made soup followed by Turkey Casserole with red cabbage, onion and apple, and a tempting dessert such as Iced Whisky and Honey Creams. Hay on Wye is a world famous centre for the second hand book trade; situated in a very peaceful part of the Welsh countryside it is ideal for all year round walking on nearby Offa's Dyke and the Wye Valley Walk. RAC Acclaimed.

Open all year. No smoking in the house. Vegetarian, diabetic by arrangement. Children: over 8s only. Pets by arrangement. 3 bedrooms en suite. Tea & coffee making & T.V. in bedrooms. Credit cards. B. & B. from £16.50.

HEREFORD

Grafton Villa, Grafton, Nr Hereford, HR2 8ED (0432) 268689
Open all year. No smoking in the house. Vegetarian & other diets by arrangement. Children welcome. Pets by arrangement. Tea/coffee-making & T.V. in all bedrooms. B. & B. from £15.

The Old Rectory, Byford, Hereford, HR4 7LD (098122) 218
Lovely Georgian house used as a rectory from 1830 until 1960.
Open Easter to Nov. No smoking throughout. Vegetarian by arrangement. No disabled access. Children welcome. Pets by arrangement. En suite in 1 room. Tea/coffee-making. T.V. in all rooms. B. & B. from £13.

KINGTON

Church House, Lyonshall, Kington, HR5 3HR (05448) 350
Small, Georgian country house with lovely views in all directions standing in 10 acres of gardens and paddocks; meals prepared from fresh local produce.
Open all year ex. Xmas. No smoking in the house. Vegetarian & other diets by arrangement. Children welcome. En suite in some rooms. Tea/coffee-making in all rooms. T.V. in lounge. B. & B. from £15, single £20.

LEDBURY

Wall Hills Country Guest House, Hereford Rd, Ledbury, HR8 2PR (0531) 2833
Elegant Georgian mansion in its own garden on the hill slopes overlooking Ledbury.
Open all year ex. Xmas. No smoking in dining room & bedrooms. Vegetarian & other diets by arrangement. Licensed. Children welcome. En suite. Tea/coffee-making in all rooms. T.V. lounge. B. & B. from £17.50.

LEOMINSTER

Copper Hall, 134 South St, Leominster, HR6 8JN (0568) 611622
Open all year ex. Xmas. No smoking in dining room & bedrooms.Vegetarian & other diets by arrangement. Children: if well behaved. Pets by arrangement. Tea/coffee-making & T.V. in all bedrooms. B. & B. from £15.

Green Haven Country House, Lucton, Leominster, HR6 9PN (0568) 85276
Charming country house in beautiful landscaped gardens surrounded by woods and fields.
Open all year. No smoking throughout. Special diets by arrangement. Children: over 10s only. Tea/coffee-making on request. T.V. B. & B. from £15. ETB Listed.

Kimbolton Court, Kimbolton, Leominster, HR6 0HH (0568) 87259
Stone-built farmhouse in an acre of partially wild garden at the end of a peaceful lane.
Open all year ex. Xmas and New Year. No smoking in bedrooms. Vegetarian & other diets by arrangement. Children welcome. En suite in some rooms. Tea/coffee-making in all rooms. T.V. in lounge. B. & B. from £13.

Ratefield Farm, Kimbolton, Leominster, HR6 0JB (0568) 2507
Lovely 18th C. house in a secluded position 1m from Kimbolton. Home-baked bread and rolls.
Open Mar. - mid Feb. No smoking in dining room & bedrooms. Vegetarian, diabetic, coeliac by arrangement.Children welcome. Pets by arrangement. Tea/coffee-making. T.V. in lounge. Amex. B. & B. from £13.50.

Withenfield, South St, Leominster, HR6 8JN (0568) 612011
Detached Georgian house furnished with many period pieces, including a four-poster bed.
Open all year. No smoking in dining room, lounge & bedrooms. Vegetarian & other diets by arrangement. Licensed. Children welcome. En suite, TV & tea/coffee-making in all rooms. B. & B. from £24.50. D. £17.50.

MORDIFORD

Orchard Farm, Mordiford, Nr Hereford, HR1 4EJ (0432) 870253
17th C. stone-built farmhouse with large, natural garden and 57 acres of traditional farmland.
Open all year ex. Xmas. No smoking ex. 1 sitting room. Vegetarian & other diets by arrangement. Licensed. Children: over 10s only. Tea/coffee-making available. T.V. available. Amex. B. & B. from £14.

MUCH BIRCH

The Old School, Much Birch, Nr Hereford, HR2 8HJ Tel: Rita Ayers (0981) 540006
Comfortable, attractive, converted Victorian school with a lovely large garden and fantastic views. Really good home-made food. Marvellous walking country. Guest lounge with colour TV and extensive library. Central heating. ETB 2 Crown Commended.
Open all year. No smoking in dining room and bedrooms. Vegetarian, vegan, diabetic and most other special diets by arrangement. Children welcome. Trained pets welcome. En suite in 2 rooms. Tea/coffee-making in all rooms. T.V in lounge, radio in all bedrooms. B. & B. from £15.

ROSS ON WYE

Aberhall Farm, St Owen's Cross, Ross on Wye, HR2 8LL (098987) 256
17th C. farmhouse forming part of working mixed farm. Tastefully decorated (all bedrooms have lovely views) and serving meals prepared from fresh produce by award-winning cook.
Open Mar. to Oct. No smoking in public rooms. Children: over 10s only. En suite in some rooms. Tea/coffee-making in all rooms. T.V in lounge. B. & B. from £14.

The Arches Country House, Walford Rd, Ross-on-Wye (0989) 63348
Small family-run guest house in ½ acre of lawns & 10 mins walk from town centre. All bedrooms overlook the garden. Very high standard of decor. RAC Acclaimed. AA listed. Routier Award.
Open all year. No smoking in the dining room & bedrooms. Vegetarian & other diets by arrangement. En suite, TV & tea/coffee-making in bedrooms. Children & pets welcome. B. & B. £15 - 20.

Brook House, Lea, Nr Ross on Wye, HR9 7JZ (098981) 710
Fine Grade II listed Queen Anne building standing on the site of a mediaeval hospice.
Open all year. No smoking ex. in lounge. Vegetarian standard. Other diets by arrangement. Children: over 7s only. Pets by arrangement. Some en suite. Tea/coffee-making in all rooms. T.V in lounge. B. & B. from £15.

Edde Cross House, Edde Cross St, Ross on Wye, HR9 7BZ (0989) 65088
Georgian Grade II listed town house with its charming walled garden.
Open Feb. to Nov. No smoking in the house. Vegetarian standard. Other special diets by arrangement. Children: over 10s only. En suite in some rooms. Tea/coffee-making & T.V in all bedrooms. B. & B. from £17.

Lavender Cottage, Bridstow, Ross on Wye, HR9 6QB (0989) 62836
Lavender Cottage is a delightful character property with parts dating back to the 17th century; it enjoys a tranquil location just one mile from Ross on Wye and has fine views of Bridstow church and May Hill; Ross church spire can be seen clearly amidst the backdrop of the trees of Chase Woods and Goodrich Castle with the Forest of Dean beyond. The cottage has been comfortably furnished and decorated and a generous breakfast is offered to guests.
Open all year. No smoking in the house. Vegetarian & other diets by arrangement. En suite in some rooms. Tea/coffee-making in all rooms. T.V. in lounge. B. & B. from £12.50.

Linden House, 14 Church St, Ross on Wye, HR9 5HN (0989) 65373
William and Mary/Georgian town house in a quiet street opposite St Marys church.
Open all year. No smoking in the house. Vegetarian & other diets by arrangement. Licensed. Children: over 8s only. En suite in some rooms. Tea/coffee-making & T.V. in all bedrooms. B. & B. from £16.50.

Rudhall farm, Ross-on-Wye, Hereford, HR9 7TL (0989) 85240
Elegant country house with landscaped garden with lake and millstream in peaceful valley.

Open 10 Jan. to 6 Dec. No smoking in the house. Vegetarian & other diets by arrangement. Tea/coffee-making & TV in bedrooms. B. & B. from £17.

ST WEONARDS

The Old Vicarage, St Weonards, HR2 8NT (09818) 278
Comfortable Victorian home in 2 acres of gardens, in charming village; panoramic views.
Open all year ex. Xmas. No smoking in the house. Vegetarian and most other special diets by arrangement. Children welcome. Tea/coffee-making & T.V. in all bedrooms. B. & B. from £16.

ULLINGSWICK

The Steppes Country House Hotel, Ullingswick, HR1 3JG (0432) 820424

The Steppes is a listed 17th C. building with a wealth of original features (beamed ceilings, inglenook fireplaces, tiled floors) in the tiny hamlet of Ullingswick - a community mentioned in the Domesday Book of 1082. It has been sympathetically renovated - the ancient dairy and cider-making cellars now forming the Cellar bar and Lounge - and the bedrooms are all tastefully furnished and decorated. The 5-course evening meal, served by candlelight, is a gourmet treat for the adventurous palate, and features an eclectic variety of dishes, ranging from ancient Medieval recipes served at Royal Banquets to revived local delicacies and Eastern delights (a more conventional menu is available for those with traditional tastes); all meals have been prepared from the finest fresh ingredients by the internationally renowned chef. Add to this the beauty of the unspoilt - and still largely undiscovered - Herefordshire countryside, and you have the perfect place for a very special holiday break.
Open all year. No smoking in most public rooms. Vegetarian & other diets by arrangement. Licensed. Disabled access: 'not for totally wheelchair bound'. Children: over 12s only. Pets by arrangement. En suite, tea/coffee-making, TV, phone, mini-bar in all bedrooms. Access, Barclaycard. B. & B. from £32.50.

Restaurants

HEREFORD

'Nutters', Capuchin Yard, Off Church St, Hereford (277447)
Vegetarian restaurant.
Open 9.30 - 5. No smoking throughout. Vegetarian standard. Licensed. Wheelchair access. Children welcome.

Intermision Restaurant, Unit 24, Maylord Orchards Shopping Centre (0432) 272500
A friendly self-service restaurant serving popular light lunches, snacks and a wide range of hot and cold drinks.
Open store hours. Smoking banned throughout. Vegetarian meals. Disabled acces. Not licensed. Children very welcome. Credit and debit cards accepted.

ROSS ON WYE

Copperfields, 29 Gloucester Rd, Ross-on-Wye (0989) 67734
Teashop serving cakes, hot and cold snacks and a choice of teas.
Open 9 - 5, Mon. to Sat. No smoking throughout.

Meader' s Hungarian Restaurant, 1 Copse Cross St, Ross on Wye, HR9 5PD (0989) 62803
Friendly restaurant serving delicious food, mainly Hungarian.
No smoking throughout. Vegetarian. Licensed. Children welcome.

Shropshire
Accommodation

BRIDGNORTH

The Old Vicarage Hotel, Worfield, Bridgnorth, WV15 5JZ (07464) 497

The Old Vicarage is a magnificent Edwardian house which stands in two acres of beautifully tended grounds, overlooking fields and farmland, in the quiet Shropshire hamlet of Worfield. The proprietors, Christine and Peter Iles, have been in residence since 1979 and since that time have lovingly restored this handsome Edwardian parsonage into a country house hotel of quite exceptional quality: decorated and furnished in keeping with the period, the en suite guest rooms are nonetheless individually styled (each is named after a local village), and offer a wide range of facilities, including a direct dial phone, a mini-bar and fresh fruit; further luxury suites (including one specifically designed for disabled guests), are available in the Coach House. The candlelit dinner is exceptionally good: the menu, which is based around the availability of fresh, regional produce, changes daily and virtually everything is home-made, including the bread, ice-cream, sorbets and preserves (there are some excellent vegetarian options); the wine list is comprehensive and includes a good selection of half bottles. The Old Vicarage is a perfect venue for parties and private functions.

Open all year. No smoking in dining room & some bedrooms. Vegetarian & other diets by arrangement. Licensed. Ramps & special suite for disabled. Children welcome. Pets by arrangement. En suite, tea/coffee-making & T.V. in all bedrooms. Access, Visa, Amex, Diners. B. & B. from £78.50 for 2 persons, D. from £19.50.

CHURCH STRETTON

Ⓦ Hope Bowdler Hall, Church Stretton, SY6 7DD (0694) 722041

Hope Bowdler Hall is an ancient stone-built manor house with a lovely large garden - complete with hard tennis court - which stands at the edge of the peaceful village of Hope Bowdler, surrounded by beautiful hills. A family home, it has been carefully modernised and now offers a very comfortable standard of accommodation; only four guests are taken at any one time which gives the place a friendly, relaxed atmosphere. Breakfast is the only meal available but a number of local places offer good evening meals. Hope Bowdler is an excellent centre for walking: you are just one and a half miles from Church Stretton and Ludlow, Shrewsbury, Ironbridge and the Welsh borders are within easy reach. Riding and golf are both available locally, and there are famous gardens at Hodnet Hall, Burford House and Powys Castle. Visitors should take the the B4371 in the village and approach by the lane leading to the church.

Open April to Oct. No smoking in the house. B. & B. from £15.

Mynd House Hotel, Little Stretton, Church Stretton, SY6 6RB (0694) 722212

Standing high above the road with extensive views across the Stretton Gap to Ragleth Hill, this small Edwardian house hotel and restaurant offers a perfect window on the Shropshire Hills. The rather severe Edwardian brick exterior belies the intimate interior of the house which Janet and Robert Hill have enhanced with period furniture and decor (a log fire blazes in the lounge in cooler weather); no reception or room numbers here: you are received as a guest in a country house. The candlelit restaurant - open to non-residents - features an excellent fixed price 4-course Table d'hote or an à la carte menu (both offer imaginative dishes and good meat-free options), and there is an outstanding wine list (the Mynd House Hotel was the 1991 winner of the Mercier Prix d'Elite award) which features over 300 selections - including English country and French organic

wines - and an incredible 100 item half bottle list. For the walker the area is a delight in all seasons - the hotel produces a booklet of six walks from the door - and your proximity to the ancient towns of Shrewsbury and Ludlow make the Mynd House Hotel a perfect destination for a short break in the Shropshire Hills. Environmentally friendly. e.g. Organic French wines available.
Open all year ex. Jan. & 1 week in Aug. No smoking ex. in bar lounge. Vegetarian by arrangement. Licensed. Children welcome. Pets by arrangement. En suite, tea/coffee-making & T.V. in all bedrooms. Credit cards. B. & B. from £28 p.p. Luxury suites from £42 p.p.

CRAVEN ARMS

The Old Rectory, Hopesay, Craven Arms, SY7 8HD (05887) 245
Delightful 17th century rectory set in 2 acres of beautiful landscaped gardens.
Open all year. No smoking throughout. Vegetarian & other diets by arrangement. Not licensed, but bring your own. Children: over 12s only. En suite, tea/coffee-making & T.V. in all bedrooms. B & B from £26, D. £16.

ELLESMERE

The Mount, St John's Hill, Ellesmere, Shropshire, SY12 OEY (0691) 622466
Quality bed and breakfast, catering for a maximum of 4 guests, in a Listed 18th C. private house at the heart of Ellesmere Conservation Area; log fires, good books and many other welcoming touches; large peaceful garden. ETB 2 Crowns Highly Commended.
Open all year. No smoking in the house. Vegetarian & other diets by arrangement. 2 guest bedrooms each with private bathroom. Tea/coffee-making & radio in all bedrooms. T.V. in sitting room. B. & B. £20.

IRONBRIDGE

The Library House, 11 Severn Bank, Ironbridge, TF8 7AN (0952) 432299

The Library House is a well-restored period house situated in a World Heritage Site of The Ironbridge Gorge about 100 yards from the Ironbridge itself; the old village library, which gives the house its name is now a comfortable guest lounge. The house has been tastefully furnished throughout, and the proprietors offer excellent accommodation in centrally heated en suite rooms. Breakfast is the only meal which is usually served at the Library House, but evening meals - in which everything has been freshly home-cooked - can be provided by prior arrangment. You are splendidly situated amidst wonderful countryside and just a short distance from the Long Mynd with its famous walks.
Open all year. No smoking throughout. Vegetarian and other special diets on request. Licensed. No disabled access. Children welcome. Pets welcome. En suite. Tea/coffee-making and T.V. in all bedrooms. No credit cards. B. & B. from £21. 3 Crown Highly Commended. AA QQQ. Free car park pass to all sites.

The Severn Trow, Church Rd, Jackfield, Ironbridge, Shrops, TF8 7ND (0952) 883551
Your hosts at the Severn Trow, Jim and Pauline Hannigan, are extending a hand of hospitality which has been proferred by successive occupants for many centuries at their home: travellers to the area would berth their trows at the wharf at the end of the garden before retiring to the Severn Trow for rest and recuperation. These days no trow-berthing is required to appreciate the Hannigan hospitality and the wonderful way in which they have renovated their unique home: some things could not be changed (the front door faces the river and its purpose died with the river trade), but some original features still enhance the character of the house, such as the wide inglenook fireplace and the magnificent Jackfield mosaic tile floor in the dining room. Accommodation is in rooms which have changed happily in both comfort and function (one was once one of several brothel cubicles), and each has a range of helpful amenities, including the ground floor suite (a good choice for guests of limited mobility - your hosts will gladly serve breakfast therein on request).
Open Jan. to end Oct. No smoking in the house. Vegetarian & other diets by arrangement. Ground floor room but not total wheelchair access. Well-behaved children welcome. En suite & tea/coffee-making in bedrooms. TV in lounge & some bedrooms. B. & B. £16-21.

LINGEN

Brook Cottage, Lingen, Bucknell, Shropshire, SY7 ODY (0544) 267990
18th C. cottage in country garden with brook in idyllic village. Vegetarian food a speciality. Books, music and tranquillity to be enjoyed!
Open Feb. - Nov. No smoking in the house. Specialises in special diets including gluten-free, milk-free, egg-free. Children & pets by arrangement. T.V. lounge. B. & B. from £15, E.M. £7.50.

LUDLOW

Corndene, Coreley, Ludlow, SY8 3AW (0584) 890324
Charming house of great charm in 2 acres of lovely gardens. Excellent wheelchair access.
Open all year ex. Xmas and New Year. No smoking throughout. Vegetarian & other diets by arrangement. "Tourism for all" accessible: excellent disabled access. Children welcome. En suite & tea/coffee-making facilities in all bedrooms. T.V. in lounge. B. & B. from £16. ETB 3 Crowns.

MINSTERLEY

Cricklewood Cottage, Plox Green, Minsterley, SY5 OHT (0743) 791229
18th C. cottage which is beautifully situated at the foot of the Stiperstones Hills
Open all year. No smoking throughout. Vegetarian and most other special diets by arrangement. En suite in 1 room. Tea/coffee-making in all bedrooms. T.V. in lounge. B. & B from £13. ETB Listed/Commended.

OSWESTRY

Bwlch y Rhiw, Llansilin, Oswestry, SY10 7PT (0691) 70261
Bwlch y Rhiw is a large Victorian farmhouse which is perched high above the Cynllaith Valley amidst 120 acres of farmland. It has been carefully restored in order to retain its original character and every modern comfort is provided in the centrally heated guest bedrooms (there is a double, a twin and a family room); there is also a pleasant lounge for guests'use. Breakfasts are served in the oak dining room with its inglenook fireplace and original bread oven and, while evening meals are not provided your hosts will provide soup and sandwiches on request and there are several good pubs and restaurants nearby. Llansilin straddles the English/Welsh border and as such is an ideal base for exploring the charms of both countries including Snowdonia, Chester & Shrewsbury.
Open Easter - Oct. inc. No smoking in the dining room. Vegetarian by arrangement. En suite, TV & tea/coffee-making in bedrooms. Children welcome. B. & B. from £16.50.

Frankton Manor, Welsh Frankton, Whittington, Oswestry, SY11 4NX (0691) 622454
Charming Victorian country house, originally the village rectory, with superb views.
Open Mar. - Oct.. No smoking in the house. Vegetarian & other diets by arrangement. Licensed. Children welcome. En suite, tea/coffee-making & T.V. in all bedrooms. B. & B. from £14.50. D. £8.

SHREWSBURY

Anton Guest House, 1 Canon St, Monkmoor, SY2 5HG (0743) 359275
The Anton Guest House is an attactive corner-positioned Victorian house which stands on a main road just 5 minutes' stroll from both Shrewsbury town centre and the 10th C. abbey church. Family-owned and run, the proprietors, Tony and Anne Sandford, offer a very friendly welcome to guests and are always on hand to help you make the most of your stay. The Anton Guest House has been very tastefully decorated, and each of the 3 bedrooms are warm and comfortable (the house is double-glazed). Breakfast is wholesome and delicious (the many repeat visits to the Anton Guest House testify to its popularity), and special diets can be accommodated by arrangement. The world-famous Brother Cadfael books, by Ellis Peters (soon to be serialised by central TV), are set in the area and visitors may be interested in retracing the intrepid monk's steps in the Brother Cadfael walks. Anton Guest House is 2 Crowns Commended.
Open all year. No smoking throughout. Children welcome. Tea & coffee-making and T.V. in all bedrooms. B. & B. £15.50. ETB 2 Crowns Commended.

Frankbrook, Yeaton Lane, Baschurch, Shrewsbury SY4 2HZ (0939) 260778
Attractive, peaceful country house with interesting gardenny. Home-grown produce.
Open all year. No smoking in the house. Vegetarian & other diets by arrangement. Children welcome. Tea/coffee-making in all bedrooms. T.V. in lounge & some bedrooms. B. & B. from £12.50. D. £6.50.

The Old House, Ryton, Dorrington, Nr Shrewsbury, SY5 7LY (0743) 73585
17th C. manor house in the small rural hamlet 6m south of Shrewsbury; 2 acres of superb gardens (complete with orchard & lily pond); most of the original timber frame & panelling remains including the oak-panelled dining room with antiques, pewter and fine paintings.
Open all year. No smoking in the house. Vegetarian & vegan standard. Other diets by arrangement.Children welcome. En suite & tea/coffee-making in all bedrooms. T.V. lounge. B. & B. from £17.50.

Restaurants

BRIDGNORTH
Old Vicarage Hotel, Worfield, Bridgnorth, WV15 5J2 (07464) 497
For further details please see under the entry in the accommodation section.

CHURCH STRETTON
Acorn Wholefood Restaurant Coffee House, 26 Sandford Ave, SY6 6BW (0694) 722495
Small family run business, recommended in many good food guides; all fare, except bread, is made on the premises from wholefood ingredients. Excellent food and friendly, efficient service.
32 seats. Open 9.30 - 5.30 winter and 10 - 6 summer, Sundays and Bank Holidays. No smoking in 75% of restaurant (sep. room).Vegetarian, vegan and other diets standard. Children welcome.

Mynd House Hotel, Little Stretton, SY6 6RB (0694) 722212
For further details please see under the entry in the accommodation section.

LUDLOW
Hardwicks Restaurant, 2 Quality Square, Ludlow (0584) 876470
Excellent vegetarian and wholefood restaurant.
33 seats. No smoking in 65% of restaurant. Vegetarian standard. Licensed. Children welcome.

NEWPORT
Royal Victoria Hotel, St Mary's St, Newport, Shorpshire (0952) 820331
Buttercross Restaurant with Victorian decor.
No smoking in part of restaurant. Vegetarian on request. Licensed. Children welcome. All credit cards accepted.

SHREWSBURY

Intermission Restaurant, Mezzanine Level, Pride Hill Centre, SY1 1BY (0743) 52393
A friendly self-service restaurant serving light lunches, snacks and hot and cold drinks.
Open store hours. No smoking. Vegetarian meals. Disabled access. Children welcome.. Credit/debit cards.

The Good Life, Barracks Passage, Wyle Cop, Shrewsbury (0743) 350455
The Good Life occupies 3 rooms of a finely restored 14th C. building which is quietly situated in one of the oldest parts of the historic and lovely county town of Shrewsbury. There is seating for 64 (plus 2 high chairs!) at clean pine tables, and the delicious wholefood menu makes a welcome change from 'chips with everything'. As the proprietors rightly point out: wholefood simply means nothing added or taken away; accordingly fresh vegetables and fruit, wholemeal flour, free-range eggs and demerara sugar are used to prepare delicious home-cooked quiches, nut loaves, cheeses and salads as well as a variety of tempting desserts and puddings; beverages (many caffeine-free) are chosen with the same care and all of the menu is available to take away.
64 seats (plus 2 high chairs!). Open 9.30 - 3.30 (4.30 Sat.) No smoking in 1 room. Vegetarian exclusively. Licensed. Disabled access. Children welcome.

TELFORD
Debenhams, Telford Centre (0952) 291500
Pavilion, a friendly self-service coffee shop serving popular light lunches, snacks and a wide range of hot and cold drinks.
Open store hours. No smoking throughout. Vegetarian meals. Disabled access. Children very welcome. Credit and debit cards accepted.

Staffordshire
Accommodation

BURTON-ON-TRENT

The Edgecote Hotel, 179 Ashby Rd, Burton on Trent, DE15 0LB (0283) 68966

The Edgecote is an attractive family-run hotel situated on the A50 Leicester road less than 5 minutes from the centre of Burton. All 12 centrally heated bedrooms are clean and comfortable - several have en suite facilities - and each is equipped with a range of helpful amenities such as a radio intercom and colour TV; there is a licensed bar and a comfortable lounge. Breakfast at the Edgecote is a real treat (the proprietors believe it to be the best in Burton!): a selection of cereals, yoghurt, fresh fruit and fruit juice is arranged on a self-service buffet, and to follow there is a choice of a traditional cooked breakfast or a lighter Continental option with home-baked rolls and croissants; dinner is served in the oak-panelled dining room and the delicious 3-course meal features imaginative vegetarian options and excellent home-cooked puds - and, at £9 it has got to be one of the best bargains to be found in Burton!

Open all year. No smoking in dining room, bedrooms & corridors. Vegetarian by arrangement. Licensed. Children welcome. Pets by arrangement. En suite in some rooms. Tea/coffee-making & T.V. in all bedrooms. Access, Visa, Amex. B. & B. from £16.50, D. £9.

ECCLESHALL

Glenwood, Croxton, Eccleshall, ST21 6PF (063082) 238

Glenwood is a charming timber-framed cottage which is beautifully situated amidst the unspoilt Staffordshire countryside; in the 16th C. it used to be a coaching inn but these days it has been tastefully renovated and comfortably furnished to provide peaceful accommodation of a very high standard to guests; indeed the proprietors have been awarded a 2 Crown Commended status by the English Tourist Board. Its peaceful location notwithstanding, Glenwood is just a short drive from junctions 14 and 15 on the M6; additionally you will find yourself within easy touring distance of the Peak District, the Potteries, the Marches and Wales.

Open all year. No smoking in dining room & bedrooms. Vegetarian & other diets by arrangement. Disabled access. Children welcome. Pets by arrangement. En suite. Tea/coffee-making in all rooms. T.V. lounge. Access, Visa. B. & B. from £13. ETB 2 Crown Commended.

LEEK

Pethills Bank Cottage, Bottomhouse, Nr Leek, ST13 7PF (0538) 304277/304555

18th C. Derbyshire stone farmhouse set on a hillside in landscaped gardens & with beautiful views.
Open Mar. to Dec. No smoking in most of the house. Vegetarian by arrangement. Children: over 5s welcome. En suite, tea/coffee-making & T.V. in all bedrooms. B. & B. from £17.50.

The White House, Grindon, Nr Leek, ST13 7TP (0538) 304250

South-facing house, 1,000 feet up in the Peak National Park; uninterrupted views of the Manifold and Hamps Valley. Retains the stone mullions and oak beams; home-baked bread & preserves
Open all year ex. Xmas and New Year. No smoking ex. in lounge. Vegetarian & other diets by arrangement. Children: over 10s only. En suite, TV & tea/coffee-making in all rooms. B. & B. from £17.

NEWCASTLE UNDER LYME

Durlston Guest House, Kimberley Rd, Newcastle under Lyme, ST5 9EG (0782) 611708

Friendly, family-run guest house 10 mins walk from the town centre. B'fast only. ETB 1 Crown.
Open all year. No smoking in dining room & on upper floor. Vegetarian by arrangement (b'fast only). Children welcome. Pets by arrangement. Tea-making & T.V. in rooms. Access, Visa, M'card. B. & B. from £15. AA listed.

STOKE-ON-TRENT

The Corrie Guest House, 13-15 Newton St, Basford, Stoke-on-Trent, ST4 6JN (0782) 614838

Fine Victorian house situated in a quiet cul-de-sac just off the A53 and A500 in the heart of the Potteries. Festival Park less than a mile away. Freshly prepared breakfasts; evening meal and snacks by arrangement. Large car park. 3 single, 2 double, 2 family and 1 twin-bedded room.
Open all year. Smoking allowed only in smokers'lounge. Vegetarian & special diets by arrangement. Children: 'no babies'. En suite in some rooms. Tea/coffee-making. T.V. in lounge. B. & B. from £15.

The Hollies, Clay Lake, Endon, Stoke-on-Trent, ST9 9DD (0782) 503252
Lovely Victorian house with large garden quietly situated in Endon village off the B5051/A53.
Open all year. No smoking in the house. Vegetarian & other diets by arrangement. Children welcome. Pets by arrangement. En suite in some rooms. Tea/coffee-making in all rooms. T.V. in lounge. B. & B. from £14.

White Gables Hotel, Trentham Rd, Blurton, Stoke-on-Trent, ST3 3DT (0782) 324882
Elegant, quiet, country-house-style hotel close to the M6 and with easy access to all city centres; beautifully decorated bedrooms.
Open all year. No smoking in the house. Vegetarian & other diets by arrangement. Licensed. Disabled access: '3 ground floor bedrooms'. Children welcome. Pets by arrangement. En suite in some rooms. Tea/coffee-making, T.V. & D.D. phones in all bedrooms. Access, Visa, Amex. B. & B. from £18.

Restaurants

BURTON-ON-TRENT

Byrkley Park Centre, Rangemore, Burton-on-Trent, DE13 9RN (0283) 716467
The Byrkley Park Centre is a garden centre with a difference; set in the beautiful countryside

around Burton-on-Trent, Byrkley Park (which is named after the 13th C. Thomas Berkley (sic.) who had a house near the site) has everything for the keen gardener including indoor and outdoor plants, garden furniture and a garden design and landscaping service; there is also the excellent Thomas de Byrkley Tea Room and Carvery which offers a wide range of delicious snacks (including home-made cakes), and selections from the Carvery and Salad Bar (there is a good selection of wines).
144 seats indoors, 80 seats outdoors. Open 10 to 4.30, Sept. to Mar.; 10 - 5.30, Apr. to Aug. & 10 - 8 p.m., Thurs. to Sat., Apr. to Aug. L. around £4. No smoking in dining room. Vegetarian & other diets on request. Licensed. Disabled access: ramps, wheelchairs, toilets. Children welcome. Credit cards.

HANLEY

Pavilion Coffee Shop, Potteries Shopping Centre (0782) 202495
A friendly self-service coffee shop serving popular light lunches, snacks and a wide range of hot and cold drinks.
Open store hours. No smoking throughout. Vegetarian meals. Disabled access. Children very welcome. Credit and debit cards accepted.

WATERHOUSES

The Old School Restaurant, Staffordshire Peak Arts Centre, Cauldon Lowe, Nr Waterhouses, ST10 3EX (0538) 308431
The Staffordshire Peak Arts Centre is housed in the atmospheric setting of a converted old moorlands village school, and it displays an exceptional range of fine art, craft work and gifts. The Old School Restaurant - housed in the same buiding - is a delightful place in which to enjoy the wide range of home-made cakes and meals which are served throughout the day. Wholesome ingredients have been used in cooking and there are some tasty vegetarian options. Families are particularly welcome - there is a garden and play area available - and on fine days you may care to walk along the Nature Trail which has been laid out nearby on a one acre site of special scientific interest.
40 seats. Open 10.30 - 5.30. Prices reasonable. No smoking throughout. Vegetarian and vegan standard. Most other special diets on request. Licensed. Disabled access. Children welcome. Access, Visa.

Warwickshire
Accommodation

HENLEY IN ARDEN

Irelands Farm Bed & Breakfast, Irelands Farm, Irelands Lane, B95 5SA (0564) 792476
Open all year, ex. Xmas & New Year. No smoking in dining room & bedrooms. Vegetarian by arrangement. Dogs by arrangement. En suite some rooms. Tea/coffee making & T.V. in all rooms. B. & B. from £15.

NUNEATON

Bosworth Firs, Bosworth Rd, Market Bosworth, Nr Nuneaton, CV13 0DW (0455) 290727
Small family-run guest house in ⅓ acre of gardens in rural situation on B585 1m from Bosworth.
Open all year. No smoking in dining room & bedrooms. Vegetarian & other diets by arrangement. Disabled access. Children welcome. Pets by arrangement. En suite. Tea/coffee-making in all rooms. T.V. B. & B. £13.

ROYAL LEAMINGTON SPA

Agape, 26 St Mary Rd, Royal Leamington Spa (0926) 882896
Pleasant guest house situated on the southern edge of town & within easy walking distance of its many attractions. Warm, friendly atmosphere. BTA member. Home-made jams for b'fast.
Open all year. No smoking in the house. Vegetarian & other diets by arrangement. Children: over 5s welcome. En suite, TV & tea/coffee-making in bedrooms. B. & B. from £18.50.

Northton, 77 Telford Avenue, Royal Leamington Spa, CV32 7HQ (0926) 425609
Northton is a private family home situated just off the A445 offering first class accommodation in a quiet and peaceful residential area on the northern outskirts of Leamington Spa; it has been very comfortably furnished - both guest rooms face south and overlook extensive gardens - and a full English breakfast is served to guests (together with national daily papers!). Northton is ideally situated for visitors to the city of Coventry (just 20 minutes drive away), its Management Training Centre and National Agricultural Centre (just 2 miles away); taxis can be arranged to and from these two centres and Northton.
Open Feb. to Oct. No smoking throughout. Vegetarian and other special diets by arrangement. Children welcome. En suite, tea/coffee-making and T.V. in all rooms. B. & B. from £15. ETB 2 Crowns Commended.

The Willis, 11 Eastnor Grove, Royal Leamington Spa, CV31 1LD (0926) 425820
Spacious Victorian town house with peaceful garden in a quiet residential cul-de-sac.
Open all year. No smoking in the house. Vegetarian & other diets by arrangement. Children welcome. Pets by arrangement. En suite in twin-bedded room. Tea/coffee-making in all rooms. T.V B. & B. from £16.

SHIPSTON-ON-STOUR

Longdon Manor, Shipston-on-Stour, CV36 4PW (0608) 82235
14th C. manor house with history and records dating from 10th C.
Open Mar. to Nov. No smoking in the house. Vegetarian diets by arrangement. Children welcome. En suite & TV in all rooms. Tea/coffee-making in rooms on request. Credit cards. B. & B. from £30.

STRATFORD UPON AVON

Abberley, 12 Albany Rd, Stratford upon Avon, CV37 6PG (0789) 295934

Abberley is an comfortable family home, centrally situated in a quiet residential part of Stratford upon Avon within easy walking distance of the three Royal Shakespeare Company theatres and the River Avon. It is an exclusively smoke-free establishment and, while breakfast is the only meal available, it is a healthy treat (home-made Seville marmalade; vegetarian breakfast options) and there are plenty of good restaurants in the town. Abberley provides the perfect base from which to visit the Shakespearean properties and explore the Cotswolds, Warwick Castle and the many nearby National Trust properties.
Open all year. No smoking in the house. Special diets by arrangement. Full private facilities en suite. Tea/coffee-making & T.V. Car parking. B. & B. from £19.

Ashburton House, 27 Evesham Place, Stratford upon Avon, CV37 6HT (0789) 292444 Fax: (0789) 415658
Small, friendly guest house close to the town centre and specialising in Japanese breakfasts and pre-theatre dinners; traditional English breakfast is also available.
Open all year ex. Xmas. Smoking banned in public rooms. Vegetarian & most other special diets by arrangement. Children welcome. Tea/coffee-making & T.V in all bedrooms. Amex. B. & B. from £16.

Avon Croft, Old Town, Stratford upon Avon, CV37 6BG (0789) 292600
16th C. listed house close to town centre, theatres and Holy Trinity Church.
Open Mar. to Nov. No smoking in the house. Special diets on request. Children welcome. En suite & tea/coffee-making in all rooms. B. & B. from £17.

Bishopton Hill Nursery, Birmingham Rd, Stratford-upon-Avon, CV37 0RN (0789) 267829
Formerly a nursery, this attractive modern bungalow stands in 4 acres of grounds 1½ miles north of Stratford-upon-Avon on the A3400 Henley-in-Arden road. It is a spacious family home, beautifully situated in an elevated position with wonderful views over Stratford-upon-Avon towards the Cotswold Hills. It is run by Muriel Hardwicke who offers a full English breakfast to guests: lacto-vegetarian and other diets can be catered for by arrangement and there are plenty of restaurants in Stratford-upon-Avon. Accommodation is in comfortable rooms which have good facilities, and there is a ground floor room. Most visitors to Stratford come to enjoy the theatres and houses associated with Shakespeare's home town, but happily they are within easy reach of many of England's other most beautiful places, such as Warwick Castle, Blenheim Palace and Oxford. The NEC and the airport are also within easy driving distance.
Open all year. No smoking in the house. Vegetarian & other diets by arrangement. Children: over 8s welcome. En suite, TV & tea/coffee-making in bedrooms. B. & B. from £17.50.

Brook Lodge, 192 Alcester Rd, Stratford upon Avon, CV37 9DR (0789) 295988
Open all year ex. xmas & New Year. Smoking banned in all public rooms. Children welcome. Pets by arrangement. En suite in most rooms. Tea/coffee-making & T.V in all bedrooms. Credit cards B. & B. from £15.

Clomendy Guest House, 157 Evesham Rd, Stratford, CV37 9BP (0789) 266957
Clomendy Guest House is a small, detached, family-run guest house which is built in the mock tudor style and stands on the main Stratford to Evesham road; there is a very pleasant garden which recently won a 'Stratford in Bloom' commendation. Breakfast is the only meal to be served at Clomendy, but you are within easy reach of Stratford town centre in which there are numerous good restaurants. Guests choosing to arrive by coach or rail can be collected free of charge from the stations, and you will find the guest house is within easy each of the theatres and Anne Hathaway's cottage, as well as within driving distance of the Cotswolds.
Open all year. No smoking in the house. Children welcome. Tea/coffee-making & T.V. in bedrooms. B. & B. from £13 - 17. ETB 2 Crowns.

Green Gables, 47 Banbury Rd, Stratford upon Avon, CV37 7HW (0789) 20557
Open all year. No smoking in the house. Children. En suite. Tea-making & T.V. B. & B. from £13.

Moonraker House, Alcester Rd, Stratford-upon-Avon, CV37 9DB Tel: (0789) 299346/267115 Fax: (0789) 295504

Moonraker House is situated in Stratford-upon-Avon, the perfect centre for exploring the Cotswolds, and is personally run by the owners, Mike and Mauveen Spencer. All the rooms have been individually designed and decorated to a very high standard of comfort and cosiness by Mauveen and her daughter, and there is a collection of Edwardian furniture in the main lounge/dining room. For an extra touch of luxury there is also a four-poster bedroom (with garden patio) a 2-room suite and a half-testa bedroom. Moonraker House is a home-from-home down to the home-made jams & marmalade which are part of the delicious, freshly cooked English breakfast.
Open all year ex. Xmas & Boxing Day. No smoking in the house. Vegetarian & any other diet by arrangement. Some ground floor rooms. Children welcome. Pets by arrangement. En suite, colour TV, clock radio, hairdryer & tea/coffee-making in bedrooms. Credit cards. B. & B. £18.50 - 29.

Moss Cottage, 61 Evesham Rd, Stratford-upon-Avon, CV37 9BA (0789) 294770
Detached cottage offering spacious en suite accommodation with TV & tea tray. Traditional b'fast; free range eggs. Close to Shakespeare properties & theatres. Reductions for 2+ nights.
Open Mar - Dec. No smoking in the house. En suite, TV & tea/coffee-making in bedrooms. B. & B. £15-19.

Pond Cottage, The Green, Warmington, Banbury, OX17 1BU Tel: (029589) 682
This much-photographed, old, stone-built cottage with honeysuckle climbing up the wall

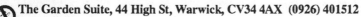

stands in a lovely, peaceful Conservation Area just 6 miles from the M40 - midway between junction 11 (Banbury), and 12 (Gaydon); it is an idyllic spot- far removed from the hustle and bustle of Warwick, Stratford-upon-Avon and the Cotswolds which are, nevertheless, within easy touring distance. The cottage has been delightfully furnished in a traditional style and great attention has been paid to detail: the double bedroom overlooks the village green and duckpond and the small, cheerfully decorated single room overlooks the garden. Your hostess, Mrs Viljoen, offers a warm welcome to guests and, on a summer's day, tea in her brightly coloured, pocket-handkerchief garden. The home-cooked food is delicious, and a typical evening meal would feature home-made Mushroom Soup followed by Chicken Breast with Almond Sauce, and a mouthwatering blackberry, plum or gooseberry Ice Cream prepared with fruit, freshly culled from the garden.
Open April - Oct. inc. No smoking in the house. Double room: shower w. basin en suite; single: bathroom next door. Tea/coffee making in both bedrooms. TV in sitting room. B. & B. £32 double, £15 single. D. £11.80.

Twelfth Night, Evesham Place, Stratford upon Avon, CV37 6HT (0789) 414595
Elegantly refurbished Victorian house. Superb pre-theatre meals available.
Open all year. No smoking in the house. Vegetarian and most other special diets at breakfast by arrangement. Children: over 5s only. En suite in most rooms. Tea/coffee-making & T.V in all bedrooms. B. & B. from £18.

WARWICK

The Croft, Haseley Knob, Warwick, CV35 7NL (0926) 484 447
The Croft is a large family house and small holding set in the picturesque village of Haseley Knob. It has a large flower and vegetable garden in which guests can relax. A friendly family atmosphere is a very important part of life at the Croft - for business or tourist traveller alike - and there are ample quantities of food, often featuring home-made produce like fresh farm eggs, vegetables and home-made jam and marmalade. There is lots to see and do in the area including visiting Warwick, Kenilworth, Stratford, Coventry and the Birmingham areas (there are leaflets at The Croft to give you information). The Croft is convenient for Birmingham airport & NEC.
Open all year. No smoking in the house. Vegetarian & other diets by arrangement. Disabled access: 'ground floor bedroom but not suitable for wheelchairs'. Children welcome. Pets by arrangement. En suite in some rooms. Tea/coffee-making & T.V in all bedrooms. B. & B. from £18.50, E.T.B. 2 Crowns commended.

The Garden Suite, 44 High St, Warwick, CV34 4AX (0926) 401512

Its owners tell me that while the origins of their lovely old home have been lost in the mists of time, it nevertheless has the dubious distinction of having been one of the first houses to have been burned in the fire of 1694; an event unlikely to be repeated as No. 44 is now a completely smoke-free establishment! It has much else to commend it: overlooking (as its name suggests) a tranquil private garden, it provides a haven of peace for visitors to this historically interesting, active old town. Accommodation is in one of two superbly appointed suites, equipped to the very highest standards, with hairdryer, fridge, a large hot drinks selection, and books and magazines - a home from home! Supper trays and evening meals are available only by prior arrangement.
Open all year. No smoking in the house. Disabled access: 1 ground floor suite of rooms suitable for families. Children welcome. Pets by arrangement. En suite, TV & tea/coffee-making in all rooms. B. & B. from £19.

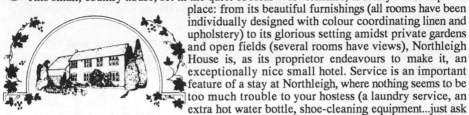

Northleigh House, Five Ways Rd, Hatton, Nr Warwick, CV35 7HZ (0926) 484203
This small, country house, set in the quiet of rural Warwickshire, is really rather a special place: from its beautiful furnishings (all rooms have been individually designed with colour coordinating linen and upholstery) to its glorious setting amidst private gardens and open fields (several rooms have views), Northleigh House is, as its proprietor endeavours to make it, an exceptionally nice small hotel. Service is an important feature of a stay at Northleigh, where nothing seems to be too much trouble to your hostess (a laundry service, an extra hot water bottle, shoe-cleaning equipment...just ask and it's there). The food is first-rate - breakfasts are freshly prepared to suit individual requirements and evening meals or supper trays are available on request (although guests might want to sample the many fine restaurants in the area).
Open all year ex. Xmas & Jan. No smoking in the house. Vegetarian and some other special diets by arrangement. Children welcome. Pets by arrangement. En suite, TV & tea/coffee-making in all rooms. Singles from £28, double from £40. Credit cards. ETB 3 Crowns Highly Commended.

Redlands Farm, Banbury Rd, Lighthorne, Nr Warwick, CV35 0AH (0926) 651241
Redlands Farm is a lovely 17th C. stone farmhouse standing in 2 acres of gardens complete with swimming pool and beautiful views across open countryside. It has been comfortably furnished throughout (there is also central heating), but the basic character of the house remains unchanged, and there are still open fires and beamed ceilings; bedrooms are very attractively decorated - one has a Victorian brass bed - and there are en suite facilities. Redlands Farm is an excellent base from which to explore the Warwickshire countryside: Stratford and the Cotswolds are all within easy touring distance, and Warwick is just 10 minutes'drive away.
Open April - Oct. No smoking in the dining room & bedrooms. Vegetarian & other diets by arrangement. Children welcome. En suite & TV available. B. & B. £14-16.

Willowbrook House B. & B., Lighthorne Rd, Kineton, Nr Warwick, CV35 0JL Tel: (0926) 640475 Fax: (0926) 641747
Very comfortable house & smallholding with sheep, chickens, gardens & paddocks in lovely rolling countryside. Nr Warwick, Stratford, Cotswolds, NEC & NAC. Furnished with antiques.
Open all year ex. Xmas. No smoking in the house. Vegetarian & other diets by arrangement. Pets by arrangement. En suite, TV & tea/coffee-making in bedrooms. B. & B. from £14. 3 miles J12 M40.

Restaurants

ROYAL LEAMINGTON SPA

The Pavilion Coffee Shop, Upper Mall, Royal Priors Shopping Centre (0926) 450133
A friendly self-service coffee shop serving lunches, snacks & a range of hot & cold drinks.
Open store hours. No smoking. Vegetarian meals. Disabled access. Children very welcome. Credit/debit cards.

STRATFORD UPON AVON

Cafe Natural, Greenhill St, Stratford upon Avon, CV37 6LF (0789) 415741
Wholefood and vegetarian restaurant (situated behind *Stratford Health Foods*) serving good range of meat-free snacks and meals.
Open Mon. to Sat. 9 - 5 p.m.. Prices various. No smoking throughout. 100% vegetarian and vegan on request. Not licensed but bring your own wine. Disabled access. Children welcome. Access, L.V.

Charlotte's Tearooms, 6 Jury St, Stratford upon Avon
No smoking in throughout.

WARWICK

Hathaway's Restaurant & Tea-room, High St, Stratford upon Avon.
No smoking in separate room.

West Midlands
Accommodation

BIRMINGHAM

Norton Place Hotel, 180 Lifford Lane, Kings Norton, B30 3NT (021) 433 5656
Country-house hotel situated within walled gardens of the Patrick Collection; excellent food.
Open all year. No smoking in dining room and in some bedrooms. Vegetarian standard. Licensed. Disabled access. Children welcome. Room service. En suite & T.V. in all bedrooms. Credit cards. B. & B. from £45.

COVENTRY

Brooklands Grange Hotel and Restaurant, Holyhead Road, CV5 8HX (0203) 601601
Open all year. No smoking in restaurant & some bedrooms. Vegetarian. Licensed. Disabled access.

Westwood Cottage, Westwood Heath Road, Westwood Heath, CV4 8GN (0203) 471084
One of 4 sandstone cottages built in 1834 and set in rural surroundings; pleasingly renovated and retaining many period features.
Open all year ex. Xmas. No smoking in dining room, bedrooms & lounge. Vegetarian by arrangement. Disabled access. Children welcome. En suite in some rooms. Tea/coffee making. T.V. lounge. B. & B. from £17.

FILLONGLEY (Nr COVENTRY)

Mill Farmhouse, Mill Lane, Fillongley, Nr Coventry, CV7 8EE (0676) 41898
Ⓝ Peace and tranquillity in country residence in idyllic countryside. Super home-cooking. Private gardens and car park. Exceptionally comfortable bedrooms. Near NEC Birmingham.
Open all year. No smoking. Vegetarian & other diets by arrangement. En suite, TV & tea/coffee-making in bedrooms. B. & B. apartment (double) £40; one person £30; single room £15 (shared facilities).

SUTTON COLDFIELD

New Hall, Walmley Road, Sutton Coldfield, B76 8QX (021) 378 2442
Open all year. No smoking in dining room. Vegetarian. Licensed. Disabled access. Children: over 7s only.

WALSALL

Abberley Hotel, Bescot Road, Walsall, WS2 9AD (0922) 27413
Well-established hotel, tastefully furnished with designer fabrics in order to complement the craftsmanship and skill of the original Victorian building. AA, RAC 2 star, HETB 4 Crowns.
Open all year. No smoking in restaurant & some bedrooms. Vegetarian by arrangement. Licensed. Disabled access. Children welcome. Pets by arrangement. En suite, TV & tea making in rooms. Access, Visa, Amex.

Restaurants & Pubs

BIRMINGHAM

Wild Oats, 5 Raddlebarn Road, Selly Oak (021) 471 2459
32 seats. Open 12 - 2, 6 - 9. No smoking. Vegetarian and vegan exclusively. Disabled access. Children.

COVENTRY

Ⓝ **Debenhams, West Orchard Shopping Centre, Smithford Way, CV1 1QL (0203) 633230**
Pavilion, a friendly self-service coffee shop serving lunches, snacks & a range of hot & cold drinks.
Open store hours. No smoking throughout. Vegetarian. Disabled access. Children welcome. Credit/debit cards.

The Old Clarence, Earlson Ave., Coventry
Three room pub with totally separate smoke-free lounge.
35 seats. Smoking banned in lounge bar. Disabled access.

DUDLEY

Ⓝ **Debenhams, The Merry Hill Centre, Pedmore Rd, Brierley Hill, DY5 1SY (0384) 480440**
Intermission, a friendly self-service restaurant serving lunches, snacks & hot & cold drinks.
Open store hours. No smoking. Vegetarian. Disabled access. Children welcome. Credit/debit cards.

Worcestershire
Accommodation

BEWDLEY

Alton Guest House and Tea Rooms, Alton House, Long Bank, Bewdley (0299) 266733
Pleasing guest house cum tea room serving home-made snacks, lunches and teas.
Open all year. No smoking ex. smoker's lounge. Vegetarian & other diets by arrangement. Children welcome.
En suite in some rooms. Tea/coffee-making & T.V. in all bedrooms. Access, Visa. B. & B. from £15.

BROADWAY

 **Orchard Grove, Station Rd, Broadway, WR12 7DE (0386) 853834**

Orchard Grove is an attractive modern detached stone house which is pleasantly situated just a few minutes' walk from the centre of the charming Cotswold village of Broadway. Orchard Grove is privately owned and run and offers an exceptionally high standard of accommodation and comfort to guests; your host, Angela McSweeney, does everything she can to make you feel welcome and at home, and will gladly give help and advice to help you plan your stay. Breakfast is the only meal to be served at Orchard Grove but there are numerous restaurants and pubs in the area and your hosts will gladly make table reservations for you in advance of your stay. You are ideally placed for touring all the many beautiful little towns and villages in the Cotswolds, and you will also find yourself within easy touring distance of Oxford, Cheltenham, Stratford and Warwick. *ETB 2 Crown Highly Commended.*
Open all year. No smoking in the house. Vegetarian & other diets by arrangement (b'fast only). Children welcome. En suite in some rooms. Tea/coffee-making & T.V. in all bedrooms. B. & B. from £17 £19.

Pye Corner Farm, Broadway, WR12 7JP (0386) 853740
Open May to Oct. No smoking. Vegetarian by arrangement. Children welcome. B. & B. from £12.

The Old Rectory, Church St, Willersey, Nr Broadway, WR12 7PN (0386) 853729

 Standing in a beautiful, flower-filled walled garden, this splendid 17th C. rectory, built of mellow Cotswold stone, has been lovingly restored by its owners who have been careful to retain all the original period features of the building such as the oak beams and quaint stone-built fireplaces. It has been charmingly decorated and furnished: the bedrooms, with charming four-poster beds, have an individual style and are very romantic (honeymooners are very welcome!); some rooms have views of Bredon and the Welsh hills. Breakfast is the only meal to be served at the Old Rectory, but it is a generous feast and vegetarian or continental options are available for meat-free or lighter appetites. The Old Rectory stands opposite the ancient church (first built in the 11th C.). Willersey, with its picturesque duck pond and quaint cottages, is typical of all that is best in the Cotswolds, and is an ideal centre for touring this lovely area. The Old Rectory was, incidentally, the RAC Guest House of the Year winner in 1991.
Open all year. No smoking ex. smoking lounge. Vegetarian b'fasts by arrangement. Children: over 8s only. En suite, tea/coffee-making & satellite T.V. in all bedrooms. Access, Visa. B. & B. from £59 double.

BROMSGROVE

Victoria Guest House, 31 Victoria Rd, Bromsgrove, B61 0DW (0527) 75777
Open all year ex. Xmas. No smoking in all public rooms. Vegetarian & other diets by arrangement. Children welcome. Tea/coffee-making & T.V. in all bedrooms. B. & B. from £13.

MALVERN

Holdfast Cottage Hotel, Welland, Nr Malvern, WR13 6NA (0684) 310288
17th C. cottage with Victorian extensions; oak-beamed hall, log fire & Victorian-style bar.
Open all year. No smoking in dining room & bedrooms. Vegetarian. Other diets by arrangement. Licensed. Children welcome. Pets by arrangement. En suite, tea-making & T.V. in all bedrooms. B. & B. from £34.

The Laurels, 108 Graham Rd, Malvern, WR14 2HX (0684) 575996
Victorian stone-built house close to town centre with its Winter Gardens, park, priory, museum and shops. Good centre for touring Wales, Cotswolds, Shropshire & Gloucestershire.
Open all year. No smoking in dining room, bedrooms & lounge. Children welcome. TV & tea/coffee-making in bedrooms. B. & B. £15.

The Nupend, Cradley, Nr Malvern, WR13 5NP (0886) 880881
Former farmhouse in 2 acres of grounds just 10 mins drive from the Malvern Hills.
Open all year. No smoking in the house. Vegetarian by arrangement. En suite, TV & tea/coffee-making in all rooms. B. & B. from £18, D. from £12.50.

Oakwood, Blackheath Way, Malvern, WR14 4DR (0684) 575508

Oakwood is one of Malvern's most notable houses: a beautiful, detached Victorian residence standing in 4 acres of grounds on the south-west slopes of the Malvern Hills looking towards Wales (on warm summer evenings guests can enjoy these views while relaxing on the terrace). There are lots of lovely little touches at Oakwood; the house is furnished throughout with antiques - the bedrooms are all prettily decorated and there is a sitting room where letters may be written on house notepaper. The cuisine is of Cordon Bleu standard (although simpler meals can be prepared for those who prefer them) and a typical evening menu would feature Melon in Port followed by Herrings in Savoury Sauce with Beef Olives and Yoghurt Pudding.
Open all year. No smoking in the house. Vegetarian & other diets by arrangement. Licensed. Children welcome. En suite most rooms. Tea/coffee-making & T.V in all rooms. B. & B. from £16. ETB 3 Crown Highly Commended.

One Eight Four, 184 West Malvern Rd, Malvern, WR14 4AZ (0684) 566544
Beautiful 5-storey Victorian house high on the western side of the Malvern hills; beautifully decorated (lots of stripped pine) and west-facing rooms each have views to the Welsh mountains.
Open all year. Smoking banned throughout the house except one lounge. Vegetarian breakfasts by arrangement. Licensed. En suite, TV & tea/coffee-making in all rooms. Access, Visa. B. & B. from £18.

The Red Gate, 32 Avenue Rd, Great Malvern, WR14 3BJ (0684) 565013
Family-run hotel close to the station & town centre yet with the atmosphere of a country home.
Open all year. No smoking in dining room & bedrooms. Vegetarian and other diets by arrangement. Licensed. Children: over 6s only. En suite most rooms. Tea/coffee-making & T.V. in all bedrooms. B. & B. from £22.

St Just, Worcester Rd, Malvern, WR14 1EU (0684) 562023

St Just is a splendid Victorian residence standing in a lovely garden overlooking a large expanse of open countryside yet is close to most amenities. It has been sympathetically restored by its present owners and beautifully decorated to provide bed and breakfast accommodation of a particularly high standard (indeed it comes to me with several high recommendations). Bedrooms are cosy and comfortable - and all very well-appointed - and the elegant dining room has lovely garden views.
Breakfast is the only meal served at St Just but there are several good restaurants in and around Malvern. St Just has a 2 Crown status. ETB 2 Crowns.
Open all year ex. Xmas and New Year. No smoking in the house. Special diets catered for. Children: over 5s only. Pets by arrangement. En suite some rooms. Tea/coffee-making & T.V in all bedrooms. B. & B. from £14.50.

MALVERN WELLS

The Cottage in the Wood Hotel, Holywell Rd, Malvern Wells, WR14 4LG (0684) 573487
Twice voted the hotel with the best view in England, this charming country hotel is in fact three separate white-painted buildings perched high in the Malvern Hills in 7 acres of woodland. *Open all year. No smoking in dining room. Vegetarian standard. Licensed. Children welcome. Pets welcome. En suite, tea/coffee-making & T.V. in all bedrooms. Access, Visa, Mastercard. B. & B. from £44.50.*

Cyprus House, 210 Wells Rd, Malvern Wells, WR14 4HD (0684) 563824
Pleasant, early Victorian house situated in the centre of the village. *Open Easter to Sept. No smoking in the house. Vegetarian and other diets by arrangement.Children welcome. Pets by arrangement. Tea/coffee-making in all rooms. T.V. in lounge. B. & B. from £12.*

PERSHORE

Samares Guest House, 11 Cherry Orchard, Charlton, WR10 3LD (0386) 860461
Comfortably furnished dormer bungalow, peacefully situated in a cul-de-sac in the pretty village of Charlton in the Vale of Evesham; excellent food home-prepared from fresh ingredients. *Open all year. No smoking in the house. Vegetarian & other diets by arrangement. Disabled access: 2 ground floor bedrooms. Children: over 10s only. Tea/coffee-making. T.V. in lounge. B. & B. from £13.50, D. from £8.*

TENBURY WELLS

Court Farm, Hanley Childe, Tenbury Wells, WR15 8QY (0885) 410265
Charming 15th C. farmhouse, with adjoining listed buildings on 200 acre mixed farm, quietly situated near the church in the pretty village of Hanley Childe. Good home-cooking. *Open Apr. to Oct. No smoking in the house. Vegetarian and most other special diets by arrangement.Children welcome. Tea/coffee-making in all rooms. T.V. in lounge.*

Restaurants

BEWDLEY

Alton Guest House and Tea Rooms, Alton House, Long Bank, DY12 2UL (0299) 266733
40 seats. Open 9 - 6. L. around £7.50. Smoking banned in tea room.
For further details please see under the entry in the accommodation section.

MALVERN WELLS

Croque-en-Bouche, 221 Wells Rd, Malvern Wells, Worcester, WR14 4HF (0684) 565612
Excellent restaurant serving exceptional cuisine (6-course table d'hote dinner). *24 seats. Open various times. D. around £28. No smoking in dining room. Vegetarian and other special diets by prior arrangement. Licensed. Disabled access: 'one four inch step'. Children welcome. Access, Visa.*

WORCESTER

Hodson's Coffee House, 100 High St, Worcester (0905) 21036

Hodson's Coffee House and Patisserie, with its lovely *al fresco* dining area, looks as though it might be more at home on a Parisian boulevard than in the heart of Worcester. But here it is, midway between the historic Guildhall and the renowned cathedral, under the watchful and ever-so-English eye of Sir Edward Elgar, offering an interesting selection of dishes, including a number of 'platters' - which in Hodson-speak is an exceedingly generous plateful of hearty fare such as Ham Platter (locally cooked old-fashioned ham with green salad) or Prawn Platter (an enormous prawn cocktail) or one of a range of ten or so other platters; follow your meal - if your are able - with a delicious patisserie treat or an ice cream sundae. Hodson's also has the city's Clean Food Award, the National Heartbeat Award & is air-conditioned throughout. Definitely a *very* healthy place to eat.
100 seats. Open 9.30 - 5; closed Sundays. No smoking in 80% of restaurant. Licensed. Disabled access. Children welcome.

East Anglia

Cambridgeshire
Accommodation

CAMBRIDGE

Arundel House Hotel, 53 Chesterton Rd, Cambridge, CB4 3AN (0223) 67701
Health-award-winning hotel converted from fine Victorian terrace near centre of Cambridge.
Open all year ex. Xmas. Smoking only permitted in small part of restaurant. Vegetarian menu. Most other special diets by arrangement. Licensed. Children welcome. En suite in most rooms. Tea/coffee-making, T.V., video, telephone, radio and hairdryer in all bedrooms. Credit cards accepted. B. & B. from £28.50.

Bon Accord House, 20 St Margaret's Square, Off Cherry Hinton Road, Cambridge, CB1 4AP. (0223) 411188/246568

Established as a guest house some 12 years ago, the Bon Accord is situated down a quiet cul-de-sac on a good bus route to Cambridge city centre. The Northrops are non-smokers themselves and decided to make the Bon Accord completely smoke-free four years ago - since which time they have found (surprise, surprise!) that their business has not collapsed and they are inundated with visitors in search of a comfortable guest house, good food - and clean air! Only breakfast is served at the Bon Accord - but there is a wide variety of options to choose from and skimmed milk and low-fat margarine are available on request. You are within easy access of Cambridge city centre from the Bon Accord (which has, incidentally, received numerous other acclaims and commendations) and the Northrops can arrange cycle hire for you if you wish.
Open all year ex. Xmas. No smoking in the house. Vegetarian & other diets by arrangement. Children welcome. 1 room en suite. Tea/coffee-making & T.V. in all bedrooms. Visa, Mastercard. B. & B. from £17.50.

The Coach House, Scotland Road, Dry Drayton, Cambridge, CB3 8BX (0954) 782439
19th C. converted coach house standing in 2 acres of delightful grounds with a lily pond.
Open mid March to Christmas. No smoking in the house. Vegetarian and most other special diets by arrangement. Disabled access. En suite & tea/coffee-making in bedrooms. T.V. in lounge. B. & B. from £19.

El Shaddai, 41 Warkworth St, Cambridge, CB1 1EG (0223) 327978
Open July to Sept. inc. No smoking in the house. Special diets if required. Children welcome. Tea/Coffee-making & T.V. in all bedrooms. B. & B. from £13.

Kings Tithe, 13A Comberton Road, Barton, Cambridge, CB3 7BA (0223) 263610
Quiet family home in pleasant village just over 3 miles south west of Cambridge.
Open all year ex. Xmas and New Year. No smoking in the house. Vegetarian by arrangement. Children: over 8s only. Tea/coffee-making & T.V. in all bedrooms. B. & B. from £15.

Purlins, 12 High Street, Little Shelford, Cambridge, CB2 5ES (0223) 842643
Relatively new house in 2 acres of maturing woodland & lawned gardens in the quiet and picturesque village of Little Shelford.
Open Feb. to Dec. 18th. No smoking in the house. Vegetarian & other diets by arrangement. Disabled access. Children: over 8s only. En suite & colour T.V. in all rooms. Tea/coffee on request. B. & B. from £19.

St. Mark's Vicarage, Barton Road, Cambridge, CB3 9J2
Victorian vicarage with garden; short walk from central Cambridge.
Open all year ex. Xmas. No smoking in the house. Vegetarian & other diets by arrangement. Children welcome. Tea/coffee-making & T.V. in all bedrooms. B. & B. from £14.

The Willows, 102 High Street, Landbeach, Cambridge CB4 4DT (0223) 860332
Centrally heated farmhouse accommodation in attractive village just 3m from Cambridge.
Open all year ex. Xmas. No smoking in the house. Vegetarian by arrangement. Disabled access: 1 ground floor room. Children welcome. Pets by arrangement. Tea/coffee-making& TV in rooms. B. & B. from £15.

ELY

Springfields, Ely Road, Little Thetford, Ely, CB6 3HJ (0353) 663637
Springfields is a lovely large home set in an acre of beautiful landscaped gardens and orchard

in which guests are invited to wander and sit awhile to enjoy the tranquillity of the setting and (in summer) to smell the roses! The guest accommodation is housed in a separate wing and consists of three pretty double rooms which have each been tastefully furnished and appointed with many delightful touches and everything you could wish to make your stay a happy and memorable one; all rooms have wash hand basins. Breakfast is served in a pleasant dining room in which guests sit around a large table to enjoy together the delicious, freshly prepared food. Springfields is set in a very quiet location yet is only two miles from historic Ely with its famous cathedral, Oliver Cromwell's house (he lived here from 1637 to 1644) and many other buildings of great architectural and historic interest, and of course it is a perfect base from which to explore the changeless beauty of the Fens!
Open all year, ex. Dec. No smoking in the house. Vegetarian by arrangement. En suite rooms available. Tea/coffee-making in bedrooms. T.V. in all rooms. B. & B. from £20.

Warden's House, Lode Lane, Wicken, Ely CB7 5XP (0353) 624165
Open all year ex. Xmas. No smoking in the house. Vegetarian breakfast standard. Dogs, by arrangement. Tea/Coffee-making in all bedrooms. B. & B. from £10.50.

PETERBOROUGH

Stoneacre, Elton Rd, Wansford, Peterborough (0780) 783283
Charming modern house in a secluded spot with views across the Nene Valley. Half mile from A1.
Open all year. No smoking in dining room. Vegetarian by arrangement. Good disabled access: 4 ground floor rooms. Children: over 5s only. En suite. Tea/coffee-making & T.V. in all bedrooms. B. & B. from £12.50.

Swallow Hotel, Peterborough Business Park, Lynch Wood, Peterborough, PE2 6GB Tel: (0733) 371111 Fax: (0733) 236725
Luxuriously appointed 163-bedroom business class hotel conveniently situated just 2 minutes from the A1 and within easy reach of Peterborough city centre.
Open all year. No smoking in 50% of dining room/pub/bar area & in 55% of bedrooms. Vegetarian, vegan and diabetic diets catered for, most other special diets by arrangement. Licensed. Disabled access. Children welcome. Dogs allowed in bedrooms. En suite, tea/coffee-making & T.V. in all bedrooms. Credit cards accepted. B. & B. from £42 p.p. sharing a twin room.

Restaurants

CAMBRIDGE

Browns Restaurant, 23 Trumpington Street, Cambridge (0223) 461655
No smoking in 45% of restaurant. Vegetarian. Licensed. Disabled access. Children.

Debenhams, 36-40 The Grafton Centre (0223) 353525
Springles, a friendly self-service restaurant serving lunches, snacks, hot and cold drinks.
Open store hours. No smoking. Vegetarian. Disabled access. Children welcome. Credit/debit cards.

Hobbs Pavilion Restaurant, Park Terrace, Cambridge, CB1 1JH (0223) 67480
Great eating place located in the pavilion of a cricket ground; imaginative menu.
Open 12 - 2.30, 7 - 10. (8.30 -10 Thurs.) D. from £7. Separate room for smokers. Vegetarian and vegan standard. Some other special diets on request. Licensed. Children welcome.

Henry's Teashop, 5A Pembroke St, Cambridge (0223) 61206
Open Mon. - Sat., 9 - 5.15, all year. No smoking throughout.

 Kings Pantry, 9A Kings Parade, Cambridge, CB2 1SJ (0223) 321551
First-rate vegetarian restaurant located in the heart of Cambridge.
52 seats. Open 8 - 5.30. 7 days & Tue. - Sat. 6.30 - 9.30. L. around £5. D. from £10. No smoking throughout. Exclusively vegetarian and vegan. Licensed. Children welcome. Credit cards.

PETERBOROUGH

 Peterborough Cathedral Shop, 24 Minster Precincts, Peterborough (0733) 555098
Pleasant café situated above gift shop.
40 seats. Open 10 - 4, Mon. to Sat. No smoking. Vegetarian. Children welcome (high chair avail.)

The Queensgate Centre, Peterborough

The Queensgate Centre in central Peterborough is comprised of 100 shops and restaurants which are built around spacious marbled malls and squares in a light, air-conditioned environment. Half the public seating areas are designated for non-smokers and there is a good selection of specialist and in-store restaurants and coffee shops - again, with a high proportion of seating for non-smokers. The number of seats in the various eating areas and the proportions designated for non-smokers are as follows:
Littlewoods: 340 seats (40%); BHS: 260 seats (73%); Boots: 90 seats (100%); John Lewis: 80 seats (100%); McDonalds: 235 seats (68%); John Menzies: 100 seats (50%); Maxine's: 144 seats (33%); Reflections: 60 seats (50%); Coffee Mill: 90 seats (36%); Poppins Restaurant: 90 seats (50%). Late night shopping until 8pm on Thursdays and also on Fridays during December.

SIX MILE BOTTOM

 Swynford Paddocks, Six Mile Bottom, Cambridgeshire (063870) 234
No smoking. Vegetarian standard. Disabled access. Children welcome. Credit cards.

Pubs & Wine Bars

CAMBRIDGE

The Cambridge Blue, 85/87 Gwydir St, Cambridge, CB1 2LG (0223) 61382
Purpose built late 19th C. terrace pub in side street off Mill Road.
No smoking in 1 bar. Vegetarian standard. Wheelchair access. Children welcome in garden only.

Free Press, Prospect Row, Cambridge (0223) 68337
Busy pub serving good food and real ales.
No smoking in snug/eating area. Vegetarian standard. Children welcome.

HOLYWELL

Olde Ferry Boat, Holywell (off A1123 in Needingworth)
Open pub hours. No smoking in 2 rooms. Vegetarian available. Children welcome.

WHITTLESFORD

The Tickell Arms, North Rd, Whittlesford, Cambridge, CB2 4NZ (0223) 833128
The Tickell Arms is a fine 18th C. building which has been attractively furnished and decorated. It is a great rarity - a pub with two large smoke-free dining and drinking areas - and not only that, it serves exceptionally good food: menus feature dishes which are imaginative and tasty and vegetarians are very well catered for. There is a Winter Garden in which smoking is permitted, and during the warmer months a large terrace, which overlooks the lovely water garden, is also used for dining.
No smoking in 2 rooms.

Essex
Accommodation

ARDLEIGH

 **Dundas Place, Colchester Road, Ardleigh, Colchester, CO7 7NP (0206) 230625**

Dundas Place is a lovely old 17th C. cottage in the centre of the pretty village of Ardleigh. It is tastefully decorated and furnished throughout and all three bedrooms are well-equipped with all amenities (including double glazing on the front windows for extra peace and quiet!). Breakfast is served in the attractive dining room (with log fire) at 8.30 a.m. - unless otherwise requested - and there are good evening meals to be had at nearby inns; there is a pleasant lounge for guests'use. Doreen and Ian Le May will make you very welcome and Ardleigh is a perfect base from which to explore Constable Country and the pretty villages of Suffolk; you are just 12 miles away from Harwich and 20 m. from Felixstowe.

Open all year ex. Xmas & New Year. No smoking throughout. Vegetarian by arrangement. Children welcome. Pets by arrangement. T.V., wash-basins & tea/coffee-making in all rooms. B. & B from £14.50-£17.

BRAINTREE

The Old House, 11 Bradford Street, Braintree, CM7 6AS (0376) 550457

Spacious 16th C. family house of great historical interest standing in an acre of gardens.
Open all year. No smoking ex. in Bar. Vegetarian by arrangement. Licensed. Disabled access. Children welcome. En suite, tea/coffee-making & T.V. in all rooms. B. & B. from £16.

CASTLE HEDINGHAM

The Old School House, St James Street, Castle Hedingham, CO9 3EW (0787) 61370

Charming Georgian building which stands in in a beautiful walled garden; separate cottage.
Open all year. No smoking in the house. Vegetarian by arrangement. Licensed. Children: over 12s only. En suite in all rooms. T.V. in sitting room and 1 bedroom. B & B from £18.50. ETB 2 Crowns Commended.

The Pottery, St James Street, Castle Hedingham, CO9 3EW (0787) 60036

Comfortable Georgian house in the charming medieval village of Castle Hedingham.
Open all year ex. Xmas. No smoking in the house. Vegetarian and most other special diets by arrangement. Children: over 12s only. Tea/coffee-making in all bedrooms. B & B from £16.50.

CHELMSFORD

Boswell House Hotel, 118 Springfield Road, Chelmsford, CM2 6LF (0245) 287587

 The Boswell House is a 19th C. town house which was beautifully renovated and converted into a charming small hotel in 1980. It has been very tastefully furnished throughout with stripped pine furniture and each of the thirteen en suite bedrooms have excellent facilities including direct dial phones. The food is very good indeed: everything has been home-prepared on the premises from fresh ingredients and the menu offers a wide selection of

traditional dishes; wedding receptions, private lunch or dinner parties may be booked for up to 25 people. Chelmsford is the county town of Essex and amongst its many features are the cathedral, Essex County Cricket Ground and shopping facilities.
Open all year ex. Xmas. No smoking in dining room, sitting room & 9 bedrooms. Vegetarian & other by arrangement. Licensed. Disabled access: good - there are ground floor bedrooms and just one step at the hotel entrance. Children welcome (cots, high chairs, baby listening service availale). No pets (ex. guide dogs). En suite, tea/coffee-making & T.V. in all bedrooms. Credit cards. B & B from £28.

Meadowview, 101 Keene Way, Galleywood, Chelmsford, CM2 8NS (0245) 259273
Open all year. No smoking in the house. Vegetarian by arrangement. Children welcome. Pets welcome. Tea/coffee-making in all bedrooms. T.V. in one bedroom. B & B from £12.00.

CLACTON-ON-SEA

 Chelsea House, Collingwood Road, Marine Parade West, CO15 1UL (0255) 424018
Open all year. No smoking in the house. Vegetarian and most other special diets by arrangement. Children welcome. En suite in 17 rooms. Tea/coffee-making in all bedrooms. T.V. on request. Credit card.

 Crockleford Grange, Bromley Rd, Colchester, CO7 7SE (0206) 864405
Attractive converted Grade II Listed barn; oak beams & thatched roof. Crystal chandeliers in bedrooms. Within easy reach of Dedham & Flatford. 20 mins Harwich, 5 mins Essex University. *No smoking. Children welcome. En suite, TV & tea/coffee in rooms. B. & B. £15, Honeymoon suite £45.*

COLCHESTER

Gill Nicholson, 14 Roman Road, Colchester, CO1 1UR (0206) 577905
14 Roman Road is a spacious Victorian town house situated in a quiet square near the centre of Colchester with easy access to both the bus and railway station. In fact those who choose to bring cars can park them and forget about driving during their visit, as all the places of interest - the castle, the museums, shops and sports facilities - are within easy walking distance of the house. A full, home-cooked English breakfast is served by Gill which features a number of home-made items - including the bread, jam and lemon curd - and some healthy, vegetarian and low-cholesterol options, such as muesli, prunes and low-fat yoghurt; the nearby Foresters Arms serves excellent home-cooked lunches and evening meals. Whether visiting Colchester on business - or just taking a holiday break in this beautiful part of Eastern England - the comfortable family atmosphere at 14 Roman Road will make your stay a special and memorable one.
Open all year ex. Xmas week. No smoking in the house. Vegetarian and most other special diets by arrangement. Children by arrangment. En suite in 1 room. Tea/coffee-making & T.V. in all bedrooms. B. & B. from £30.

Kings Vineyard, Fossetts Lane, Fordham, Nr Colchester, C06 3NY (0206) 240377
 Lovely detached house on southfacing slope in gentle rolling countryside. Beautiful views.
Open all year. No smoking in the house. Vegetarian standard. Children welcome. Private bathroom available. Tea/coffee-making & T.V. facilities. Amex. B. & B. from £16.

DUNMOW

The Four Seasons Hotel, Walden Rd, Thaxted, Nr Dunmow, CM6 2RE Tel: (0371) 830129 Fax: (0371) 830835

The Four Seasons Hotel is a lovely, quiet country hotel set in approximately 2 acres of carefully maintained grounds with lawned gardens and natural pond on the outskirts of the beautiful mediaeval town of Thaxted. Whilst many of the original features of the building have been retained, the hotel has been sympathetically modernised to a very high standard and offers comfortable accommodation in each of the centrally heated, en suite guest bedrooms. Meals served in the dining room have been prepared with care from fresh, local produce, and the à la carte menu features such dishes as Seafood Crêpes, Breast of Duck in Châtelaine Sauce and a selection of desserts; there is a traditional Sunday lunch menu (reservation only). The Four Seasons Hotel is an ideal choice for the business traveller: there is a fax/photocopying service plus excellent conference and seminar facilities, & the location - 20 mins from Stansted Airport & 15 mins from the M11 - make business meetings easy to arrange.
Open all year. No smoking in the dining room, some bedrooms, part of the bar & the lounge. Licensed. Children; over 12s only. En suite, TV, DD phones & tea/coffee-making in bedrooms. Credit cards. B. & B. from £32.50.

FRINTON-ON-SEA

Uplands Guest House, 41 Hadleigh Road, Frinton-on-Sea, CO13 9HQ (0255) 674889
Open all year ex. Xmas. No smoking in dining room and bedrooms. Licensed. Children: over 6s only. En suite in 4 rooms. Tea/coffee-making in all bedrooms. T.V. in lounge. Ample car parking. B. & B. from £18.50.

GREAT DUNMOW

 'Greys', Ongar Road, Margaret Roding, Nr Great Dunmow, CM6 1QR (024531) 509
Greys was formerly two cottages and now has three double bedrooms for guests - one with twin beds. Pleasantly situated on the family arable and sheep farm, the house is beamed throughout, with dining and sitting rooms and a large garden. Ideal for short breaks and exploring pretty villages, old towns, creeks and estuaries. Greys is situated just off the A1060 by the telephone box in the village and is 8 miles from Great Dunmow (it's advisable to check the map before travelling). *Open most of year. No smoking in the house. Vegetarian by arrangement. Children: over 10s only. Tea/coffee always available. T.V. downstairs. B & B from £16.*

MANNINGTREE

Dimbols Farm, Wrabness, Manningtree, CO11 2TH (0255) 880328
No smoking in dining rooms & bedrooms. Vegetarian breakfast by arrangement. Children welcome. Tea/coffee-making in all bedrooms. T.V. in sitting room. B & B from £14.

SOUTHEND-ON-SEA

Strand Guest House, 165 Eastern Esplanade, Southend-on-Sea, SS1 2YB (0702) 586611
Open April to Nov. No smoking in dining room & 1 bedroom. Vegetarian by arrangement. Children welcome. Most rooms en suite. Free coffee in lounge. T.V. in all bedrooms. B. & B. from £16.

THAXTED

Piggot's Mill, Watling Lane, Thaxted, CM6 2QY (0371) 830379
A range of traditional Essex barns, with many original features, now a farmhouse standing in a secluded yet central position in the mediaeval village of Thaxted; lovely garden; very good b'fast. *Open all year (no meals at Xmas). No smoking in dining room & bedrooms. Vegetarian & other diets by arrangement. Children: over 12s only. En suite, TV & tea/coffee-making in all bedrooms. B. & B. from £19.50.*

The Swallow Hotel, Old Shire Ln., Waltham Abbey, Essex, EN9 3LX Tel: (0992) 717170 Fax: (0992) 711841

The Swallow Hotel at Waltham Abbey is a spacious modern 4-star hotel which stands near J26 of the M25. All 165 en suite bedrooms are equipped with D.D. phone, mini-bar, hairdryer and trouser press, and 55 rooms are designated non-smoking. There is a Coffee Shop, Cocktail Bar and two restaurants to choose from: the Glade Restaurant offers a range of à la carte and table d'hôte dishes while the Brooks Brasserie has a more informal atmosphere, the menu featuring a lunchtime carvery and a choice of continental meals. The Swallow Leisure Club has a pool, steam room, mini-gym and solarium - an ideal place to relax after an intense business meeting - and the conference and meeting rooms have facilities for up to 250 delegates.
Open all year. No smoking in part of dining room, some bedrooms & Leisure Club. Vegetarian & other diets. Children welcome. Wheelchair access. En suite, TV & tea/coffee in rooms. Credit cards.

Restaurants

CASTLE HEDINGHAM

Rumbles Castle Restaurant, St James St, Castle Hedingham, CO9 3EJ (0787) 61490
Open all year. Barbecue menu £12.50, à la carte £16.50-£19.50. No smoking in dining room, allowed in coffee lounge & bar area. Vegetarain standard. Licensed. Disabled access. Children welcome. Access, Visa.

CHELMSFORD

Debenhams, 27 High St, Chelmsford (0245) 355511
Springles, a friendly self-service restaurant serving lunches, snacks & hot and cold drinks. *Open store hours. No smoking. Vegetarian. Disabled access. Children welcome. Credit/debit cards.*

Scott's, The Street, Hatfield Peverel, Chelmsford, CM3 2DR (0245) 380161
Open Mon. - Sat., 7 until late by booking. No smoking. Vegetarian. Licensed. Disabled access.

Farmhouse Feast, The Street, Roxwell, Chelmsford, CM1 4PB   (0245) 48 583

Farmhouse Feast is a charming restaurant housed in a late 15th C. building in the centre of Roxwell village. The food is first-rate - everything has been home-cooked on the premises from fresh ingredients - and there are some excellent vegetarian options; indeed Farmhouse Feast has hosted some exclusively vegetarian events such as a Good Friday meat-free meal featuring Vegetable Kebabs in curried batter with yoghurt dip followed by Red Cabbage and Apple Soup, Lentil Terrine with Cream and Mushroom Sauce and Ricotta Stuffed Pears in Apricot dressing. As well as catering for individuals, Farmhouse Feast is especially adept at hosting small parties and will also undertake outside catering: their menus are imaginative and their prices very keen - and, more pertinently for our purposes, a whole floor is smoke-free.

Open all year, including Xmas Day. Gourmet evenings last Fri. in month. No smoking in 75% of restaurant (on separate floor). Vegetarian & special diets by arrangement. Licensed. Disabled access. Children welcomed.

COLCHESTER

Debenhams, 34 Culver St West   (0206) 763434
Intermission, a friendly self-service coffee shop serving popular light lunches, snacks and a wide range of hot and cold drinks.
Open store hours. No smoking. Vegetarian meals. Disabled access. Children welcome. Credit/debit cards.

DUNMOW

Rumbles Cottage Restaurant, Braintree Road, Felsted, Dunmow, CM6 3DJ (0371) 820996
Open all year. Guinea pig menu £12.50, à la carte £16.50-£19.50. Separate dining rooms for non-smokers by prior arrangement. Vegetarian standard. Licensed. Disabled access. Children welcome. No pets. Access, Visa.

ROMFORD

Debenhams, Market Place, Romford (0708) 766066
Intermission, a friendly self-service restaurant serving popular light lunches, snacks and a wide range of hot and cold drinks.
Open store hours. No smoking. Vegetarian meals. Disabled access. Children welcome. Credit/debit cards.

SOUTHEND-ON-SEA

Debenhams, The Royals, High St, Southend (0702) 460237
Pavilion, a friendly self-service coffee shop serving popular light lunches, snacks and a wide range of hot and cold drinks.
Open store hours. No smoking. Vegetarian meals. Disabled access. Children welcome. Credit/debit cards.

THURROCK

Debenhams, Lakeside Shopping Centre, Thurrock (0708) 860066
Intermission, a friendly self-service restaurant serving popular light lunches, snacks and a wide range of hot and cold drinks.
Open store hours. No smoking. Vegetarian meals. Disabled access. Children welcome. Credit/debit cards.

Pubs & Wine Bars

CHELMSFORD

Seabrights Barn, Galleywood Rd, Gt Baddow, Nr Chelmsford (0245) 478033
Open Mon. to Sat. 12 - 2, 6 - 11, Sun. 12 - 10. Smoking banned in conservatory family room. Vegetarian standard. Other special diets catered for on request at any time. Wheelchair access. Good facilities for children. Access, Visa.

Norfolk
Accommodation

BLAKENEY

Flintstones Guest House, Wiveton, Blakeney, NR25 7TL (0263) 740337

Flintstones Guest House is a charming single storey residence set in picturesque surroundings near to the village green in the quiet village of Wiveton one mile from the sea at Cley and Blakeney. It has been beautifully furnished throughout - the bedrooms have each been very comfortably appointed - and a friendly and relaxed atmosphere prevails. Food is of the good old-fashioned British variety and is served in good old-fashioned quantities, too: a typical evening meal would feature fresh grapefruit followed by Roast Chicken with all the trimmings and a home-made dessert such as Sherry Trifle; tea and coffee would complete the meal. The area is perfect for walkers and birdwatchers: the heathland at Salthouse and Kelling have stunning scenery, and the North Norfolk Coastal Path passes nearby. *Open all year. No smoking. Vegetarian and some special diets by arrangement. Licensed. Children welcome. Pets by arrangement. En suite, tea/coffee-making & T.V. in all rooms. B. & B. from £15.*

CASTLE ACRE

The Old Red Lion, Bailey Street, Castle Acre, PE32 2AG (0760) 755557
Open all year. No smoking throughout. Vegetarian by arrangement. Children welcome.

CROMER

Beverley Holiday Flats, 17 Alfred Rd, Cromer, NR27 9AN (0394) 450343

Maureen and Barry Marshall, the proprietors of Beverley Holiday Flats, are proud to be able to say that they are the five times winner of the Norfolk Tourism Award for Excellence. And deservedly so, I might add: their beautiful self-catering apartments are situated just a stone's throw from the seafront in a very pleasant part of Cromer and have been furnished with just about everything that you could wish for including microwaves, coffee percolators and, on the beds, excellent orthopaedic mattresses. Cromer is an excellent base for visiting the many attractions in the area which include historic houses, nature reserves and the North Norfolk Steam Railway. *Open May to Sept. No smoking throughout.*

Birch House, 34 Cabbell Rd, Cromer, NR27 9HX (0263) 512521
Birch House is a warm, friendly guest house, close to all the amenities of Cromer; it has been tastefully furnished thourhgout - everything is scrupulously clea - and there is a residents'lounge. The extensive b'fast menu includes oak-smoked kippers and haddock. Cromer is 'bright but breezy' in summer but its fine, sandy beaches are very beautiful & you are just a short walk from the pier..
Open all year. No smoking. Vegetarian and other special diets by arrangement. Children welcome. Pets by arrangement. Some en suite. Tea/coffee-making & T.V. in all rooms. B. & B. from £15.

Corner Cottage, Water Lane, West Runton, Cromer, NR27 9QP (0263) 758180
Corner Cottage is a small, friendly guest house which is situated on the North Norfolk coast near train and bus stops and just 3 mins' walk from the excellent beach at West Runton (renowned for its fossil remains). It offers very comfortable accommodation in its centrally heated bedrooms and there is a full English breakfast. There is lots to see and do locally: there are three golf courses, a swimming pool at Sheringham and a stable at the Shire Horse Centre (which puts on an excellent show including a video on the use of Shire Horses); additionally there are many good walks nearby & N. T. houses at Felbrigg & Blickling.

Open all year. No smoking in the house. Car parking. Children: over 5 yrs welcome. Tea/coffee making in all rooms. T.V. in lounge. B. & B. from £14.

DISS

The Old Rectory, Gissing, Diss, IP22 3XB Tel: (037 977) 575 Fax: (037 977) 4427

The Old Rectory is a large, spacious Victorian house standing amidst 3 acres of garden and woodland in the peaceful hamlet of Gissing; the village has an abundance of mature trees from the time when it formed part of a private estate and the church has an unusual round tower and double hammer beam roof. The guest bedrooms at the Old Rectory are large and beautifully appointed: each has en suite or private facilities and fresh flowers, hairdryers and notepaper in addition to the usual amenities; the elegant drawing and dining room each have welcoming open fires. A delicious 4-course evening meal, or lighter option, is available by prior arrangement, and packed lunches can be prepared on request; breakfast, which is often served in the conservatory, offers an extensive menu choice. There is much to enjoy - guests may play croquet on the lawns, swim in the indoor heated pool, or relax on the terrace - while those venturing a little further afield will find much to enjoy nearby including the part-Tudor town of Diss, Bressingham Gardens, Thetford Forest and the unspoilt coast-line at Southwold and Walberswick.

Open all year. No smoking in dining room, bedrooms & most public areas. Vegetarian and low-fat diets by arrangement. En suite, TV & tea/coffee-making in all rooms. B. & B. from £23.

Ingleneuk Lodge, Hopton Rd, Garboldisham, Diss, IP22 2RQ (095 381) 541

Ingleneuk Lodge is a lovely modern single storey home standing in 11 acres of grounds and woodlands; its quiet rural situation makes it a haven for wildlife, and guests in search of peace, tranquillity and a comfortable and homely atmosphere need look no further. Food is first-rate: (witness the numerous visitors who return annually) and there is a sunny south-facing patio overlooking the garden and pond on which guests can relax and enjoy a pre-dinner drink. Cooking is imaginative and a typical evening meal would feature Celery and Leek Soup followed by Stuffed Pork Chops with Cider and a delicious home-made dessert, such as Chocolate Rum Truffle; cheese and biscuits with tea or coffee complete the meal.

Open all year. No smoking in dining room & some bedrooms.Vegetarian by arrangement. Licensed. Disabled access. Children welcome. Pets by arrangement. En suite in most rooms. Tea/coffee-making, Colour T.V., telephone and electric blankets in all rooms. Access, Visa, Amex, Mastercard, Eurocard. B. & B. from £17 to £23.50 sharing. Singles welcome. D. £13.50. Special D., B. & B. breaks available all year ex. Xmas.

Strenneth Farmhouse, Old Airfield Rd, Fersfield, Diss (0379) 888182

This beautiful red brick 16th/17th C. former farmhouse stands in a lovely lawned garden close to the market town of Diss; it has been renovated to a very high standard indeed while retaining the period features of the building - oak beams, casement windows, open fires, window seats - and the bedrooms are decorated and furnished with taste and style (one has a four-poster and the rooms in the newer East wing are all on the ground floor); there is an especially attractive residents' lounge which has been furnished with period and reproduction furniture to harmonise with the beamed ceilings and walls. The food is of a very high standard indeed - special diets are treated sympathetically and there is a high proportion of home-baking and home-cooking. Diss is a charming little town and is central to most of East Anglia's tourist attractions.

Open all year. No smoking in part of dining room & 1 lounge. Vegetarian and other special diets, but not vegan, by arrangement. Licensed. Children welcome. Pets by arrangement. En suite in most rooms. Tea/coffee-making in all rooms. T.V. in lounge. Credit cards. B. & B. from £20. D. £12.50.

Swan House Country Crafts and Tea Room, Swan House, Hopton Rd, Garboldisham, Nr Diss, Norfolk, IP22 2PQ (095381) 8221

Swan House is an attractive 17th C. former coaching inn situated in the village of Garboldisham, midway betwen Thetford and Diss. Built around 1690, Swan House has retained much of its original character complete with beams, inglenooks and, in one of the outhouses, the original cooking ovens. Your hosts, Tracy and Michael Eldridge, offer a warm and friendly welcome (with tea and biscuits), and there are three comfortable guest rooms, each with its own character, including exposed beams. Traditional home-made fare is served in the tearoom - all the bread, rolls and cakes have been home-baked - and a log fire blazes in the grate in cooler weather; there is a quality range of crafts, antiques & paintings on display and in summer the enclosed country garden is the perfect setting in which to relax and enjoy a clotted cream tea. You are within easy reach of a number of interesting places at Swan House including Norwich, Great Yarmouth and Bressingham Gardens. ETB Approved and listed.

Open all year ex. Xmas & Jan. No smoking throughout. Vegetarian by arrangement. Wheelchair access to teashop. Children welcome in tea shop only. T.V. in bedrooms. Diners card. B. & B. from £15.

FAKENHAM

Manor Farmhouse, Stibbard Rd, Fulmodestone, NR21 0LX (032 878) 353

Lovely white-painted Georgian farmhouse with beautiful lawned gardens; lots of home-prepared food from fresh or home-produce, including lamb, free-range eggs and poultry.

Open all year. No smoking in the house. Vegetarian and other special diets by arrangement. Access, Visa. B. & B. from £17. ETB 1 Crown Commended.

GREAT YARMOUTH

The Driftwood, 82-84 Walpole Rd, Gt Yarmouth, NR30 4NE (0493) 857878

Open April to Oct. No smoking in dining room, sitting room and some bedrooms. Children welcome. Tea/coffee making and T.V. in all rooms. B. & B. from £12-£15.

Siesta Lodge, 53/54 York Rd, Gt Yarmouth, NR30 2NE (0493) 843207

Tastefully decorated guest house with a friendly, welcoming atmosphere.

Open all year. No smoking in dining room and bedrooms. Special diets by arrangement. Licensed. Children welcome. Tea/coffee making facilities. T.V. in lounge. B. & B. from £10.

HUNSTANTON

Salacia Lodge, 56 Greevegate, Hunstanton, PE36 6AE (0485) 533702

Salacia Lodge is a warm, friendly well-established guest house which offers superb, well-appointed accommodation and an excellent breakfast. You are conveniently situated close to several sports and recreational facilities, and additionally you are just a few minutes'walk from the town centre, theatre and sea front; there are a number of good eating places in the town. Hunstanton is a perfect centre for walkers and birdwatchers.

No smoking thoughout. Vegetarian & other diets by arrangement. En suite in all rooms. B. & B. from £15.

KINGS LYNN

Knights Hill Hotel, Knights Hill Village, South Wootton, Kings Lynn, PE30 3HQ (0553) 675566

Knights Hill Hotel is one of a number of charming buildings which make up Knights Hill village - a unique conversion of barns, farmhouses and other structures. Standing atop one of the highest points in West Norfolk, and set in 11 acres of parkland and gardens, Knights Hill Village is made up of The Farmers Arms and Restaurant, Knights Barn Conference and Exhibition Centre, and the Knights Hill Hotel itself which was built in 1588 and, in its former life as Rising Lodge, was much used as a hunting lodge. These days the lodge, with its classical dimensions and Georgian facade, offer a very high standard of accommodation to guests: a number of bedrooms overlook the garden and grounds, while a further selection of 'Courtyard Apartments'lead through French windows to a patio area. Guests dine in the Garden Restaurant on a selection of freshly prepared meals.

Open all year. Smoking banned in main part of restaurant & some bedrooms, and part of bar. Vegetarian standard. Licensed. Some disabled access. Children welcome. Pets by arrangement. En suite, TV & tea/coffee making in all rooms. All major credit cards accepted. B. & B. from £56.

 'Homelands', 79 Sutton Rd, Terrington St Clement, Kings Lynn, PE34 4PJ (0553) 828401

Pleasant detached house in an acre of pretty lawned gardens in lovely village.

Open March to Nov. No smoking in the house. Vegetarian and other special diets by arrangement. Children welcome. Twin bedded room with shower, double room en suite. Tea/coffee-making & T.V. in some rooms. B. & B. from £14-£17, (with 5% discount for 3 or more days).

NEATISHEAD

Regency Guest House, Neatishead, Nr Norwich, NR12 8AD (0692) 630233

Lovely 18th C. house in the unspoilt village of Neatishead; beautifully furnished rooms (Laura Ashley). Exceptionally generous breakfasts; good vegetarian options.

Open all year. No smoking in dining room & all public areas. Vegetarian & other diets by arrangement. Children welcome. Pets by arrangement. En suite. Tea/coffee-making & T.V. all rooms. B. & B. from £16.50.

NORTH WALSHAM

Toll Barn, Norwich Rd, North Walsham, NR28 0JB (0692) 403063

Converted 18th C. barn with cosy en suite lodges around a delightful garden.

Open all year. No smoking throughout. Vegetarian by arrangement. Wheelchair access 'possible'. Children and pets welcome. En suite. Tea/coffee-making facilities and T.V. in all bedrooms. B. & B. from £18.

NORWICH

fax 0603-270-548

Gables Farm, Hemblington Hall Rd, Hemblington, Norwich, NR13 4PT (0605) 49548- 239 -
Beautiful period thatched farmhouse in the centre of Broadland between Norwich and Great Yarmouth. Family room available for up to 4 people.

Open all year. No smoking in the house. En suite, tea/coffee making & T.V. in all rooms. B. & B. from £20.

The Beeches Hotel, 4-6 Earlham Rd, Norwich, NR2 3DB (0603) 621167

The Beeches Hotel began life as private mansions in the 19th C. for successful Norwich businessmen; Henry Trevor, one such resident, devoted some 15 years to creating an idyllic Italianate garden in his grounds. Sadly the houses and gardens were neglected until 1980 when they were rediscovered, beautifully renovated and revived, and now they stand surrounded by 3 acres of tranquil wooded gardens just 10 minutes stroll from the centre of Norwich. The houses - known collectively as the Beeches Hotel - provide a luxurious and unique holiday or business destination: accommodation is in prettily furnished bedrooms and the bistro-style dining room which overlooks the garden is a pleasant airy room in which excellent home-cooked meals are served.

Open all year. No smoking in dining room & 75% of bedrooms. Vegetarian by arrangement. Licensed. Disabled access. Children welcome. En suite, tea-making, TV & DD phone in all rooms. Access, Visa. B. & B. from £37.

Fuchsias Guest House, 139 Earlham Rd, Norwich, NR2 3RG (0603) 51410

A friendly, family-run Victorian guest house convenient for city, UEA & countryside of Norfolk & Suffolk. Good bus routes. Central heating. Washbasins & personal keys to bedrooms.

Open all year. No smoking in the dining room, some bedrooms & public areas. Vegetarian & other diets by arrangement. En suite. TV & tea-making. Children welcome. B. & B. from £15 single, £28 double, £32. family

Grey Gables Country House Hotel and Restaurant, Norwich Rd, Cawston, Norwich, NR10 4EY (0603) 871259
Formerly Brandiston Rectory, this beautiful house offers very comfortable accommodation and fine food prepared from fresh ingredients, served by candlelight. Excellent 200 item wine list.
Open all year. No smoking in dining room. Vegetarian choice available. Other special diets by arrangement. Licensed. Some disabled access. Children: over 5s only. En suite in most rooms. Tea/coffee-making, T.V. and phone in all rooms. Access, Visa. B. & B. from £23. Bargain breaks: D., B. & B. £64 p.p. for 2 nights.

Kingsley Lodge, 3 Kingsley Rd, Norwich, NR1 3RB (0603) 615819
Kingsley Lodge is a friendly, Edwardian house which is conveniently situated in the centre of the city close to the bus station and just a few minutes'walk from the Market Place and shops. Each of the four comfortable guest rooms has an en suite bathroom and a range of amenities including tea and coffee-making facilities and a colour T.V. A full English breakfast - or a vegetarian option - is served to guests in a pleasant lounge or (in summer) in the conservatory. Kingsley Lodge is ideally placed for exploring historic Norwich (there is street parking with permits outside the house) and your host, Sally Clarke, will gladly advise you of the most interesting places to visit. *Open all year. No smoking throughout. Vegetarian & other diets by arrangement. En suite, TV & tea/coffee-making in all rooms. B. & B. from £18-£25.*

Park Farm Hotel, Hethersett, Norwich, NR9 3DL Tel: (0603) 810264 Fax: (0603) 812104

Park Farm Hotel occupies a tranquil and secluded location in beautifully landscaped grounds just 5m south of Norwich on the B1172. The original Georgian farmshouse has been carefully extended and the hotel now offers accommodation of an exceptionally highstandard: each of the 38 en suite bedrooms have been luxuriously decorated and equipped with every convenience - including phones and trouser presses - and there are some executive rooms available which have 4-poster beds and whirlpool baths. There is a first-rate leisure complex with indoor heated pool, sauna, steam room, solarium, jacuzzi and gymnasium and there is also croque and putting, plus an outdoor hard tennis court (the hotel also has affiliation with a local 18-hole golf course). The restaurant is totally non-smoking and there is a wide selection of menus - all prepared with care from fine ingredients - plus an excellent wine list. Six conference rooms cater for delegations of between 6 and 150 people and there is a helipad and light aircraft landing strip in the grounds . *Open all year. No smoking in the dining room & some bedrooms. Vegetarian & other diets by arrangement. En suite, TV & tea/coffee-making in bedrooms. Licensed. Wheelchair access. Children welcome. Credit cards.*

Pine Trees, Holly Lane, Blofield, Norwich, NR13 4BV (0603) 713778
Large, modern house in quiet rural area 1m from Blofield & by-pass. Ground floor suite for 2 - 6 people; private bath & entrance. Range of healthy b'fasts. Close Norwich, Broads & coast. *Open all year, ex. Xmas. No smoking in the house. Vegetarian & vegan standard. Other diets by arrangement. Some disabled access. Children welcome. Tea & coffee-making facilities. T.V. in lounge. B. & B. from £10-£17.*

SHERINGHAM
Achimota, 31 North St, Sheringham, NR26 8LW (0263) 822379

Achimota is a small, comfortable guest house which is quietly situated just a few minutes'stroll from the sea in the charming town of Sheringham on the North Norfolk coast; it derives its name from a small village in Ghana where the proprietors, John and Margaret Flowerdew, lived for some while. The Flowerdews offer comfortable, relaxed accommodation with good English cooking to their guests; there are several excellent choices on the breakfast menu (including Cley Smokehouse kippers!), and the evening meal features a good variety of home-prepared dishes such as Minestrone Soup followed by Chicken Paprika Casserole and a tempting dessert such as Chocolate Orange Trifle. You are perfectly

Achimota for visiting a number of National Trust Properties, and Sandringham, Norwich and the Broads are each just one hour's drive away.
Open all year. Smoking banned throughout. Vegetarian and most other special diets by arrangement. Well-behaved children & pets welcome. Tea/coffee-making facilities in all bedrooms. T.V. in lounge and bedrooms on request. B. & B. from £15. ETB 2 Crowns Commended.

SLOLEY

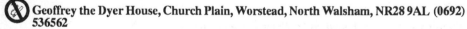 **Cubitt Cottage, Low St, Sloley, Nr Norwich, NR12 8HD   (069) 269295**
18th C. cottage in an acre of pretty gardens with 100 varieties of old-fashioned rose.
Open all year. No smoking throughout. Vegetarian, vegan, diabetic and other special diets on request. Children welcome. Tea/coffee-making in all rooms. T.V. in lounge. B. & B. from £18.50. D. £10.

SWAFFHAM

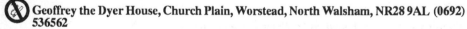 **Corfield House, Sporle, Nr Swaffham, PE32 2EA (0760) 23636**
     Corfield House is a beautiful brick-built country house standing amidst half an acre of lawned gardens in the peaceful village of Sporle near Swaffham. The accommodation is in very comfortable en suite bedrooms some of which have fine views across the fields and each of which has a range of amenities including a T.V., clock radio, hairdryer and fact-file on places to visit in the area; there is a twin-bedded ground floor room with easy access for the disabled. A full English or continental breakfast is served to guests, and a delicious 4-course evening meal can be prepared on request offering some tasty home-cooked dishes followed by an extensive cheeseboard; vegetarian and special diets can be prepared by arrangement and packed lunches are available on request. Swaffham is an attractive town with a lively Saturday market and open-air auction; additionally you are well-placed for visiting a number of National Trust properties, Sandringham, Thetford Forest and the historic towns of Kings Lynn and Norwich.
Open Easter to Dec. No smoking throughout. Vegetarian & diabetic by arrangement. Licensed. Some disabled access. Children welcome. Pets by arrangement. En suite in 5 rooms. T.V. in all rooms. Credit cards accepted. B. & B. from £18.50. ETB 3 Crowns Highly Commended.

WALSINGHAM

The Old Rectory, Waterden, Walsingham, NR22 6AT (0328) 823298
Beautiful Victorian rectory on the Holkham Estate in peaceful rural surroundings; beautifully furnished with antiques.
Open all year. No smoking ex. 1 bedroom. Vegetarian & other diets by arrangement. Disabled access. Children welcome. Pets by arrangement. En suite & tea/coffee-making in all rooms. T.V. in 1 room. B. & B. from £16.

WALTON HIGHWAY

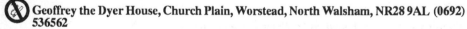 **Stratton Farm, West Drove North, Walton Highway, PE14 7DP (0945) 880162**
     Open all year. No smoking in the house. Vegetarian & diabetic by arrangement. Good access for wheelchair users. Children: over 5s only. En suite rooms. Tea/coffee & T.V in all rooms. B. & B. from £18-£20.

WORSTEAD

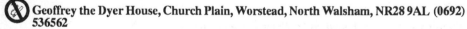 **Geoffrey the Dyer House, Church Plain, Worstead, North Walsham, NR28 9AL (0692) 536562**

 Geoffrey the Dyer House stands across the village square from Worstead's famous church which was built in the 13th C. by Flemish weavers. The beams and stays that hold up the house's lofty ceilings once supported the looms that made the famous Worstead cloth; careful restoration of this 17th C. listed building has preserved its unique character while creating a comfortable (and centrally heated) home of great charm: all the guest bedrooms have en suite facilities but the oak beams are intact and it is still possible to warm yourself in front of the inglenook fireplace on cooler evenings. Worstead is a conservation village in which the most dominant feature is its famous church; the village and the surrounding area have a beautiful, unspoilt quality despite the fact that Norfolk's

most popular amenities and attractions are so near at hand (Norwich 12 miles, the coast 8 miles and the Broads 2 miles). Worstead railway station is just 1 mile from the village.
Open all year. No smoking in the house. Vegetarian & other diets on request. Children welcome. Pets by arrangement. En suite, tea/coffee-making& T.V. in all rooms. B. & B. from £16. D. £8.50.

Restaurants

CASTLE ACRE
The Old Red Lion, Bailey St, Castle Acre, PE32 2AG   (0760) 755557
For further details please see under entry in the accommodation section.

DISS
The Waffle House, Market Place, Diss   (0379) 650709
This is a family restaurant offering good food at reasonable prices with friendly service. The 'daily specials'include dishes prepared from organic meat and produce, as well as a choice of vegetarian and vegan dishes; delicious home-made cakes and scones are baked on the premises daily. Children are very welcome - there are highchairs available - and party bookings can also be arranged.
No smoking in 70% of seating area - separate area. Open Mon.-Thurs. 10 - 5, Fri. 9 a.m. - 5 p.m., Sat. 9 - 9, Sun. 10 - 6. Last orders 1 hr before closing. Vegetarian standard. Wheelchair access. Party bookings taken.

GREAT YARMOUTH
Ⓝ **Lanes Bistro, No. 3, Row 75, Howard St South, Gt Yarmouth   (0493) 330622**
22 seats. Open 8.30 - 4. No smoking throughout. Vegetarian standard.

KINGS LYNN
Ⓝ **Debenhams, 19 - 16 High St, Kings Lynn   (0553) 772668**
Pavilion, a friendly self-service coffee shop serving lunches, snacks & a range of hot & cold drinks.
Open store hours. No smoking. Vegetarian meals. Disabled access. Children welcome. Credit/debit cards.

NORWICH
Ⓝ **The Almond Tree, 441 Dereham Rd, Costessey, NR5 0SG   (0603) 748798/749114**
No smoking. Licensed. Disabled access. Children welcome. Visa, Amex, Mastercard, Diners.

Ⓝ **The Assembly House, 12 Theatre St, Norwich, NR2 1RQ   (0603) 626402**
No smoking. Vegetarian standard. Licensed. Disabled access. Children welcome.

Ⓝ **Debenhams, Oxford Place, Norwich   (0603) 626181**
Springles, a self-service restaurant serving lunches, snacks & a range of hot & cold drinks.
Open store hours. No smoking. Vegetarian meals. Disabled access. Children welcome. Credit/debit cards.

Lloyd's of London St Restaurant, 66 London St, Norwich, NR2 1JT   (0603) 624978
50% no-smoking. Vegetarian standard. Children welcome, 'but not the very young'. Credit cards.

Pizza Express, 15 St Benedicts St, Norwich   (0603) 622157
No smoking in part of restaurant. Vegetarian standard. Licensed. Disabled access. Children welcome.

Pizza One Pancakes Too!, 24 Tombland, Norwich, NR3 1RF   (0603) 526099

Exceptionally popular pizza restaurant in the centre of Norwich. Situated alongside the ancient cathedral walls with cobblestones along the front and the famous spire of Norwich cathedral as a backdrop, it has long been one of Norwich's favourite eating places. The tempting menu includes pizzas, pancakes, excellent pasta dishes and delectable puddings (crepes with maple syrup, roasted almonds, peaches and cream - you name it, and you can have it!). The proprietors are nothing if not accommodating to guests: you can order pancakes without fillings and fillings without pancakes - for dessert you can choose a bowl of toppings. There is also a welcome sense of humour: there is a monthly competition for the best poem, comment or doodle and the winner has the honour of having his/her contribution displayed on the giant doodleboard as well as winning a meal for two.

110 seats. Open 12 - 11. Smoking banned in 60% of restaurant. L. around £5.25. Vegetarian standard. Licensed. Disabled access. Children welcome. Credit cards accepted.

La Tienda, 10 St Gregory's Alley, Norwich, NR2 1ER (0603) 629122
No smoking. Vegetarian, vegan, diabetic & gluten-free avail. Licensed. Some disabled access. Children.

Tree House Restaurant, 16 Dove St, Norwich (0603) 625560

The Treehouse Restaurant is situated above a wholefood shop in the centre of Norwich and is close to the city's famous 800 year-old market; the restaurant interior is warm and bright (with natural pine floors and furniture, and lots of plants and flowers), while the extensive window seating provides a lively view of the city. Run by an enthusiastic co-operative team, the Tree House is renowned for its warm and welcoming atmosphere; the food is fabulous - a wide range of vegetarian, vegan and gluten-free food is available on the daily-changing menu (all at affordable prices!) - and all meals are freshly prepared on the premises (the restaurant sensibly offers two meal sizes - one for the ravenous and one for the meek!). Lunches are served from 11.30 a.m. to 3 p.m. and afternoon teas - with a tempting selection of vegan, gluten-free and sugar-free cakes - are served from 3 to 5 p.m.; the evening trade commences at 6 p.m. and last orders are at 10 p.m. A good selection of organic wines and beverages are also available.

48 seats. Open 11.30 a.m. - 10 pm. No smoking throughout. L. around £4, D. from £5 to £15. Vegetarian, vegan, sugar-free and gluten-free standard. Children welcome (high charis available).

The Waffle House, 39 St Giles St, Norwich, NR2 1JN (0603) 612790
No smoking on first floor of restaurant and in 60% of downstairs seating area.

SHERINGHAM
The Jolly Tar, 55 Station Rd, Sheringham, NR26 8RG (0263) 822475
No smoking in 50% of restaurant (2 separate rooms). Licensed. Disabled access..

WELLS-NEXT-THE-SEA
The Moorings Restaurant, 6 Freeman St, Wells-next-the-Sea, NR23 1BA (0328) 710949

The Moorings Restaurant is, as its name suggests, situated in a charming old building a short walk from the beach at Wells-next-the-Sea. Unsurprisingly, much of the delicious home-cooked food has a marine flavour: home-smoked mussels, spicy fish soup or a half dozen locally raised oysters feature as appetisers on the extensive menu (even the Taramasalata is made from

Bernard and Carla Phillips

locally caught cods' roe), followed by Monkfish Fillet with Cumin and Coriander or Filo Parcel of Sea Bass as a main course. There are several good non-fish selections, too, such as Wild Mushroom Soup followed by Gratin of Pasta and Aubergine. Puddings are scrumptious (Butterscotch Pie with Walnut Crust or Special Trifle with Marsala, Amaretto & Almonds), and coffee with home-made chocolates completes the meal.

40 seats. No smoking throughout. D. around £15. Vegetarian standard. Licensed. Disabled access. Children

Pubs & Wine Bars

BLAKENEY
The Kings Arms, Westgate St, Blakeney, Holt, Norfolk, NR25 7NQ (0263) 740341
Unspoilt and original well-established pub serving good reasonably priced bar food home-prepared using much local produce; lovely large garden and children's play area.
No smoking in 1 room. Vegetarian standard & other diets on request. Children welcome. Wheelchair access.

Suffolk
Accommodation

BURY ST EDMUNDS

The Angel Hotel, Bury St Edmunds (0284) 753926
The hotel has 2 restaurants, one in the 12th C. undercroft, the other overlooking the square and Abbey gateway. Recommended by Mr Pickwick!
Open all year. No smoking main dining room & some bedrooms. Vegetarian & other diets by arrangement. Licensed. Children welcome. Pets by arrangement. En suite in all rooms. Credit cards. B. & B. from £50.

Hamilton House, 4 Nelson Rd, Bury St Edmunds, IP33 3AG (0284) 702201
Elegant Edwardian villa in a quiet cul-de-sac 3 mins from town & with easy access to the A45.
Open all year. No smoking. Vegetarian & other diets by arrangement. Children welcome. En suite in 2 rooms. Tea/coffee-making & T.V. in all bedrooms. Credit cards. B. & B. from £17.

EYE

Barley Green Farm, Laxfield Rd, Stradbroke, Eye, IP21 5JT (037984) 281
Tudor farmhouse in 8 acres, surrounded by attractive garden & ponds, near village.
Open Mar. to Oct. No smoking in the house. En suite 1 room. Tea/coffee in rooms. B. & B. from £15.

Oldcott, Laxfield Rd, Fressingfield, Nr Eye, IP21 5PU (037986) 8186
Oldcott is a 16th C. oak-beamed house which stands well back from the road in a large garden, at the centre of the village of Fressingfield. The accommodation is comfortable (it has been awarded a 2 Crowns Highly Commended Status by the English Tourist Board), and there is a sitting room and separate dining room for guests' use. You are offered a warm welcome with afternoon tea served on arrival, and the breakfast features toast, cereals and home-made wheaten scones as well as a cooked option; evening meals are available locally just five minutes' walk away. Fressingfield is an excellent base from which to explore the countryside of Suffolk, Norfolk and Cambridgeshire.
Open all year. No smoking in the house. Vegetarian & other diets by arrangement. Small babies welcome. En suite, tea/coffee-making & T.V. in all rooms. B. & B. from £17.50. ETB 2 Crowns Highly Commended.

FELIXSTOWE

Dorincourt Guest House, 16 Garfield Rd, Felixstowe, IP11 7PU (0394) 270447
Open all year. No smoking in the house. Vegetarian & other diets by arrangement. Children welcome. Tea/coffee-making & T.V. in all bedrooms. B. & B. from £15.

FRAMLINGHAM

Shimmens Pightle, Dennington Rd, Framlingham, IP13 9JT (0728) 724036
Open all year ex. Xmas. No smoking in the house. Vegetarian & other diets by arrangement. Disabled access. Children: over 8s only. Tea/coffee-making. T.V. lounge. B. & B. from £15.50. E.T.B Crown Commended.

IPSWICH

College Farm, Hintlesham, Ipswich, IP8 3NT (047387) 253

College Farm is a lovely oak-beamed 15th C. farmhouse which forms part of a 600 acre working farm of arable crops and a beef herd. The farmhouse has tremendous character - it was once owned by Cardinal Wolsey - and has been furnished in keeping with the age of the building; there is a lovely, large garden, complete with pond and a grass tennis court (summer use, only!). College Farm enjoys a wonderfully peaceful position well off the busy A1071 road - but just 6 miles of West of Ipswich with its shops and sporting facilities. There is much to see and do within easy reach of College Farm including visiting the old Wool Towns of Hadleigh and Lavenham, and enjoying 'Constable Country' on the Essex border.

Open all year ex. Xmas & New Year. No smoking in dining room & bedrooms. Vegetarian & other diets by arrangement. Children: over 5s. En suite 1 bedroom. Tea-making in all rooms. T.V. lounge. B. & B. from £15.

Otley House, Helmingham Rd, Otley, Ipswich, IP6 9NR Tel & Fax: (0473) 890253

Otley House has origins in the 17th C. but subsequent modernisations have created a building of great charm and it now boasts a Georgian facade and a fine listed Georgian staircase; it has been beautifully decorated and appropriately furnished (it has a lovely relaxed atmosphere) and it stands in its own spacious grounds, complete with small lake, surrounded by mature trees. Your hostess, Lise Hilton, is Danish and the excellent breakfast and evening menus feature a number of Scandinavian dishes as well as more traditional English fare. Otley House is within easy reach of a number of local attractions including the Concert Hall at Snape Maltings, Minsmere Bird Sanctuary and the coast at Aldeburgh.

Open Mar. to Oct. inc. No smoking ex. in billiard room. Vegetarian & other special diets by arrangement. Licensed. Children: over 12s only. En suite all rooms. T.V. 3 bedrooms. B. & B. from £24, single £34, D. £15.50.

Pipps Ford, Norwich Rd, Needham Market, Ipswich IP6 8LJ (044979) 208

16th C. farmhouse in a delightful old-fashioned garden on beautiful stretch of the River Gipping

Open mid-Jan. to mid-Dec. No smoking in dining room & bedrooms. Vegetarian & other diets by arrangement. Licensed. Disabled access. Children: over 5s. En suite & tea-making in rooms. T.V. in 2 lounges. B. & B. £26-29.

Redhouse, Levington, Ipswich, OP10 OLZ (0473) 659670

Redhouse is a substantial Victorian farmhouse which stands in 3 acres of gardens and paddocks surrounded by farmland. It is situated on the edge of the tiny village of Levington in an area of Outstanding Natural Beauty with magnificent views over the Orwell estuary; the proprietors, Mr and Mrs Matthews, are organic gardeners and keep horses and small livestock. Although Redhouse is primarily a bed and breakfast establishment, an evening meal can be obtained by prior arrangement and there are restaurants and pubs within easy reach. You will find Redhouse an ideal base for exploring the rich variety of the Suffolk countryside - including its Heritage Coast and mediaeval wool villages - and additionally there is an equestrian centre nearby and lots of lovely walks for ramblers.

Open Mar. to Nov. No smoking in part of dining room & bedrooms. Vegetarian & other diets by arrangement. Children welcome. Tea/coffee-making in all bedrooms. T.V. in lounge. B. & B. from £13.

The White House. Bucklesham, Ipswich (0473) 659325

The White House is a substantial private country house set in large gardens in the quiet village of Bucklesham; the bedrooms are all tastefully decorated and each have views of the garden and fields. There is also a self-catering annexe which sleep 2/3 and is fully equipped with a kitchen, sitting room, bedroom and bathroom (ideal for the disabled). The excellent meals have been prepared from fresh ingredients - including some garden produce wherever possible - and almost everything has been home-made, including the bread. Although Ipswich and Felixstowe are just 6 miles away, you are in the heart of the unspoilt countryside immortalised by John Constable; indeed Bucklesham itself is surrounded by panoramic rural views, and there are no less than three rivers nearby.

Open all year. No smoking in the house. Vegetarian by arrangement Children welcome. En suite in 1 room. Tea/coffee-making in all bedrooms. T.V. in lounge. B. & B. from £14-£16. D. £7.50.

LAVENHAM

The Swan Hotel, High St, Lavenham (0787) 247477
Open all year. No smoking in dining room & some bedrooms. Vegetarian standard. Other diets by arrangement. Licensed. Disabled access. Children welcome. En suite, TV & tea/coffee-making in all bedrooms.

LOWESTOFT

Fair Havens Christian Guest House, 8 Wellington Esp., NR33 OQQ (0502) 574927
Open all year ex. Xmas. No smoking in the house. Vegetarian and most other special diets by arrangement. Children welcome. Tea/coffee-making in all bedrooms. T.V. lounge. B. & B. from £14.50.

SUDBURY

Borley Place, Borley, Sudbury (next to the Parish Church) (0787) 71120
18th C. farmhouse set amidst rolling countryside in Constable country.
Open all year. No smoking in dining room, bedroom & sitting room. Children welcome. En suite. Tea/coffee-making if requested. T.V. lounge. B. & B. from £15.

Bulmer Tye House, Nr Sudbury, CO10 7ED (0787) 269315
Historic and characterful house with an informal, friendly atmosphere in a beautiful garden.
Open all year. No smoking. Vegetarian by arrangement. Children welcome. B. & B. from £16.

WOODBRIDGE

Old School, Saxtead, Woodbridge, IP13 9QP (0728) 723887
Exclusively vegetarian & vegan accommodation in converted school.
Open all year. No smoking in the house. Exclusively vegetarian. Vegan standard. Other diets by arrangement. Children welcome. Pets by arrangement. En suite in 2 rooms. Tea/coffee-making. B. & B. from £10. D. £6.

Priory Cottage, Low Corner, Butley, Nr Woodbridge, IP12 3QD (0394450) 382
Open all year ex. Xmas/Boxing Day. No smoking in the house. Vegetarian and most other special diets by arrangement. Children: over 5s only. Pets by arrangement. T.V. lounge. B. & B. from £14. D. £12.50.

Restaurants

BRANDON

Copper Kettle, 31 High St, Brandon (0842) 814185
Open Tue. - Fri., 10 - 5, 10 - 6 Sat. & Sun. No smoking throughout.

BURY ST EDMUNDS

The Angel Hotel, Bury St Edmunds (0284) 753926
No smoking. Vegetarian standard. Licensed. Disabled access. Children welcome. Credit cards.

HADLEIGH

The Spinning Wheel, 117/119 High St, Hadleigh, IP7 5EJ (0473) 822175
Pleasant restaurant housed in 17th C. building.
60 seats. Open 12 - 2, 7 - 11. Smoking banned in 50% of restaurant. Vegetarian and other special diets standard. Credit cards accepted. Licensed. Children welcome. Credit cards.

IPSWICH

Debenhams, Waterloo House, Ipswich (0473) 221313
Springles, a friendly self-service restaurant serving lunches, snacks & a range of hot & cold drinks.
Open store hours. No smoking throughout. Vegetarian meals. Children welcome. Credit/debit cards.

LOWESTOFT

Hampers Sandwich Bar & Buttery, 11A Grove Rd, Lowestoft, NR32 1EB (0502) 500316
26 seats. Open 10 - 4. Vegetarian standard. No smoking throughout. Children welcome.

East Midlands

Derbyshire
Accommodation

ALKMONTON

Ⓝ Dairy House Farm, Alkmonton, Longford, Derby, DE6 3DG (0335) 330359
Open all year. No smoking in the house. Vegetarian & other diets by arrangement. Licensed. Children: over 5s. En suite 3 rooms. Tea-making in bedrooms. T.V. lounge. B. & B. from £14.50. ETB 3 Crowns Commended.

ASHBOURNE

Ⓝ The Manse Vegetarian and Vegan Guest House, Wetton, DE6 2AF (033527) 259
Open all year ex. Xmas and New Year. No smoking in the house. Exclusively meat-free, mainly vegan. Children welcome. Pets by arrangement. En suite 1 room. Tea/coffee-making. T.V. in sitting room. B. & B. from £12.50.

The Old Chapel, Wetton, Nr Ashbourne, DE6 2AE (033527) 378
Charmingly converted 19th C. chapel. Excellent home-cooked food.
Open Feb. to Nov. No smoking in dining room & bedrooms. Vegetarian & other diets by arrangement. Children: over 7s only. Pets by arrangement. En suite & tea/coffee-making in bedrooms. T.V. available. B. & B. from £26.

BAKEWELL

Ⓝ Holly Cottage, Rowland, Nr Bakewell, DE4 1NR (0629) 640624
Beautiful 18th C. Farmhouse in peaceful rural setting; panelled hall with log fires for guests'use.
Open Jan. to Oct. No smoking throughout. Vegetarian by arrangement. Children welcome. Tea/coffee-making in all bedrooms. B. & B. from £16.50.

Ⓝ Riverside Country House Hotel, Ashford in the Water, DE4 1QF (0629) 814275
Exceptionally beautiful Georgian house set in mature gardens overlooking the river Wye.
Open all year. No smoking in the house. Vegetarian standard. Licensed. Disabled access to restaurant only. Children welcome. Dogs by arrangement. En suite, TV & tea/coffee-making in bedrooms. B. & B. from £41.

Ⓝ Sheldon House, Chapel Street, Monyash, Nr. Bakewell, DE4 1JJ (0629) 813067
Beautiful 18th century listed building in the picturesque village of Monyash in the heart of the Peak District National Park, recently renovated to a very high standard. Healthy b'fasts.
Open all year ex. Xmas and New Year. No smoking in the house. Vegetarian and most other special diets by arrangement. Children: over 7s only. En suite, tea/coffee-making in bedrooms. T.V. avail. B. & B. from £16.

BELPER

Dannah Farm Country Guest House, Dannah Farm, Bowmans Lane, Shottle, Nr Belper, DE56 2DR Tel: (0773) 550 273 or 630 Fax: (0773) 550590

Dannah Farm is an attractive Georgian building serving a 128 acre mixed farm on the beautiful Chatsworth Estate. The accommodation is very comfortable, and there is a superb 4-poster suite available. Joan Slack is very interested in (and knowledgeable about) healthy food and uses wholefood ingredients where possible in cooking. Muesli, yoghurt and fruit are always available at breakfast and the imaginative evening menu might feature Spinach and Cottage Cheese Filo, followed by Earl Grey Sorbet, Seafood Pie and a delicious dessert such as Stuffed Apple Pancakes with Cream. Joan recently opened her highly acclaimed non-residential restaurant, The

Mixing Place, on the Dannah Farm site, offering the same superlative food; the excellence of her achievements have been recognised by the English Tourist Board (Dannah Farm is 3 Crown Highly Commended) and she has won the National Award for Farm Catering. Lots to see and do in the area which is, incidentally, excellent for walking.

Open all year ex. Xmas. No smoking in bedrooms & dining room. Vegetarian & other diets by arrangement. Licensed. Children welcome. All rooms private facilities, tea/coffee-making & colour T.V. Credit cards. B. & B. from £24. AA 4Q Selected, RAC Highly Acclaimed. Finalists in 1992 Alternative Farmer of the Year.

BUXTON

Alpine Guest House, Hardwick Mount, Buxton, SK17 6PS (0298) 26155

The Alpine Guest House is a traditional Victorian Guest House with private parking which is situated in the beautiful market town of Buxton just a few minutes walk from the opera house, pavilion gardens and railway station; surrounded by the spectacular scenery of the Peak District National Park, Buxton is an excellent touring centre and is famous for its architecture and spa water. The food at the Alpine Guest House is nourishing and wholesome: everything is prepared on the premises and both traditional and vegetarian menus are available. A typical traditional evening meal would feature Crispy Mushrooms followed by Pork and Bean Cassoulet, and the imaginative vegetarian meal might feature Sliced Melon with Cherry Sauce followed by Nut Wellington with Herb and Mushroom Gravy. Puddings are delicious, such as Brandied Mince Tart with Tofu and Honey Cream or Spiced Brown Bread Pudding with Greek Yoghurt.

Open all year. No smoking in the house. Vegetarian standard. Most other special diets by arrangement. Children welcome. Tea/coffee-making & T.V. in all bedrooms. B. & B. from £14, D. £8.

Biggin Hall, Biggin-by-Hartington, Buxton, SK17 0DH (0298) 84451

Open all year. No smoking in dining room & sitting room. Vegetarian & other diets by arrangement. Licensed. Pets by arrangement. En suite in most rooms. Tea/coffee-making & T.V. in apartments & in sitting room.

Coningsby Guest House, 6 Macclesfield Road, Buxton, SK17 9AH (0298) 26735

Conveniently situated within walking distance of the major attractions of this lovely spa town, this elegant Victorian house has been most tastefully decorated and furnished by its proud owners, John and Linda Harry. Meals are prepared by Linda and her mother who are careful to use *fresh* produce wherever possible in cooking, and in offering a varied - and imaginative - menu to guests. Accordingly a typical evening meal might feature Mushroom and Stilton Soup, followed by Pork Fillet in Sherry Sauce and a selection of tempting desserts, such as Home-made Apple, Rum and Raisin Pie or Iced Raspberry Souffle. Buxton is a charming town in its own right although visitors are equally well-placed for visiting other attractions such as Chatsworth, Haddon Hall and the Castleton Caverns.

Open all year ex. Xmas. No smoking in the house. Vegetarian and most other special diets by arrangement. En suite shower, tea/coffee-making & T.V. in all bedrooms. ETB 3 Crowns Highly Commended. B. & B. from £18.

Ivy House, Newhaven, Biggin by Hartington, Buxton, Derbyshire, SK17 0DT (0298) 84709

19th C. former Grade II listed coaching inn recently renovated yet retaining many original features including flag stone floors. Log fires. Ideal for walking, cycling, touring. Ground floor apartment.

Open all year. No smoking in the house. Vegetarian & other diets by arrangement. Ground floor apartment. Children & pets welcome. En suite, TV & tea/coffee-making in bedrooms. B. & B. from £19-25.

Lynstone Guest House, 3 Grange Rd, Buxton, SK17 6NH (0298) 77043

A warm welcome awaits you in this small family-run guest house which stands in a quiet location just 5 minutes walk from the Opera House, Pavilion Gardens, Pooles Cavern, railway station and shopping centre of Buxton. All bedrooms are spacious, tastefully decorated and spotlessly clean. and each has shaver point, tea & coffee-making facilities and colour TV. A very generous breakfast is served to guests (traditional or vegetarian) and there are lots of good eating places in town.

Open Feb. - Dec. No smoking in the house. Vegetarian & other diets by arrangement. TV & tea/coffee-making in bedrooms. Children welcome. B. & B. from £14.

Milne House, Millers Dale, Buxton, DE4 1JJ (0298) 872315
Charming converted watermill situated near wooded hills in the heart of Derbyshire.
Open all year. Smoking allowed only in the lounge. Vegetarian and most other special diets by arrangement. Licensed. Children welcome.Tea/coffee-making facilities. T.V. available. B. & B. from £11.

Oldfield Guest House, 8 Macclesfield Rd, Buxton, SK17 9AH (0298) 24371

Oldfield Guest House is a large detached Victorian property which was built around 1870. It has recently been restored and is now run as a friendly family guest house - which is exceptionally clean and offers a very high standard of accommodation. Each of the spacious en suite bedrooms - some of which are on the ground floor - has tea-making facilities and a colour TV; there is a lovely large garden and ample space for parking. At Oldfield you are within walking distance of all the attractions of Buxton including the Opera House and Pavilion Gardens. The Oldfields also have a self-catering cottage - for further details see below.
Open all year. No smoking in the house. Vegetarian by arrangement. En suite, TV & tea/coffee-making in bedrooms. Children welcome. B. & B. from £16.

Self-catering, 1 Silverlands Cottage, Trinity Passage, Buxton (0298) 24371
This lovely stone cottage has a small garden and is attractively positioned in a tranquil cul de sac. The living accommodation consists of a kitchen cum dining room, a sitting room, two bedrooms and a bathroom; the cottage has been fully equipped with a Teletext TV and video and an automatic washing machine. You are within easy walking distance of the town centre with the Opera House and Pavilion Gardens - and of course are ideally placed for visiting all the other attractions of the Peak District National Park. There is safe, private parking. Sleeps 4 - 5.
Open all year. No smoking in the cottage. Children welcome. £120 - 220 per week.

CHESTERFIELD *from train station :*

Sheeplea Cottage Farm, Baslow Road, Eastmoor, Chesterfield (0246) 566785
Open Mar. to Oct. inc. No smoking throughout. Vegetarian standard. Other diets by arrangement. Children: over 12s only. Pets by arrangement. Tea-making in bedrooms. T.V. in lounge. B. & B. from £12.50.

MATLOCK BATH

Cliffeside Bed & Breakfast, Brunswood Rd, Matlock Bath, DE4 3PA (0629) 56981
Cliffeside is a friendly, family-run bed and breakfast with a lovely garden, complete with patio and ponds, set in the heart of the beautiful Derbyshire Dales with spectacular country views. Accommodation is in very comfortable rooms - there is a new double en suite bedroom with an adjacent room with bunk beds which is ideal for families (a cot and highchair is available, and baby-sitting can be arranged); the other double room has the use of a private bathroom with a corner bath. The breakfast is hearty and delicious - a real treat to set you up for the day - and there are plenty of restaurants and pubs nearby where you may enjoy an evening meal. Matlock Bath is a beautiful town, and you are near to Chatsworth House, Haddon Hall & Gulliver's Kingdom.
Open all year. No smoking in the house. Vegetarian & other diets by arrangement. Children & pets welcome. 1 double/family en suite; 1 double. TV & tea/coffee-making in both rooms. B. & B. from £13.

MATLOCK

Derwent House, Knowleston Place, Matlock, DE4 3BU (0629) 584681
Charming 17th C. Grade II listed building built of Derbyshire gritstone in secluded backwater just 50 yards from Hall Leys Park. Each of the 5 comfortably furnished guest rooms are named after Derbyshire rivers. Family owned and children very welcome.
Open all year ex. Xmas and New Year. No smoking in the house. Vegetarian standard. Children welcome. Pets by arrangement. En suite in 1 bedroom. Tea/Coffee-making & T.V. in rooms. B. & B. from £16.

Lane End House, Green Lane, Tansley, DE4 5FJ (0629) 583981

Lane End is a small Georgian farmhouse set behind Tansley village green near to the church and with open fields and green hills to the rear. It is owned by a very welcoming couple, David and Marion Smith, who brought their 10 years of experience in running a very successful country house hotel in Leicestershire to bear on a smaller - and, they hope, therefore more personal - enterprise just three years ago. Much love and care has gone into the internal decoration and refurbishment of the house - there is a downstairs bedroom with shower room for those unable to cope with stairs - and the bedrooms are equipped, in addition to the usual facilities, with bathrobes, current magazines, tapes, fresh fruit and flowers. The food is prepared with a similar amount of attention to detail: everything is home-made - including the soups and patés - and vegetables are nearly always steamed; fromage frais - or yoghourt - is served as an accompaniment to the delicious desserts. There is much to see and do within the area: Chatsworth House, Haddon Hall and Hardwick House are just a short drive away, while the famous Tissington Trail, Dovedale Valley, Black Rock, and the new Carsington Reservoir are very easily accessible to walkers. *Open all year. No smoking in the house. Vegetarian and most other special diets by arrangement. Licensed. Disabled access: 2 steps at front door. Children welcome. Pets by arrangement. Each bedroom has a private bathroom. Tea/coffee-making & T.V. in all bedrooms. Access, Visa, Mastercard. B. & B. from £21.*

Sunnybank Guest House, 37 Clifton Rd, Matlock Bath, Matlock, DE4 3PW (0629) 584621

Spacious, comfortable Victorian residence offering excellent accommodation in peaceful surroundings with lovely views of the Derwent Valley. Ideal centre for touring & walking. *Open all year. No smoking in the house. Vegetarian & other diets by arrangement. Children; over 10s only. En suite in 3 rooms. TV in lounge & 3 rooms. Tea/coffee-making in all bedrooms. Credit cards. B. & B. from £17.*

WIRKSWORTH

Avondale Farm, Grangemill, Nr Wirksworth, DE4 4HT (0629) 650820

Avondale offers peaceful and private bed and breakfast in a tastefully converted barn on a non-working farm in the small hamlet of Grangemill in the Peak District National Park. The accommodation is of an exceptionally high standard and is totally self-contained and centrally heated: designed for two people, guests enter by their own small hallway into the spacious dining/sitting area with its cosy log burner, and the adjoining bedroom has comfortable twin beds and a private bathroom. The breakfast is excellent with lots of healthy treats including local honey, bread and croissants as well as real coffee from a cafetiere! Baskets of magazines are provided and some helpful information about the area. Grangemill is situated twixt Ashbourne and Bakewell and there is lovely walking to be had on the nearby wild and wind-blown moors. *Open all year. No smoking in the house. Vegetarian & other special diets by arrangement. Children & pets by arrangement. Private bathroom. Tea/coffee making, T.V., radio & hairdryer in room. B. & B. from £19.50.*

Restaurants & Pubs

BAKEWELL

Green Apple, Diamond Court, Water Street, DE4 1EW (0629) 814404

Tucked away in Diamond Court in central Bakewell, this charming little restaurant has recently been converted from five old cottages. Retaining the beamed ceilings and the exposed stone walls of the original building, this pleasing bistro offers an imaginative menu of home-prepared food typically featuring Melon with Elderflower Sorbet followed by Chicken with Celery Sauce and a tasty choice of desserts (the Fresh Fruit Brulée is especially recommended). Lunchtime diners, in sunny weather, might choose to eat *al fresco* in the patio garden. *Open 12 - 2, 7 - 9.30. Teas 2 - 5.30 (summer). L. from £5.75. D. from £12. Take-away service. No smoking. Vegetarian. Licensed. Disabled access. Children. Credit cards (+4%).*

BELPER

 The Mixing Place, Dannah Farm Country Guest House, Dannah Farm, Bowmans Lane, Shottle, Nr Belper, DE5 2DR (077) 389273/630
For further details please see under the entry in the accommodation section.

CHESTERFIELD

The House of York, 26 The Green, Hasland, Nr Chesterfield (0246) 211241
Separate dining room for non-smokers. Vegetarian standard. Licensed. Children welcome. Credit cards.

Royal Oak Inn, High Street, Barlborough, Chesterfield (0246) 810425
Separate smoke-free section . Vegetarian standard. Licensed. Children allowed. Access, Visa.

DERBY

The Brunswick Pub, 1 Railway Terrace, Derby (0332) 290677
Smoking banned in one room.

 Debenhams, 17 - 24 Victorian St, Derby (0332) 44252
Springles, a friendly self-service restaurant serving lunches, snacks & hot & cold drinks.
Open store hours. No smoking. Vegetarian meals. Disabled access. Children welcome. Credit/debit cards.

Orchard Restaurant, 21 Friargate, Derby (0332) 40307
Smoking banned in most of restaurant. Mainly vegetarian food. Licensed. Children welcome.

 Quatties Restaurant, 109 Normanton Road, Derby (0332) 368701
No smoking throughout. Vegetarian standard. Licensed. Well-behaved children welcome.

MELBOURNE

John Thompson Inn, Ingleby, Melbourne, DE7 1HW (0332) 862469
A 16th C. country pub with its own brewery and extensive gardens and picture gallery. 4 miles from Calke Abbey, 2 miles from Melbourne Hall and 5 miles from E. Midlands airport.
Open all year. Smoking banned in separate lounge. Meals available. Wheelchair access to smoke-free lounge. Children's room available for evenings.

TICKNALL

 Daisy's Tearoom, The Old Coach House, Hayes Farm, Ticknall, DE7 1JZ (0332) 862696

Daisy's Tearoom is situated in the coach house of a lovely large Georgian farmhouse in beautiful Ticknall. It stands in lovely informal gardens (customers are welcome to wander therein!), and a further attraction is the antiques showroom to the rear of the tea room. Lace tablecloths, fresh flowers, gentle background music all create a peaceful ambience - and very friendly service from your host, Zoe Salisbury. The food is excellent - booking is advisable, especially on Sunday when traditional roasts lure guests from far and wide - and the set teas, which are served from 2.30 p.m., offer a mouthwatering choice: Summer Garden Tea with Smoked Salmon, Daisy Jones Cream Tea, Cricketer's teas . . . you could spend a whole afternoon making up your mind! Everything is home-made and wholesome and, with seating for just 25, rarely overcrowded & always relaxed
Open 10.30 - 5.30. L. around £5. Teas around £3. Smoking banned throughout. Vegetarian standard. Some other special diets on request. Children welcome.

Leicestershire Accommodation

BROUGHTON ASTLEY

⊗ The Old Farmhouse, Old Mill Rd, Broughton Astley, LE9 6PQ (0455) 282254
Open all year. No smoking in the house. Vegetarian and other special diets by arrangement. Children welcome. Tea/coffee making in all rooms. B. & B. from £13.50.

COTTESMORE

⊗ The House of Alice (incorporating The Looking Glass, Natural Therapies & Madhatters Tearoom), 35 Main St, Cottesmore, LE15 7DH (0572) 813264
300-year-old thatched cottage functioning as both a centre for natural healing & a tea room serving home-made snacks and cakes. 3 miles from Rutland Water in the small town of Cottesmore.
Open all year (tearoom closed Oct. - April). No smoking throughout. Vegetarian & other diets by arrangement. Children welcome. Pets by arrangement. Tea/coffee-making & T.V. B. & B. from £18.

LEICESTER

Leicestershire Moat House, Wigston Rd (B582), Oadby, Leicester, LE2 5QE (0533) 719441

Although of modern interior design and totally refurbished, the oldest part of this excellent, business-class hotel was once a gentleman's residence with parts dating back to 1898. Offering excellent facilities in each of its 57 en suite bedrooms, including in-house movies, trouser presses and direct dial phones, this well-appointed hotel is conveniently situated in the village-like residential area of Oadby yet has easy access to Leicester city centre and the M1. A wide variety of food is offered, from the tasty, home-made bar snacks served in the lounge bar to the succulent roasts served from the carvery in the Czar's Restaurant adjoining the upper bar; a typical restaurant menu selection would feature Rollmop Herring and Lemon Cream followed by Roast Chicken with Bread Sauce (served with a selection of fresh vegetables), and a choice of sweets from the trolley.
Open all year. No smoking in restaurant & some bedrooms. Vegetarian. Licensed. Disabled access. Children welcome. Pets by arrangement. En suite, TV & tea-making in rooms. Credit cards. B. & B. from £30.50-£72.50.

⊗ Richard's Backpacker's Hostel, 157 Wanlip Ln., Birstall, LE4 4GL (0533) 673107
Independent hostel for cyclists, backpackers & young tourists. Bus services from Stand B at the city bus station to the hostel's nearest stop at Windmill Avenue, Birstall. Home-made bread.
Open all year. No smoking throughout. Vegetarian and vegan standard. Other special diets by arrangement. Not licensed, but bring your own. Children: over 5s only. B. & B. from £8.

LUTTERWORTH

⊗ Highcross House, Highcross, Lutterworth, LE17 5AT (0455) 220840
16th C. Grade II listed building at the historic crossing of Fossways and Watling Street; flowers & refreshments to greet you! Picnic basket on request.Tasteful rooms. Fresh, home-made food.
Open all year. No smoking throughout. Vegetarian & other diets by arrangement. Licensed. Disabled access. Children welcome. Pets by arrangement. En suite. Tea/coffee-making & T.V. in all rooms. B. & B. from £20.

Wheathill Farm, Church Lane, Shearsby, Lutterworth, LE17 6PG (0533) 478663
Open all year. No smoking in dining room, lounge & bedrooms. Vegetarian by arrangement. Children welcome. Disabled facilities. En suite. Tea/coffee making in all rooms. T.V. in lounge. B. & B. from £15.

MELTON MOWBRAY

Stapleford Park Country House Hotel, Stapleford Park, LE14 2EF (057 284) 522
16th C. stately home converted to use as a hotel of almost indescribable grandeur and eclecticism of style; 2 acres of walled gardens; designer bedrooms creating 'a museum of interior design'.
Open all year. No smoking in dining room. Vegetarian and other special diets by arrangement. Licensed. Disabled access. Pets by arrangement. En suite in all rooms. T.V. facilities. Credit cards. B. & B. from £125.

UPPINGHAM

Rutland House, 61 High St East, Uppingham, Rutland (0572) 822497
Open all year. Smoking banned in dining room and some bedrooms. Disabled access. Children welcome. Pets by arrangement. En suite, TV & tea/coffee making in all rooms. B. & B. from £18.50.

Restaurants & Pubs

ASHBY-DE-LA-ZOUCH

 **Staunton Stables Tea Room, The Ferrers Centre, Staunton Harold, Nr Ashby-de-la-Zouch, LE6 5RU (0332) 864617**

Staunton Stables is situated in a converted stable block, surrounding a magnificent Georgian courtyard behind Staunton Harold Hall in the beautiful Vale of Staunton Harold near Calke Abbey. Home-made cakes, pastries and light lunches are served therein on lovely Rose Chintz pottery, and the indoor seating is supplemented by more tables and chairs in the courtyard for sunny al fresco dining. The Staunton lunches consist of one daily hot 'special', such as Casserole or Beef Cobbler, traditional oven-baked potatoes with various fillings, soup, toasted sandwiches and hot puddings; roast dinners are available on Sunday, and cream teas and Hovis teas are served every afternoon. Home-made cakes, home-made preserves and Twinings Speciality Teas are available for sale, and The Stables also houses a number of craft workshops, a gift shop and the Ferrers Gallery.

Open 10.30 - 5. Smoking banned throughout. Vegetarian standard. Disabled access. Children welcome.

COTTESMORE

Madhatters, 35 Main St, Cottesmore, LE15 7DH (0572) 812550
Smoking banned throughout. Vegetarian standard. Some disabled access. Children welcome.

EMPINGHAM

White Horse Pub, 2 Main St (A606), Empingham (078 086) 221
Smoking banned in part of lounge bar.

LEICESTER

Debenhams, The Shires Centre, St Peters Lane, Leicester (0533) 515300
Intermission, a friendly self-service restaurant serving lunches, snacks & hot & cold drinks.
Open store hours. No smoking. Vegetarian. Disabled access. Children welcome. Credit/debit cards.

Parsons Gallery, 399 Ratby Ln., Kirby Muxloe, Leicester, LE9 9AQ (0533) 393534
Open 10 - 5, Wed. to Sat. No smoking throughout. Only well-behaved children welcome.

The Good Earth, 19 Free Lane, Leicester, LE1 1JX (0533) 626260
Smoking banned in 50% of restaurant (separate floor). Vegetarian and vegan standard. Licensed.

LOUGHBOROUGH

The Greenhouse, 27/29 Biggin St (first floor), Loughborough, LE11 1UA (0509) 262018
No smoking throughout. Vegetarian exclusively. Licensed. Children welcome.

OAKHAM

Muffins Tea Rooms, 9 Mill St, Oakham, Rutland, LE15 6EA (0572) 723501
No smoking throughout. Wheelchair access. Children welcome.

UPPINGHAM

Baines Tea Room, High St West, Uppingham (0572) 823317
Open Mon. to Sat., 9 - 5., (closed Mon. & Thurs. p.m. in winter). No smoking throughout.

Lincolnshire
Accommodation

BOSTON

⚜ Poundsworth, Main St, Mareham-le-Fen, Boston, PE22 7QJ (0507) 568444

Open all year. No smoking throughout. Vegetarian by arrangement. Children welcome. B. & B. from £14.

CASTLE BYTHAM

⚜ Bank House, Castle Bytham, Nr Grantham, Lincs, NG33 4SQ (0780) 410523

Bank House is located just 3 miles east of the A1 between Stamford and Grantham. Owned

by Richard and Marian Foers, this country home has the rare and prestigious quality grading of De Luxe awarded by the English Tourist Board. It was voted Bed and Breakfast of the Year in the Middle England Best of Tourism Awards and was the runner-up in the national England for Excellence Awards. It is a superbly appointed and comfortable private home, set in well-maintained secluded grounds and overlooking rolling Lincolnshire countryside on the edge of the peaceful and historic conservation village of Castle Bytham. The spacious guests'lounges, dining room and two twin bedrooms each have their own individually designed and created furnishings. Value for money, attention to detail and visitors'needs are of paramount importance to your hosts: menus feature healthy, home-made foods and there is an individually caring and personal service, which enables guests to fully enjoy the many attractions of the area such as country houses and castles, local walks, bird-watching, riding, water sports, golf and other country pursuits.

Open all year. No smoking in the house. Vegetarian & other diets by arrangement. En suite, TV & tea/coffee-making available. B. & B. from £20, Dinner £6.

EAST BARKWITH

The Grange, Torrington Lne, East Barkwith, LN3 5RY (0673) 858249

Welcoming Georgian farmhouse quietly situated amidst extensive grounds with herb beds and lawn tennis court; the spacious bedrooms have views of the farm and gardens.

Open all year. No smoking in bedrooms & most public areas. Vegetarian, diabetic and other special diets by arrangement. Children welcome. En suite in all rooms. B. & B. from £18.50. ETB 2 Crowns De Luxe.

GRANTHAM

The Lanchester Guest House, 84 Harrowby Rd, Grantham, NG31 9DS (0476) 74169

Open all year. No smoking in dining room, bedrooms & most public areas. Vegetarian by arrangement. Children welcome. En suite in some rooms. Tea/coffee making & T.V. in all rooms. B. & B. from £15.

⚜ Sycamore Farm, Bassingthorpe, Grantham, Lincs. NG33 4ED (0476) 85274

Sycamore Farm is a working family farm with a spacious Victorian farmhouse which stands

amidst the peaceful countryside of South Lincolnshire. It has been very comfortably furnished throughout: each of the spacious guest bedrooms have beautiful unspoilt views and have been well-equipped with wash handbasins or en suite facilities (hairdryers are available on request). Your hosts will do all they can to make you feel welcome and at home: they have provided maps and guide books in the sitting room - which is, incidentally, a welcoming haven with comfy chairs and a warming fire on chillier evenings. Sycamore Farm is easily located and is just 5 miles from the A1; there are numerous walks to be enjoyed nearby and you are within easy reach of Lincoln, Rutland Water and many historic houses.

Open Mar. - Oct. No smoking in the house. En suite 1 room. TV & tea/coffee-making in bedrooms. Children: over 6s welcome. B. & B. from £14.

HAINTON

The Old Vicarage, School Lane, Hainton, LN3 6LW (0507) 313660
Open all year. No smoking throughout. Children: over 12s only. No pets. Private bathroom available. Tea/coffee making & T.V. in all rooms. B. & B. from £13.50.

LINCOLN

ABC Guest House, 126 Yarborough Rd, Lincoln, LN1 1HP (0522) 543560

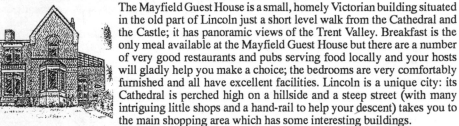

The ABC Guest House is a large, detached red brick built house overlooking the Trent Valley by the side of the old Lincoln race course and just 10 minutes walk from the cathedral and city centre. All bedrooms have been comfortably furnished and have pleasant views of the common and the Carholme golf course; some of the rear bedrooms have balconies. Your hosts, Wendy and Terry Cain, offer just breakfast to guests but it is a generous meal and there are lots of good pubs and restaurants just a short walk away in the cathedral area of the city. With its lovely green views, yet convenient proximity to the city centre, the ABC is a perfect choice for business travellers to Lincoln, or those seeking a short break in this historically interesting city.
Open all year. No smoking throughout. Vegetarian and other special diets. Disabled access.   Pets by arrangement. Some en suite rooms. Tea/coffee & T.V. in all rooms. B. & B. from £14.

Mayfield Guest House, 213 Yarborough Rd, Lincoln (0522) 533732

The Mayfield Guest House is a small, homely Victorian building situated in the old part of Lincoln just a short level walk from the Cathedral and the Castle; it has panoramic views of the Trent Valley. Breakfast is the only meal available at the Mayfield Guest House but there are a number of very good restaurants and pubs serving food locally and your hosts will gladly help you make a choice; the bedrooms are very comfortably furnished and all have excellent facilities. Lincoln is a unique city: its Cathedral is perched high on a hillside and a steep street (with many intriguing little shops and a hand-rail to help your descent) takes you to the main shopping area which has some interesting buildings.
Open all year. No smoking throughout. Vegetarian standard. Children welcome. En suite, tea/coffee making & T.V. in all rooms. Visa. B. & B. from £14.

LOUTH

Wickham House, Church Lane, Conisholme, Nr Louth, LN11 7LX (0507) 358465
Attractive 18th C. cottage standing in pleasant gardens near Conisholme church. All bedrooms have en suite facilities and have been attractively furnished; guest sitting room and library.
Open all year. No smoking. Bring your own wine. Children: over 8s only. En suite, tea/coffee making & colour T.V. in rooms. B. & B. from £17.50. ETB 3 Crown Commended.

MARKET RASON

The Waveney Guest House, Willingham Rd, Market Rason, LN8 3DN (0673) 843236

Waveney is a tudor-style cottage which has been converted from an old stable and now provides a happy, comfortable family home. It stands in mature, traditional-style gardens complete with fish pond and plenty of car parking space. There are three twin-bedded rooms - one of which has bunk beds and is a comfortable family room (a cot and high chair are also available) - and all rooms are centrally heated and have been tastefully furnished. Meals are home-cooked from

fresh, local produce (your host, Liz Margrave is a retired Home Economics teacher), and guests have use of their own lounge complete with TV, lots of books and games, and a record player. Waveney is within easy reach of a number of interesting places including the beautiful Lincolnshire Wolds (just 2 miles away) and the historically significant city of Lincoln (15 miles); other attractions include the National Hunt Race Course, a sports centre, and two golf courses. *ETB 2 Crowns Commended.*
Open all year. No smoking in the house. Vegetarian & other diets by arrangement. Children & pets welcome. En suite, TV & tea/coffee-making in bedrooms. B. & B. from £15, D. B. & B. from £21. Family rate from £40.

NORTH THORESBY

The Hen House, Hawerby Hall, North Thoresby, DN36 5QL (0472) 840278
Hen House is a handsome Georgian manor house surrounded by gardens, fields and woods which has now been established for several years as a unique venue for women to come 'for reunions, celebrations, holidays, short breaks...or just to unwind'. Wonderful food & numerous walks.
Open all year. No smoking almost throughout. Vegetarian & other diets by arrangement. Licensed. Good disabled access. Children welcome. En suite some rooms. T.V. in lounge. D., B.& B. from £32.

SPALDING

Guy Wells Farm, Whaplode, Spalding, PE12 6TZ (0406) 22239
Guy Wells is a lovely Queen Anne family home on a flower farm. Your hosts, Anne and Richard Thompson offer a warm welcome to guests; choice of dinner or light supper.
Open all year. No smoking throughout. Vegetarian and other special diets on request. One room en suite. Wash basins in all rooms. Tea/coffee making in all rooms. T.V. in lounge. B. & B. from £16.

STAMFORD

Birch House, 4 Lonsdale Rd, Stamford, PE9 2RW (0780) 54876
Family-run house in a quiet location less than 1m from Stamford.
Open all year. No smoking throughout. Children welcome. Tea-making & T.V. in all rooms. B. & B. from £14.

Casterton Taverner Motor Inn, Casterton Hill, Stamford, PE9 4DE (0780) 52441
Open all year. No smoking in dining room. Vegetarian and other special diets by arrangement. No disabled access. Children welcome. Pets by arrangement. En suite, tea/coffee making & T.V. in all rooms. price?

Hillcroft House, 25 High St, Easton-on-the-Hill, Nr Stamford, PE9 3LN (0780) 55598

Open Apr. to Sept. Smoking banned throughout the house. Vegetarian and other special diets by arrangment. Children: over 12 yrs only (no reduction). Dogs by arrangement. Some private facilities. Tea/coffee-making in all rooms. T.V. B. & B. from £14-£18. ETB 2 Crowns Commended.

The Priory, Ketton, Stamford, Lincs. (0780) 720215

The Priory is a large 16th C. house which was described in Pevsner's *Buildings of England.* It was not, in fact, a priory at all but a prebendal manor house until 1723 at which time it became a private residence. It has been meticulously restored in recent years and is now a charming family home with a limited number of rooms for guests. The house faces south towards the River Chater and large gardens which are a year-round delight with lawns, formal rose beds, herbaceous borders and yew hedges. Most of the guest rooms overlook the gardens and have the added charm of panelled walls and working shutters at the windows. The north side of the house is dominated by the presence of the very large 12th C. village church. Guests at the Priory are treated to delicious home-cooked food in either the formal dining room or the Garden Room.*ETB 3 Crown Highly Commended.*
Open all year. No smoking ex. in guest lounge. Vegetarian & other diets by arrangement. En suite, TV, DD phones & tea/coffee-making in all bedrooms. Children welcome. Wheelchair access. B. & B. from £17.50 p.p.

WASHINGBOROUGH

Washingborough Hall Country House Hotel, Church Hill, Washingborough, LN4 1BE (0522) 790340

Beautiful country house quietly situated amidst 3 acres of lawns and woodland on the edge of Washingborough village; very good food.

Open all year. No smoking in dining room and some bedrooms. Vegetarian and other special diets by arrangement. Licensed. Children welcome. Pets by arrangement. En suite, TV & tea/coffee making in all rooms. Credit cards. B. & B. from £42.

Restaurants

GRANTHAM

Claire's Concoctions, 15A Bridge St, Grantham, NG31 9AE (0476) 76981

Vegetarian restaurant serving 'imaginative and healthy cuisine' with an emphasis on wholefood and on catering for special diets.

40 seats, plus 25 in courtyard. Open Tues. - Sat. No smoking in 2 of 3 rooms. Any special diet either standard or by arrangement. Licensed. Disabled access. Children welcome.

LOUTH

Mr Chips Fish Restaurant, 17-21 Aswell St, Louth, LN11 9BA (0507) 603756

Licensed self-service fish and chip restaurant with modern decor and lighting; fully air-conditioned; good amenities for the physically disabled; mother and baby room available.

300 seats. Open 6 days, 9 - 11. No smoking in 40% of restaurant. Vegetarian standard. Licensed. Disabled access. Children welcome.

 Crustys, Pawn Shop Passage, Louth

Open Tues. & Wed., Fri. & Sat., 10 - 4. No smoking throughout.

SLEAFORD

 Bumbles Bistro, 7 Handley Court Mews, Southgate, Sleaford (0529) 413996

36 seats plus 16 on patio. Open 10 - 9. No smoking throughout. Vegetarian standard. Licensed. Disabled access. Children welcome. Amex, Mastercard.

STAMFORD

Casterton Taverner Motor Inn, Casterton Hill, Stamford, PE9 4DE (0780) 52441

Restaurant situated in two Pullman dining cars which once ran as part of the Yorkshire Pullman.

Open all day. No smoking in restaurant. Special diets on request. Licensed. Children welcome. Credit cards accepted.

Northamptonshire Accommodation

NORTHAMPTON

Forte Post House Hotel Northampton/Rugby, Crick, NN6 7XR (0788) 822101
Open all year. No smoking in 50% of dining room & all bedrooms. Vegetarian standard. Licensed. Some disabled access. Children welcome. Pets by arrangement. En suite, TV & tea/coffee-making in all rooms.

Hollington Guest House, 22 Abington Grove, Northampton, NN1 4QW (0604) 32584
Small, friendly B. & B. close to town centre. Easy access to M1, Kettering & Wellingborough.
Open all year ex. Xmas. No smoking in the dining room. Vegetarian & other diets if required. Children welcome. TV & tea/coffee-making in bedrooms. B. & B. from £12.50 (single £16, family of 3: £33; family of 4: £40.

Wold Farm, Old, Northampton, NN6 9RJ (0604) 781258
Open all year. No smoking in dining room & bedrooms. Vegetarian and other special diets by arrangement. Children welcome. Pets by arrangement. En suite. Tea/coffee making. T.V. in lounge. B. &. B. from £17.

Winwick Manor, Winwick, Northampton, NN6 7PD (078 887) 274
Open all year. No smoking. Vegetarian by arrangement. Children welcome. En suite. B. & B. from £20.

WELLINGBOROUGH

High View Hotel, 156 Midland Rd, Wellingborough Tel: (0933) 278733 Fax: (0933) 225948
Situated in a quiet tree-lined area between station & town centre. Pleasant bar.
Open all year. No smoking in the dining room. Vegetarian meals available. En suite, TV & tea/coffee-making in bedrooms. Children & pets welcome. Licensed. B. & B. from £22.50 (reduced w/e rates).

YARDLEY GOBION

Old Wharf Farm, Yardley Gobion, Nr Towcester, NN12 7UE (0908) 542454
Open all year. No smoking in dining room, bedrooms & most public areas. Vegetarian by arrangement. Children welcome. Pets by arrangement. Ad-lib tea & coffee. B. & B. from £17.

Restaurants & Pubs

BRIGSTOCK

Hill Farm Herbs, Park Walk, Brigstock, NN14 3HH (0536) 373694
Smoking banned throughout. Wheelchair access. Children welcome.

NORTHAMPTON

Cafe Kilkea, 9 George Row, Northampton (0604) 37173

Debenhams, The Drapery, Northampton, NN1 2EZ (0604) 34391
Pavilion, a friendly self-service coffee shop serving lunches, snacks & hot & cold drinks.
Open store hours. No smoking throughout. Vegetarian meals. Children welcome. Credit/debit cards.

The Manna House, St Giles St, Northampton (0604) 22666
Open all day. No smoking throughout. Some disabled access. Children welcome.

THURNING

The Tithe Barn at Thurning, Home Farm, Thurning, Nr Oundle, PE8 5RF (08323) 511
No smoking throughout. Vegetarian available. Wheelchair access. Children play area. Credit cards

TWYWELL

The Old Friar, Twywell, Nr Kettering, NN14 3AH (08012) 2625
No smoking in 1 dining area (28 seats). Vegetarian. Licensed. Wheelchair access. Children welcome.

Nottinghamshire
Accommodation

NEWARK

 The Appleton Hotel, 73 Appletongate, Newark, NG24 1LN (0636) 71616
Open all year. No smoking throughout. Vegetarian standard. Licensed. Children welcome. En suite, tea/coffee making, T.V. & direct dial phones in all rooms. Credit cards accepted. B. & B. from £25.

NOTTINGHAM

 Laurel Farm, Browns Lane, Stanton-on-the-Wolds, Nottingham, NG12 5BL (06020 373488
Lovely old farmhouse with 4 acre garden for guests'use. Fresh local produce & own eggs.
Open all year. No smoking in the house. Vegetarian & other diets by arrangement. Children welcome. En suite in 1 room. TV & tea/coffee-making in bedrooms. B. & B. from £15.

 The Lucieville Hotel, 349 Derby Rd, Nottingham, NG7 2DZ Tel: (0602) 787389 Fax 0602 790346
Executive-class hotel just 1 mile from the city centre & a short drive from exit 25 of the M1
Open all year. No smoking throughout. Vegetarian standard. Licensed. Disabled access. En suite in all rooms. Tea/coffee making, T.V., telephone and hairdrier in all rooms. Visa, Access. B. & B. from £49.50.

Nottingham Moat House, Mansfield Rd, Nottingham, NG5 2BT (0602) 602621
The Nottingham Moat House is a modern, business-class 172-bedroomed hotel which is conveniently situated less than a mile from the city centre and has free parking for 300 cars. Each of the comfortably furnished en suite bedrooms has been tastefully decorated and equipped with a range of amenities including colour TV, in-house movie channel, radios, trouser-presses and beverage-making facilities; 50% of the rooms are non-smoking. A wide range of delicious meals are served in the restaurants, one of which is a completely smoke-free a la carte dining room and two of which have smoke-free areas.
Open all year. No smoking in 1 restaurant, parts of 2 other restaurants & 50% of bedrooms. Vegetarian standard. Some other diets on request. Disabled access. Children welcome. En suite, tea/coffee making & T.V. in all rooms. Access, Visa, Amex, Diners. B. & B. from £62. Special w/e rates.

SOUTHWELL

 Old National School Hotel, Nottingham Rd, Southwell, NG25 0LG (0636) 814360
Former Victorian school which has been tastefully converted into a charming guest house; some of the beamed bedrooms have four-posters.
Open all year. No smoking in dining room & lounge. Vegetarian & other diets by arrangement. Disabled access. Children welcome. En suite & T.V. in all rooms. Credit cards. B. & B. from £20 p.p., singles £28.

TROWELL

Church Farm Guest House, 1 Nottingham Rd, Trowell, NG9 3PA (0602) 301637

 Church Farm Guest House is a 300 year old former farmhouse which stands amidst pleasant, mature gardens in a prominent position on the the A609 overlooking Trowell village. Your hosts, Carole and Philip Singer, cater for private parties and functions - including marquee weddings, business parties and trade exhibitions - as well as for individual guests. The food is excellent (the hosts are recent winners of the Salon Culinaire Bronze Medal) and the lunch and supper menu features a range of tasty and reasonably-priced options such as Home-made Broth followed by Beef Bourguignonne (with fresh vegetables) and a tempting selection of home-made desserts; the à la carte menu offers a similarly enticing choice of home-prepared dishes.
Open all year. No smoking throughout. Vegetarian & other diets by arrangement. Children welcome. T.V. in dining room. Credit cards. B. & B. from £16-£18.50.

WORKSOP

Duncan Wood Lodge Guest House, Carburton, Nr Worksop, S80 3BP (0909) 483614
A former estate lodge for the Duke of Portland, Duncan Wood Lodge is set deep in the heart of Sherwood Forest amidst an acre of secluded gardens. It has been tastefully modernised and now offers comfortable accommodation in well-equipped single, double and family bedrooms (some of which are on the ground floor); there are also facilities for small conferences and training seminars (its road and rail links make it an excellent choice for this function). Evening meals, snacks & light lunches are all available on request & are served in a pleasant dining room overlooking the gardens.
Open all year. No smoking in the dining room & some bedrooms. Vegetarian & other diets by arrangement. Children & pets welcome. B. & B. from £15, D. £9.50.

Restaurants

CALVERTON

 Painters Paradise Restaurant, Patchings Farm Art Centre, Oxton Rd, Calverton, NG14 6NU (0602) 653479

 Patchings Farm Art Centre is, I feel fairly confident in saying, a unique enterprise: based on a 38 acre rural site it consists of a conversion of farm buildings in which are housed two galleries; art, pottery and textiles studios; a gift and antique shop, and a restaurant (smoke-free, of course and serving delicious and imaginative lunches and snacks). The newly opened Painters' Paradise consists of beautiful gardens complete with a lake (over which there is a reproduction of Monet's Bridge) and around which there are beautiful gazebos in which visitors can rest and enjoy the view; there is also a striking Norwegian-style log building and restaurant, studio space and lounge area, in which more of the same delicious meals are served to visitors and where accommodation is available for larger groups. Admission to the galleries and studios is free of charge and tickets to the grounds and gardens are just £1.50 with concessions (daily painting tickets are also available and group visits can be arranged).

Patchings Farm
ART·CENTRE

Open 9 a.m. to 10 p.m. (gardens close at 6 p.m.). Prices reasonable. No smoking. Vegetarian, diabetic and additive-free diets on request. Licensed. Disabled access. Credit cards.

MANSFIELD

 Debenhams, 40 Four Seasons Cente, Mansfield (0623) 35311
Pavilion, a friendly self-service coffee shop serving lunches, snacks and hot and cold drinks.
Open store hours. No smoking. Vegetarian. Disabled access. Children welcome. Credit/debit cards.

NEWARK

 Gannets Café/Bistrot, 35 Castlegate, Newark, NG24 1AZ (0636) 702066

 Gannets was established in 1979 by Hilary and David Bower in an attractive Grade II listed Georgian building overlooking the castle on the main road through Newark. Over 12 years later they are still going strong and a second generation of Nottinghamshire diners can enjoy morning coffee, lunches and afternoon teas in the downstairs café throughout the week (a charming plant-filled outdoor patio garden has a further 6 tables in sunny weather) with a choice of wonderful home-made cakes and 'adventurous' salads (made from more than 25 ingredients). Upstairs, in the bistro, lunchtime and evening diners can enjoy a wider choice of dishes ranging from salads and patés to char-gilled fish and steaks; a typical lunch time selection might feature Mushroom, Walnut and Fresh Basil Paté, followed by Cod and Prawn au Gratin and Warm Baked Apple Cake with

Custard. Everything on the menu has been home-made from fresh (always) and additive-free (wherever possible) ingredients.

Café 36 seats, upstairs bistrot 38 seats. Café open 10 - 4.30 daily. Bistrot open Tues. to Sat., 12 noon - 2.30 & 6.30 - 9.30 Smoking banned throughout cafe and bistrot. Vegetarian always available. Licensed. Children welcome.

NOTTINGHAM

Debenhams, Long Row, Nottingham (0602) 475577
      Springles, a friendly self-service restaurant serving popular light lunches, snacks and a wide range of hot and cold drinks.
Open store hours. No smoking throughout. Vegetarian meals. Disabled access. Children very welcome. Credit and debit cards accepted.

Debenham's Intermission Coffee Shop, Flying Horse Walk, Nottingham
      Intermission, a friendly self-service coffee shop serving popular light lunches, snacks and a wide range of hot and cold drinks.
Open store hours. No smoking throughout. Vegetarian meals. Disabled access. Children very welcome. Credit and debit cards accepted.

Maxine's Salad Table, 56-58 Upper Parliament St, Nottingham (0602) 473622
Vegetarian restaurant serving home-made food; good vegan options.
75 seats. Open 9a.m. - 5p.m. No smoking in 75% of restaurant (sep. room). Vegetarian and vegan standard. Licensed. Children welcome.

Pubs & Wine Bars

SCAFTWORTH
King William, Scaftworth (off A361) (0302) 710292
No smoking in one room.

Cumbria & the North West

Cumbria
Accommodation

ALSTON

The High Fell Hotel, Alston, CA9 3BP (0434) 381597
Open all year. No smoking in dining room. Vegetarian & other diets by arrangement. Licensed. Children: over 14s welcome. En suite & tea/coffee-making in bedrooms. T.V. lounge. Credit cards. B. & B. from £24.75.

🚭 **Loaning Head Wholefood Vegetarian Guesthouse, Garrigill, Alston (0434) 381013**
17th C. stone barn; woodburning stove in the lounge with its exposed beams and splendid views; well-stocked bar (including organic & vegan wines). Home-baked bread.
Open all year. No smoking in the house. Vegetarian exclusively. Licensed. Ground floor bathroom and bedroom for the less mobile. Children: over 2s welcome. Tea/coffee-making in all bedrooms. B. & B. from £14. D. £9.

🚭 **Shield Hill House, Garrigill, Alston, Cumbria, CA9 3EX (0434) 381238**
Stone-built former farmhouse with extensive views in the heart of the North Pennines. Spectacular scenery, peace & tranquillity. Convenient for Borders, Lakes, Northumbria & Dales.
Open all year ex. Xmas. No smoking in the house. Children welcome. En suite & tea/coffee-making in all bedrooms. TV lounge. Credit cards. B. & B. from £16.25-17.50. ETB 2 Crowns.

AMBLESIDE

Borrans Park Hotel, Borrans Road, Ambleside, LA22 0EN (05394) 33454

Borrans Park Hotel is an exceptionally comfortable and well-appointed hotel standing in its own grounds so near and yet so far from the bustling centre of Ambleside. Bedrooms are superbly furnished and appointed: the *de-luxe* rooms have not only a double four-poster bed but also a private bathroom with a bubbling spa bath! Luxury indeed. A traditional English menu is served in the elegant Borrans Park dining room: all food is either home-baked or home-cooked and a typical evening menu would feature Mushroom and Coriander Paté served with fresh salad and melba toast, followed by roast ham with Cumberland Sauce and a tempting selection of home-made desserts; a selection of fine cheeses are served to round off your meal; and the menu has a helpful wine recommendation chosen from among the 150 cases in the Borrans Park cellar.
Open all year. No smoking in bedrooms & dining room. Vegetarian & other diets by arrangement. Licensed. Disabled access. Children. En suite, tea/coffee-making & T.V. in bedrooms. Credit cards. B. & B. from £27.50.

Compston House Hotel, Compston Road, Ambleside (05394) 32305
Family-run hotel with superb views of park and fells. Recommended by most major guides.
Open all year. No smoking in dining room & 2 bedrooms. Vegetarian & other diets by arrangement. Licensed. Children: over 5s only. En suite, tea/coffee-making & T.V. in all bedrooms. B. & B. from £17.50. D. £8.50.

🚭 **Cross Parrock, 5 Waterhead Terrace, Ambleside, LA22 0HA (05394) 32372**

Cross Parrock is a charming Lakeland stone guest house conveniently situated just one minute's walk from the shores of Lake Windermere. Comfortably furnished, and with prettily decorated bedrooms, Cross Parrock offers a high standard of accommodation to the Lakeland visitor in search of a warm welcome, peaceful surroundings and good food. On the latter point it is worth noting that Mrs Siddall, the proprietor, prides herself on offering imaginative, but traditional, home-prepared meals to guests: a typical evening menu featuring a home-made soup (such as Courgette and Cumin) followed by a pork chop (in Apricot and Paprika Sauce) with all the trimmings, and a delicious home-baked

pud, such as Apple and Raisin Pie. Coffee and mints complete the meal.
Open all year. No smoking throughout. Vegetarian by arrangement. Children welcome. Tea/coffee-making in bedrooms. T.V. in lounge. B. & B. from £13. D. £8.

Grey Friar Lodge Country House Hotel, Clappersgate, Ambleside, (05394) 33158
Open weekends from Feb; fully open from Easter to end Oct. No smoking in dining room & bedrooms. Licensed. Children: over 12s only. En suite , tea/coffee-making & T.V. in all bedrooms. B. & B. from £35.

Horseshoe Hotel, Rothay Rd, Ambleside, LA22 0EE(05394) 32000

The Horseshoe Hotel is an exceptionally pleasant 2 star hotel which stands conveniently close to the centre of Ambleside yet has magnificent mountain views. The hotel has been superbly appointed throughout - all bedrooms are comfortable and tastefully decorated - and there is a separate lounge for smokers. The food is excellent - everything has been home-made from fresh ingredients - and there are some good low-fat and vegetarian items on the evening menu. You are perfectly placed for visiting all of the Lake District.
Open all year. No smoking in dining room, some bedrooms & other public areas. Vegetarian standard. Some special diets by arrangement. Licensed. Disabled access to ground floor, restaurant, bar and lounge. Children welcome. Pets by arrangement. En suite in most rooms. Tea/coffee-making & T.V. in all bedrooms. Visa, Mastercard, Amex. Private car park. B. &. B. from £25. Mini breaks available.

Riverside Lodge Country House, Near Rothay Bridge, Ambleside, LA22 0EH (05394) 34208
Beautiful ivy-clad building in a splendid riverside setting; self-catering also available.
Open all year. No smoking in all public areas. Vegetarian by arrangement. Licensed. Children welcome. Pets in cottages. En suite, TV & tea/coffee-making in bedrooms. Credit cards. B. & B. from £22.50-£27.50.

Rothay Garth Hotel, Rothay Road, Ambleside, LA22 0EE (05394) 32217
Fine hotel, beautifully constructed of traditional Lakeland stone and set in attractive gardens.
Open all year. No smoking ex. in bar. Vegetarian standard. Licensed. Disabled access. Children welcome. Pets by arrangement. En suite in all rooms. Tea/coffee-making& T.V. in all bedrooms. B. & B. from £32.

Rothay Manor Hotel, Rothay Bridge, Ambleside, LA22 0EH (05394) 33605
Hotel offering, in addition to tourist accommodation, a number of winter courses and special weekends (e.g. 'Music in Imperial Russia'), and free use of local leisure centre.
Open early Feb. to end Dec. No smoking in dining room & 1 lounge. Vegetarian by arrangement. Licensed. Disabled access. Children welcome. En suite, TV & tea/coffee-making in all bedrooms.

Ⓝ Rowanfield Country House, Kirkstone Rd, Ambleside, LA22 9ET   (05394) 33686

Rowanfield is a beautiful period country home which stands in its own gardens amidst peaceful countryside with panoramic views of Lake Windermere and the surrounding mountains. The house has been carefully restored by its current owners who have complemented the original features of the house - such as its window seats, flagged floors and pine doors - with lots of Laura Ashley and Liberty fabrics. Bedrooms are comfortable and well-appointed with power showers, excellent beds and heated towel rails; there is a cosy guest lounge with a woodburning stove. The food is outstandingly good (your host, Philip Butcher, is renowned in the area for his culinary skills); everything is prepared from the finest of fresh, local produce. Evening meals are served by candlelight with gentle background classical music. Another superb meal is served in the morning with all the little extras that are so typical of Philip and Jane's standards; freshly squeezed orange juice, home-made bread rolls and home-made marmalade.Rowanfield is an excellent base from which to explore the Lake District, and additionally many good walks begin from the front door.
Open Feb. to Dec. No smoking in the house. Vegetarian & other special diets by arrangement. Licensed. Wheelchair access. Children: over 5s only. Pets welcome. En suite, TV & tea/coffee-making in bedrooms. Credit cards. B. & B. from £22, D., B. & B. from £31.

Ⓝ Rydal Holme, Rydal, Ambleside (05394) 33110
No smoking in the house. Vegetarian. En suite. Tea-making & T.V. in lounge. B. & B. from £18.

Summer Hill Country House, Hawkshead Hill, Ambleside, LA22 0PP (09666) 311
Open Mar. to Dec. No smoking in the house. Vegetarian food by arrangement. Children: over 10s only.
En suite, tea/coffee-making & T.V. in all bedrooms. B. & B. from £19.

APPLEBY

The Friary, Battlebarrow, Appleby in Westmorland, CA16 6XT (07683) 52702
Open all year. No smoking in the house. Cordon Vert vegetarian, demi-veg, diabetic, vegan, arthritic,
gluten-free and any other special diet by prior arrangement. Licensed. Children: over 6s only. En suite & tea
/coffee making in all bedrooms. T.V. in lounge. B. & B. from £18.

ARNSIDE

Stonegate Guest House, The Promenade, Arnside, LA5 DAA (0524) 761171
Open Feb. to Dec. No smoking in the house. Vegetarian and vegan standard. Children welcome. Pets by
arrangement. Tea/coffee making in bedrooms. T.V. B. & B. from £15. E. M. £8.50.

BASSENTHWAITE LAKE

The Pheasant Inn, Bassenthwaite Lake, Nr Cockermouth, CA13 9YE (07687) 76234

The Pheasant Inn was a farm in the 18th C. but has been a hotel since 1826. A listed building, it has retained all its period character including the original old bar with its mellow brown walls, and oak beamed dining room; the proprietors have decided to further eschew 20th C. discomforts by deciding not to have television or piped music and smoking has never been allowed in the dining room - thus ensuring that the timeless atmosphere of the inn and the peacefulness of its tranquil surroundings in the countryside between Bassenthwaite Lake and Thornthwaite Forest, are unmarred. The hotel has been furnished in an elegant, but unobstrusive style: each of the 20 en suite bedrooms is comfortable and pleasingly decorated, and a log fire blazes in the lounge inglenook in cooler weather; the food is excellent, and packed lunches and afternoon teas are also available. Bassenthwaite has been designated a "Quiet Lake" by the National Park Authority and as such is an important wild life centre; those in search of sailing, boating, fishing, walking and other outdoor activities will find numerous opportunities to pursue them, while those seeking nothing more than peace, quiet, an armchair by the fire and the prospect of a delicious dinner in the evening will also find that they have picked the right destination.
Open all year, ex. Xmas. No smoking in dining room & 1 resident's lounge. Vegetarian standard. Licensed.
Disabled access. Pets by arrangement. En suite in all rooms. B. & B. from £49.

BRAMPTON

Cracrop Farm, Cracrop, Kirkcambeck (06978) 245
Open all year ex. Xmas. No smoking in the house. Children welcome. No pets. En suite, tea/coffee-making
& T.V. in all bedrooms. B. & B. from £16.

Hullerbank, Talkin, Brampton, CA8 1LB (06977) 46668

Hullerbank is a 17th C. Georgian farmhouse set well back from the road and standing in its own grounds complete with orchard and gardens; adjoining the house is 14 acres of pastureland on which your hosts, Sheila and Brian, keep a small flock of commercial sheep. "A peaceful retreat" is how one guest recently described Hullerbank - an apt description given its situation in unspoilt countryside, notwithstanding its proximity to such places of interest as Hadrian's Wall, Talkin Tarn Country Park and the Lake District (just one hour's drive away). The house itself has been comfortably furnished and tastefully decorated: an open fire supplements the central heating in chilly weather and each of the three bedrooms has en suite or private bath facilities, together with a range of other helpful amenities including an electric under-blanket. Good home-cooking prepared from fresh, home-grown ingredients is served in the dining room - the speciality being home-produced lamb - and packed lunches are also available. *Open all year ex. Xmas & New Year. No smoking in the house. Vegetarian & other diets by arrangement. Children: over 10s only. En suite/private bath & tea-coffee making in bedrooms. TV lounge. B. & B. £17-17.50.*

BUTTERMERE VALLEY

Pickett Howe, Brackenthwaite, Buttermere Valley, CA13 9UY (0900) 85444
After a successful first two years at Pickett Howe, a '17th C. Lakeland statesman's long house'David and Dani Edwards, (ex of the highly acclaimed Low Hall) are looking forward to welcoming a third season of guests to their lovely home in the beautiful Buttermere Valley. With characteristic flair and meticulous attention to detail the Edwards have clearly taken great pleasure in decorating and furnishing their lovely home: bedrooms are individually styled and Laura Ashley fabrics, lace bedspreads, and elegant furniture (the bedsteads are restored Victorian) recreate the 17th & 18th centuries while power showers and whirlpool baths wash away the cares of the 20th; the original features, such as mullioned windows, flagged floors and oak beams have been retained and add to Pickett Howe's already considerable charm. Dani's culinary skills are as exceptional as ever; and the 5-course evening menu includes such delights as Spiced Apple Soup, Fennel, Lemon and Walnut in a Gougere Pastry Ring and Juniper Pudding. Crystal, candlelight and chamber music all combine to provide the all important sense of occasion which is the hallmark of dining in the Edwards' home.
Open March to Nov. Smoking banned throughout. Vegetarian and meat dishes standard. Most other special diets by arrangement. Licensed. Children: over 10s welcome. En suite & tea/coffee-making in bedrooms. T.V. available on request. D., B. & B. from £45. ETB de luxe grading.

CALDBECK

High Greenrigg House, Nr Caldbeck, CA7 8HD (06998) 430
High Greenrigg House is a carefully restored stone-built 17th C. farmhouse situated at the foot of the Caldbeck Fells in the Lake District National Park. This little known Northern area of the National Park remains uncrowded even at the height of the season and, with its proximity to the Cumbria Way (just half a mile) and the Northern and Central Fells it forms an ideal centre for fell-walkers. The house itself has been comfortably furnished and appointed with an eye to enhancing and complementing the original features of the building: the lounge retains the original flagged floor and exposed beams, and guests can sit round the cosy open fire in cooler weather. The food is wholesome and imaginative: all meals have been home-prepared from fresh produce and are served in an attractive beamed dining room, and the evening meal consists of 3 courses plus a cheeseboard and coffee. Your hosts, Fran and Robin Jacobs, are used to accommodating intrepid fell-walkers, but for the days when the weather is inclement enough to deter the hardiest of them, there is a well-equipped games room complete with table tennis, darts and snooker.
Smoking banned in most of house. Special diets by arrangement. Licensed. Disabled access. Children welcome. Pets by arrangement. En suite in all rooms. Tea/coffee-making in T.V. lounge. B. & B. from £17.

CARLISLE

Angus Hotel, 14 Scotland Rd, Carlisle, CA3 9DG (0228) 23546
Cosy Victorian family-run hotel on the Northern approach to this historic border city; built on site of Hadrian's wall. Close to castle, Tullie House Museum, cathedral, Sands Sports Centre.
Open all year. No smoking in dining room & 7 bedrooms. Vegetarian & other diets by arrangement. Children welcome. Pets by arrangement. En suite 7 rooms. Tea/coffee-making in bedrooms. TV in lounge & bedroom on request. B. & B. from £15.50.

Bank End Farm, Bewcastle, Roadhead, CA6 6NU (06978) 644 [(06977) 48644 from 1.4.93]
Luxurious, private suite for two with twin-bedded room in warm, peaceful farmhouse. Delicious home-cooking including bread, cakes, soups. Historically interesting area.
Open all April - Nov. inc. No smoking throughout. Not licensed, but bring your own wine & spirits. En suite, tea/coffee-making & TV in own sitting room. B. & B. from £21.

CONISTON

Arrowfield Country House, Little Arrow, Torver, Coniston, Cumbria, LA21 8AU (05394) 41741
Arrowfield is an attractive Victorian house standing amidst lovely gardens with beautiful views of the surrounding countryside; completely refurbished throughout, the bedrooms are comfortable and attractive and there is a spacious lounge with an open fire. Meals are served in a cosy dining room - again with a log fire - and everything is home-cooked from fresh ingredients, a typical evening meal featuring Salmon Mousse followed by Lemon Braised Lamb with white wine and herbs, and a treat of a pudding such as Tiramisu; cheese biscuits and coffee complete the meal. There are many interesting places to be visited nearby - including the residences of Wordsworth and Ruskin - while those wishing to enjoy a good country walk will have immediate access to the fells and find numerous bridlepaths and quiet lanes within the vicinity of Arrowfield itself.
Open Mar. to Oct. inc. No smoking in the dining room & bedrooms. Vegetarian & other diets by arrangement. Licensed. Children: over 3s only. En suite in 2 bedrooms. TV & tea/coffee-making in bedrooms. B. & B. £16-20.

Beech Tree, Yewdale Road, Coniston, LA21 8DB (05394) 41717
Open all year. No smoking in the house. Health food and vegetarian diets standard. Children: babies and over 6s only. Pets by arrangement. En suite in some rooms. Tea/coffee-making. T.V. in lounge. B. & B. from £14.

Black Beck Cottage, East Side of the Lake, Coniston (05394) 41607
Open Apr. to Oct. No smoking in the house. Vegetarian by arrangement. Disabled access. Children welcome. Tea/coffee-making & T.V. in all bedrooms. B. & B. from £14.

Coniston Lodge Hotel, Coniston, LA21 8HH (05394) 41201

Coniston Lodge Hotel is managed by Anthony and Elizabeth Robinson - who are the 3rd generation of hoteliers to have been looking after visitors since 1911! It offers a high standard of accommodation and comfort - bedrooms are all attractively decorated and furnished, one with a four-poster - and the dining room and lounge are very much of the country-cottage school of interior design, with lots of antique accessories and bits and pieces to add to their charm. Food is of especial importance at Coniston Lodge where traditional English and local dishes are presented with originality and flair (dine on freshly caught Consiton Char, for instance - a fish peculiar to Coniston and 3 other lakes, or set yourself up for the day with a stupendous breakfast in which local Cumberland sausage, and wholemeal toast and croissants are just some of the attractions). Coniston is just far enough away from the bustle of the centre of Lakeland to provide a base for a truly relaxing holiday. It is a haven for ramblers - and your hosts, who are experienced fell-walkers, will happily give you guidance and advice. **RAC Small Hotel of the year 1992 (Northern Region).**
Open all year ex. Xmas. Smoking banned throughout the house. Vegetarian and diabetic diets by arrangement. Licensed. Children: under 10s by arrangement. En suite, tea/coffee-making & T.V. in all bedrooms. Credit cards accepted. B. & B. from £26. RAC Highly Acclaimed, ETB Highly Commended and AA 'Select' status.

Oaklands Bed & Breakfast, Yewdale Road, Coniston, LA21 8DX (05394) 41245
Open all year. No smoking in the house. Tea/coffee-making & T.V. in bedrooms. B. & B. from £13.

Thwaite Cottage, Waterhead, Coniston, LA21 8AJ (05394) 41367
17th C. Lakeland farmhouse in 2 acres of gardens just ½m E of Coniston village. B'fast only.
Open Feb. to Nov. No smoking in the house. Vegetarian and most other special diets by arrangement. Children welcome. Tea/Coffee-making & T.V. in sitting room. B. & B. from £15-16.

ENNERDALE BRIDGE

The Shepherds Arms Hotel, Ennerdale Bridge (0946) 861249
Family-owned and run hotel in the centre of the village. Log fires, real ale, good walks locally. An emphasis on the use of fresh and seasonal ingredients (salmon is home-smoked).

Vegetarian by arrangement. Open all year. No smoking in dining room & residents'lounge. Licensed. Disabled access: 2 steps to dining room. Children welcome. Pets by arrangement. En suite in 3 rooms. Tea/Coffee-making in bedrooms. T.V. lounge. B. & B. from £20. D. £13.50.

GLENRIDDING

Moss Crag Guest House, Glenridding, CA11 0PA (07684) 82500

Moss Crag, a family-run guest house, is a charming stone-built house situated opposite Glenridding Beck in the heart of the Lake District hills and fells. Just 300 yards away is the hauntingly beautiful Lake Ullswater and, although you can fish, sail, canoe or windsurf thereon, it is best enjoyed (I feel) by just looking at it - perhaps the fishermen have got it right. Freshly prepared food is a feature of a stay at Moss Crag where a typical evening menu would feature Parton Bree (Crab Soup) followed by Beef and Noodle Bake or Spinach and Leek Pancakes and a delicious home-made dessert such as Citrus Condé or Coffee Fudge Pudding. Morning coffee, light lunch and afternoon tea are also served.

Open Feb. to Nov. inc. No smoking in the house. Vegetarian, diabetic and some other special diets by arrangement. Licensed. Children welcome. En suite in some rooms. Tea/Coffee-making & T.V. in all bedrooms. B. & B. from £15.50 - 19.50. D., B. & B. from £28 - 32. All inclusive D., B. & B. breaks available from Nov. to March incl., ex Dec., Jan. 10% reduction on B. & B. only for weekly stay in summer.

GRANGE-OVER-SANDS

Abbot Hall, Kents Bank, LA11 7BG (05395) 32896

Open all year. No smoking in the house. Vegetarian and most other special diets by arrangement.Disabled access. Children welcome. En suite. Tea/coffee-making in bedrooms. T.V. in lounges. B. & B. from £20.

GRASMERE

Lancrigg Vegetarian Country House Hotel, Easedale, Grasmere, LA22 9QN (05394) 35317

It is now almost 6 years since a chance stay at Lancrigg inspired me to compile the fist edition of *The Healthy Holiday Guide.* Happily (and unsurprisingly) Robert and Janet Whittington have continued to go from strength to strength in their provision of quite exceptional vegetarian hospitality. The house itself, set in 27 acres of gardens overlooking Easedale, has been converted from the Westmorland farm it originally was (a favourite haunt of the Wordsworths) and has been charmingly decorated - the sitting room with large, floral prints and ample armchairs, and the dining room with beautiful reproduction and period furniture, polished oak floor and prints by the lakeland artist W. Heaton Cooper. The 5-course evening menu is prepared from local organic produce (some home-grown) and would typically feature Greek Marinated Vegetables with Feta Cheese and wholemeal toast, followed by Spinach soup, Savoury Stuffed Vine Leaves and a choice of desserts, such as Sticky Toffee and Date Pudding (digestion is enhanced by the gentle music of Telemann & Vivaldi).

Open all year. Smoking banned in lounge and dining room. Vegetarian exclusively. Vegan and other special diets by arrangement. Licensed. Disabled access. Children welcome. Pets by arrangement. En suite in most rooms. Tea/coffee-making in bedrooms. T.V. in all bedrooms. Credit cards accepted. D., B. & B. from £35.

HAWKSHEAD

Foxgloves, Hawkshead, LA22 ONR (05394) 36352

Private house with beautiful views situated on the edge of the picturesque village of Hawkshead.

Open all year. No smoking in the house. Vegetarian standard. Children: over 12s only. En suite in one room. Tea/coffee-making in all bedrooms. T.V. in lounge. B. & B. from £14.

KENDAL

⊗7 Thorny Hills, Kendal (0539) 720207
Open Jan. to Nov. No smoking in the house. Vegetarian by arrangement. Children welcome. En suite in one room. Tea/coffee-making & T.V. in all bedrooms. B. & B. from £12, D. £8. ETB 1 Crown Commended.

⊗ Birslack Grange, Levens, Nr Kendal (05395) 60989
Open all year. No smoking in the house. Special diets by arrangement. Disabled access. Children welcome. Pets by arrangement. En suite in 3 rooms. Tea/coffee-making & T.V. in all bedrooms. B. & B. from £13.

⊗ Fairways, 102 Windermere Rd, Kendal, Cumbria, LA9 5EZ (0539) 725564
Victorian guest house with lovely views. 4-poster bedroom. Private parking.Golf nearby.
Open all year. No smoking in the house. Vegetarian & other diets by arrangement. Children welcome. En suite, tea/coffee-making & TV in all bedrooms. B. & B. from £15-17.

Garden House Hotel, Fowl-ing Lane, Kendal Tel: (0539) 731131 Fax: (0539) 740064
Beautiful 19th C. house in 2 acres of wooded grounds; excellent food and service.
No smoking in restaurant & most bedrooms. Vegetarian by arrangement. En suite, TV & tea/coffee-making in bedrooms. Ground floor room. Children & pets welcome. Licensed. Credit cards. B. & B. from £22.50.

⊗ Holmfield, 41 Kendal Green, Kendal, LA9 5PP (0539) 720790
Large Edwardian house of unusual, attractive design in an acre of quiet pretty gardens.
Open all year. No smoking throughout. Vegetarian & other diets on request. Children: over 12s only. Tea/coffee making in rooms. T.V. in lounge & 1 bedroom. Private parking. B. & B. from £15. ETB Highly Commended

⊗ Punchbowl House, Grayrigg, Nr Kendal, Cumbria, LA8 9BU (053984) 345
Large, Victorian stone-built farmhouse in the centre of Grayrigg village, just outside Kendal. Fully modernised throughout, spacious rooms & log fires. B. & B. and self-catering. Walkers welcome.
Open all year. No smoking throughout. Vegetarian & other diets by arrangement. Children: over 5s welcome. En suite in one room. Tea/coffee-making & TV in all bedrooms. B. & B. from £15-18.

KESWICK

⊗ Anworth House, 27 Eskin Street, Keswick, CA12 4DQ (07687) 72923
Anworth House is a small, friendly guest house which is conveniently situated just a few minutes walk from the attractive centre of Keswick with its interesting shops and pencil museum! Your hosts, Mandy and Dave Lanchester, offer an especially warm and friendly welcome to guests and do everything they can to make your stay enjoyable: the food is tasty and wholesome - everything having been prepared on the premises - and the comfortable bedrooms each have en suite facilities; packed lunches are available on request. You are within walking distance of local parks & Lake Derwentwater, and close to the beautiful fells and valleys of the Northern Lakes.
Open all year. No smoking in the house. Special diets by arrangement. Children welcome. En suite, TV & tea/coffee-making in bedrooms. B. & B. from £16.50.

Brienz Guest House, 3 Greta St, Keswick, CA12 4HS (07687) 71049
⊗Small, friendly guest house within easy walking distance of town centre, lakes & parks. High standards of comfort. Imaginative home-cooked food & menu choice. ETB Commended.
Open all year ex. Xmas & New Year. No smoking. Vegetarian & other diets with notice. Licensed. Wheelchair access. Children:over 6s only. Rooms with showers. Tea-making & TV in rooms. B. & B. from 12.50., D. £8.

Chaucer House Hotel, Ambleside Road, Keswick (07687) 72318
Open Easter to Dec. inc. No smoking in dining room & lounge. Vegetarian by arrangment. Licensed. Lifts to all floors. Children: over 4s only. Pets by arrangement. En suite. Tea/coffee-making & T.V. in rooms. B. & B. from £19, D. £11.50.

⊗ Clarence House, 14 Eskin Street, Keswick, CA12 4DQ (07687) 73186
Charming guest house situated within easy walking distance of the centre of Keswick.
Open all year ex. Xmas. No smoking in the house. Vegetarian by arrangement. Licensed. Children welcome. Pets by arrangement. En suite most rooms. Tea/coffee-making. T.V. in all bedrooms. B. & B. from £17.

Cottage in the Wood Hotel, Whinlatter Pass, Braithwaite, Keswick (07687) 78 409
The Cottage in the Wood is a charming 17th C. former coaching house which is beautifully

situated atop Whinlatter Pass in the heart of the pine forest with superb views of the Skiddaw mountain range. It offers peaceful and pleasant seclusion to guests yet is just 10 minutes drive from the centre of Keswick. The Cottage in the Wood has been very comfortably furnished: log fires in the welcoming lounge greet guests on colder days and each of the seven bedrooms has been tastefully decorated and well-appointed with private facilities; there are two Honeymoon Suites with four-poster beds. The food is excellent: meals are served in an elegant dining room and

all dishes have been home-prepared from fresh ingredients; the 5-course evening meal has been thoughtfully planned to include some traditional Lakeland dishes and vegetarian and other special diets can be accommodated by arrangement; light lunches and afternoon teas are also available .
Open Mar. to Nov. No smoking throughout. Vegetarian & other diets by arrangement. Licensed. Disabled access: all public rooms ground floor (no steps), bedrooms 1st floor. Children welcome. Pets by arrangement. En suite & tea-making in bedrooms. B. & B. from £27, D. £8.50 for residents, D. £13.50 - £16 for non-residents.

Croft House, Applethwaite, Nr Keswick, CA12 4PN (07687) 73693
Open Feb. to Nov. No smoking in the house. Vegetarian by arrangement. Licensed. Children welcome. Pets by arrangement. En suite in all rooms. Tea/coffee-making facilities. T.V. in lounge. B. & B. from £13.

Dalegarth House Country Hotel, Portinscale, Keswick, CA12 5RQ (07687) 72817

Dalegarth House is a spacious, Edwardian property standing in a sunny elevated position, amidst nearly an acre of gardens, in the village of Portinscale just one mile from Keswick. The resident proprietors, John and Carolyn Holloway, have worked hard to create a comfortable, relaxing atmosphere; indeed two guests phoned me just recently to enthuse about the service and hospitality they had enjoyed at Dalegarth House. The food is wholesome, delicious and home-cooked, a typical 6-course evening menu featuring prawn cocktail or

home-made soup with hot, fresh rolls, followed by Poached Salmon with Dill Sauce and a choice of home-made sweets; cheese, biscuits and coffee would complete the meal and packed lunches are also available on request. Dalegarth House enjoys superb views of the beautiful northern fells which provide walks for both skilled climbers and ambling strollers; those seeking to explore the Lake District by car will find Dalegarth an ideal touring base.
Open all year. No smoking in the house. Vegetarian food by arrangement. Licensed. Children: over 5s only. En suite, TV & tea/coffee-making in bedrooms. Access, Visa. B. & B. from £24. D., B.& B. £35.

Derwent Cottage, Portinscale, Keswick, CA12 5RF (07687) 74838

Derwent Cottage is no mere cottage say the proprietors, Mike and Sue Newman, for the original 18th C. dwelling was greatly extended in Victorian times in the picturesque but rather grand style favoured by those who built estates in the Lake District in those days. The result is generously proportioned rooms with high ceilings oriented to the full advantage of the site. The house is set well back from the road through the quiet village of Portinscale in well-established grounds of nearly an acre with terraced lawns and stately conifers. The accommodation, which has full central heating, includes 5 spacious en suite rooms with elegant furnishings, and a bar and lounge, both of which have open fires in the cooler months. A candle-lit 4-course table d'hôte meal of fresh home-cooked food, plus coffee, is served at 7 p.m. in an

attractive dining room with crisp linen, silver and sparkling crystalware; background classical music accompanies the meal; a residential licence enables drinks to be served throughout a relaxed evening. Derwent Cottage is 1 mile from Keswick and close to the shores of lake Derwentwater, and is an ideal location for fell-walking and touring through the National Park, or for sailing, boating and other water sports. *ETB 3 Crowns Highly Commended.*
Open Mar. - Nov. No smoking in the house. Special diets by arrangement. Children: over 12s welcome. En suite, TV & tea/coffee-making in bedrooms. Licensed. Credit cards. D., B. & B. from £32.

Glencoe Guest House, 21 Helvellyn St, Keswick, CA12 4EN (07687) 71016
Glencoe is an attractive guest house offering comfortable, reasonably-priced accommodation, just five minutes walk from the centre of Keswick. The proprietors are life-long Keswickians and have extensive local knowledge to help you to make the most of your stay. Your hosts are also both qualified caterers and offer excellent home-cooked meals to guests: a typical four-course evening menu might feature Herb Cheese with Fresh Fruit, followed by traditional roast duckling (with fresh vegetables) and a delicious dessert, such as Crème Brulée with Shortbread; breakfast is a hearty feast and includes the famous Cumberland Sausage - although a Continental option is available for lighter appetites. Keswick is an ideal base for walkers keen to explore the surrounding fells - while the town itself offers a range of recreational amenities including facilities for enjoying water sports on nearby Derwentwater and Bassenthwaite.
Open all year ex. Jan. No smoking in the house. Vegetarian and most other special diets by arrangement. Children welcome (family rooms avail.). Tea/coffee-making & T.V. in bedrooms. B. & B. from £11.

Heatherlea, 26 Blencathra Street, Keswick, CA12 4HP (07687) 72430
Traditional Lakeland stone house quietly situated near Keswick town centre; freshly cooked breakfast served in dining room with views of Skiddaw fells.
Open all year ex. Xmas and New Year. No smoking in the house. Children: over 5s only. Pets by arrangement. En suite, TV & tea/coffee-making in bedrooms. B. & B. from £15.

Jenkin Hill Cottage, Thornthwaite (0596) 82443
Open all year. No smoking in the house. Vegetarian and most other special diets by arrangement. Children: over 12s only. En suite, tea/coffee-making & T.V. in all bedrooms. B. & B. from £17.50.

Kendoon, Braithwaite, Keswick, CA12 5RY (07687) 78430
"A warm welcome for wet walkers!" Panoramic views from sitting room.
Open Feb. to Nov. Smoking banned throughout. Vegetarian, vegan and other special diets by arrangement. Pets by arrangement. Tea/coffee making in lounge. B. & B. from £12.

Lynwood, 12 Ambleside Rd, Keswick, CA12 4DL Tel: (07687) 72081 Fax: (07687) 75021

Lynwood is a large Victorian house situated in a quiet residential area just 5 minutes' walk from the centre of Keswick. The proprietors, Kelvyn and Christine Sheppard, cater exclusively for non-smokers and accordingly pride themselves on providing a friendly, relaxed but above all *clean* atmosphere. The food is excellent, too - everything is home-cooked and served in generous portions (very welcome for walkers returning from a heavy day's calorie expenditure!) - and vegetarian meals and wholesome packed lunches can also be provided on request. Each of the 6 spacious bedrooms has en suite facilities, and there is even a bedroom with a fourposter (champagne, flowers and hand-made chocolates can be provided therein on request). Keswick is the Northern centre of the Lake District National Park and as such provides much *in situ* entertainment (there is boating on Derwentwater, a new Leisure Pool, and even a pencil museum!), while those venturing farther afield will find the town an ideal base for travelling to and from all the places of interest within the National Park.
Open all year. No smoking in the house. Vegetarian & other diets by arrangement. Licensed. Children welcome (cot & highchair available). En suite, tea/coffee-making & TV in all bedrooms. B. & B. from £18.

Orchard House, Borrowdale Road, Keswick, CA12 5DE (07687) 72830
Exclusively vegetarian guest house offering superb, freshly-cooked 4 course dinners prepared from locally grown organic fruit and vegetables in season; attractively decorated, cosy rooms. *Open mid Feb. to mid Nov. plus Xmas. No smoking throughout. Vegetarian exclusively, vegan and other special diets by arrangement. Licensed. Children welcome. Dogs by arrangement. En suite in some rooms. Tea/Coffee-making in bedrooms. T.V. in separate lounge. D., B. & B. from £27. Open to non-residents for dinner.*

Skiddaw Grove Hotel, Vicarage Hill, Keswick, CA12 5QB (07687) 73324
Georgian mansion on a quiet lane atop a small hill just 10 mins' walk from the centre of Keswick. *Open all year ex. Xmas. No smoking ex. in bar. Vegetarian by arrangement. Licensed. Children welcome. En suite & tea/coffee-making in bedrooms. T.V. in lounge, and in rooms on request. B. & B. from £19.*

Squirrel Lodge, 43 Eskin Street, Keswick (07687) 73091
Attractive guest house in the centre of Keswick, with an emphasis on home-cooking. *Open all year. No smoking in the house. Vegetarian by arrangement. Licensed. Children welcome. Tea/coffee-making & T.V. in all bedrooms. Credit cards. B. & B. from £13, D. £7.*

Thwaite Howe Hotel, Thornthwaite, Nr Keswick, CA12 5SA (07687) 78281

Some years ago Mike and Penny Sutton made their escape from the pressures of professional life to take refuge in beautiful Thwaite Howe, a Victorian stone-built country house standing amidst two and a half acres of lovely gardens looking out over the Derwent valley to the mountains beyond. They have succeeded in achieving their dream of living and working amidst peace and tranquillity - and now offer to share their home with others in search of solitude and rest! Everything about Thwaite Howe - including the friendly, informal hospitality of your hosts - is conducive to relaxation: from the delicious 5-course, home-cooked evening meals (served in a lamp-lit dining room with wonderful views) to the comforts provided in the spacious bedrooms (phones, hairdryers, radios, electric blankets, easy chairs . . .) and the welcoming log fire blazing in the lounge in inclement weather. Those who can tear themselves away from the home-from-home comforts at Thwaite Howe will find themselves within easy reach of Keswick, Cockermouth, Ambleside & all the other attractions of the Lake District, while those seeking not to venture too far from the Thwaite Howe front door will find forest trails and walks in the immediate vicinity of the house. *Open Mar. - Oct. inc. No smoking in dining room & lounge. Vegetarian & other diets by arrangement. Licensed. Children: over 12s only. Pets welcome. En suite, TV & tea/coffee-making in bedrooms. B. & B. from £25. D. B. & B. from £35.*

Winchester Guest House, 58 Blencathra St, Keswick (07687) 73664
Winchester Guest House is a spacious, end-of-terrace Victorian town house which stands just a few minutes' walk from the centre of the attractive market town of Keswick. Entirely smoke-free, the Winchester guest house has a clean, pleasant atmosphere and each of the centrally heated bedrooms has been attractively furnished (some have views of Skiddaw, Blencathra and Latrig); there is a comfortable lounge for guests' use. Home-cooked breakfasts are served in a pleasant dining room - and traditional evening meals may be enjoyed during winter months. Keswick is the northern centre of the Lake District National Park and as such has easy road access to all the places of interest within Cumbria; there are numerous walks to be enjoyed - many of which begin from the Winchester front door - or, for the less nimble, a lazy stroll along the nearby riverbank. *Open all year. No smoking in the house. Vegetarian by arrangement. Children: over 3s welcome. Tea/coffee-making & TV in all bedrooms. B. & B. from £13.50, D. £7.*

KIRKBY LONSDALE

Lupton Tower Vegetarian Country Guest House, LA6 2PR (04487) 400
Open all year ex. Xmas. No smoking in the house. Exclusively vegetarian. Licensed. Children welcome. Pets by arrangement. En suite in most rooms. Tea/coffee-making in all bedrooms. B. & B. from £14.50

KIRKBY STEPHEN

Annedd Gwyon, 46 High St, Kirkby Stephen, Cumbria, CA17 4SH (07683) 72302
This late Victorian home is run along 'green' lines, with home-cooked wholefoods & a relaxing, healthy environment. Meditation room & guest lounge.
Open Jan. 7 - Dec. 22. No smoking in the house. Vegetarian standard. Tea/coffee-making. TV on request. Children & pets welcome. B. & B. £13.50.

KIRKOSWALD

 Howscales Hol. Cottages for Non-Smokers, Howscales, Kirkoswald, CA10 1JG (0768) 898666 Fax:(0768) 898710
Open all year. No smoking throughout. Children: over 12s only. Access, Visa, Diners.

THE LORTON VALE

 New House Farm and The Barn, Lorton, Cockermouth, CA13 9UU (0900) 85404
Open all year. No smoking. Fully licensed. Vegetarian. Dogs welcome. D., B. & B. from £45.

MILLOM

 Whicham Hall Farm, Silecroft, Millom, LA18 5LT (0229) 772637
Open all year. No smoking in the house. Vegetarian by arrangement. Disabled access. Children welcome. Pets by arrangement. En suite 1 room. Tea/coffee-making T.V. available. B. & B. from £10.

MOSEDALE

Mosedale House, Mosedale (07687) 79371
An emphasis on home-made and home-grown provision: vegetables, fruit, produce (such as eggs and lamb), home-baked bread and rolls. Vegetarians very welcome.
Open all year. No smoking in the house. Diets by arrangement. Disabled access. Children welcome. Pets by arrangement. En suite 4 rooms. Tea-making in rooms. T.V. most bedrooms. B. & B. from £18, D. from £11.

PENRITH

'Fair Place' Wholefood and Vegetarian Guest House, Fair Place, Watermillock, Nr Penrith, CA11 0LR (07684) 86235

 This handsome rag-stone building, set in secluded grounds 200 yards past Watermillock Church, used to be the village school. Its proprietors, whose family home it has been, converted it over 30 years ago, and it has been beautifully renovated and modernised. Now a charming small guest house (though retaining many of the original features), it is an exclusively vegetarian and vegan B. & B., serving only the best and freshest of free-range and 'whole' breakfasts. The bedrooms are all en suite (and have very comfortable beds), and, if you like music, there is an especially good room for listening (bring your own CDs). Drive if you must- but there is ample countryside within walking distance of 'Fair Place', Aira Force, a spectacular waterfall is just over 3 miles away; and Ullswater is an especially lovely Lakeland haunt.
Open Feb. to Nov. No smoking in the house. Vegetarian & vegan b'fast standard, Other diets by arrangement. Children welcome. Pets by arrangement. En suite, tea-making & T.V. in all rooms. B. & B. from £17.50.

Netherdene Guest House, Troubeck, Nr Penrith, CA11 0SJ (07684) 83475
Small, country guest house standing in its own quiet grounds with extensive mountain views 9 miles from Penrith on the A5091 to Ullswater (just off the A66). Four comfortable bedrooms. Cosy lounge with log fire. Pony-trekking, golf, fell-walking, boating, all nearby.
Open Feb. - Nov. No smoking in dining room & some bedrooms. Special diets by arrangement. Children: over 7s only. En suite, TV & tea/coffee-making in all bedrooms. B. & B. from £14.50.

The White House, Clifton, Nr Penrith (0768) 65115
Beautiful 18th C. farmhouse in the village of Clifton. Exclusively for non-smokers.
Open Jan. to Nov. No smoking throughout. Vegetarian, diabetic & gluten-free by arrangement. Licensed. Children welcome. En suite 2 rooms. Tea/coffee-making in all bedrooms. B. & B. from £14, D. £9.

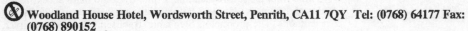 **Woodland House Hotel, Wordsworth Street, Penrith, CA11 7QY Tel: (0768) 64177 Fax: (0768) 890152**

An elegant and spacious licensed private hotel with a large car park, just five minutes walk from the centre of the town. All rooms are en suite and all have tea/coffee making facilities and a colour T.V. The meals are delicious and have been prepared from the best of fresh and local produce and, with notice, special dietary requirements can be catered for. There is a large library of maps and books for walkers, nature-lovers and sightseers and the proprietors will gladly help you plan your stay. Woodland House Hotel is an ideal centre for exploring the Lake District, Northern Pennines, Borders, Eden Valley, and is a perfect spot for an overnight stop on journeys to and from Scotland.
Open all year. No smoking in the house. Vegetarian & most other special diets by arrangement. Residential license. Children welcome. En suite, tea/coffee-making & T.V. in all bedrooms. B. & B. from £19.

SEDBERGH

Ash-Hining Farm, Howgill, Sedbergh, LA10 5HU (05396) 20957
Open March to Oct. No smoking throughout. Vegetarian by arrangement. Children: over 5s only. Pets by arrangement. T.V. in lounge. Credit cards. B. & B. from £15.

Cross Keys Hotel, Cautley, Sedbergh, LA10 5NE (05396) 20284
The Cross Keys is a tiny 400 year-old inn magnificently situated at a dramatic corner of the Howgill Fells in the Yorkshire Dales National Park; the view of Cautley Spout, one of the country's highest waterfalls, can be enjoyed from the dining room. Owned by the National Trust, most of the original features of the building have been retained, including the very low-beamed ceilings, flag stone floors, mullioned windows and open fireplaces. Even the atmosphere is special: 'homely, traditional, informal and relaxing', and the delicious food, which includes home-made bread, biscuits, preserves and icecreams, definitely predates the convenience food era. You will be very warmly welcomed - there are maps and guide books to help you plan your stay - and, as Cross Keys is unlicensed, you are asked to bring your own wine to enjoy with your meal.
Open Easter to New Year. No smoking throughout. Vegetarian & other diets by arrangement. Not licensed, but bring your own. Children welcome. En suite 1 room. Tea/coffee making in bedrooms. B. & B. from £23-£26.50.

ULVERSTON

Appletree Holme Farm, Blawith Via Ulverston, LA12 8EL (0229 85) 618
Open all year. Smoking allowed only in one sitting room. Vegetarian & other diets by arrangement. Licensed. En suite, tea/coffee-making & T.V. in all bedrooms. Visa, Amex. D., B. & B. from £49.

The Coach House, Hollow Oak, Haverthwaite, Ulverston, LA12 8AD (05395) 31622
Converted coach house with original features such as oak beams. Garden for guests. Ideal base for touring South lakeland, Coniston, South Grizedale and Windermere.
Open Mar. to Oct. No smoking in the house. Children welcome. TV & tea/coffee-making in bedrooms. B. & B. from £12.

 WINDERMERE

Aaron Slack, 48 Ellerthwaite Rd, Windermere, LA23 2BS (05394) 44649

Aaron Slack is a small guest house in a quiet part of Windermere about ½ mile from the railway station, 1 mile from the main access to the lake at Bowness Bay and within walking distance of shops and restaurants. The proprietor, Stephanie Townsend, is a keen painter, fell-walker and naturalist, and has an in-depth knowledge about this beautiful part of the world which she is happy to share with guests to help them make the most of their stay. There are two double and one twin-bedded rooms for guests: each has a colour TV and tea/coffee-making facilities, and there is a cosy sitting room. Breakfast is the only meal to be served at Aaron Slack, but visitors can look forward to a hearty meal of locally produced sausages and free-range eggs to set them up for the day; there are many restaurants and pubs serving food in Windermere village. Windermere is an ideal holiday choice for Lakeland visitors who want easy access to the unspoilt parts of the National Park but who enjoy the hustle and bustle - and leisure amenities - of staying in a popular holiday village.

Open all year. No smoking in the house. Vegetarian & other diets by arrangement. Children by arrangement. En suite 2 rooms. TV & tea/coffee-making all rooms. Credit cards. B. & B. from £12.

**Ashleigh Guest House, 11 College Road, Windermere (05394) 42292**

Ashleigh is a delightful Victorian guest house which is peacefully situated in Windermere village in the heart of the Lake District National Park; comfortably furnished and tastefully decorated throughout (there are fresh flowers in the bedrooms), many rooms have glorious mountain views. There is a very warm and friendly atmosphere at Ashleigh and your host offers a first-rate English breakfast and optional evening meal.

Open all year. No smoking in the house. Vegetarian by arrangement. Children: over 12s welcome. En suite available. Tea/coffee-making & T.V. in all bedrooms. B. & B. from £14.

The Archway, 13 College Road, Windermere (05394) 45613

This guest house was the one about which I received the most readers' recommendations when I was compiling the second edition of the Healthy Holiday Guide. A small, 'impeccable' Victorian guest house furnished tastefully throughout with antiques, paintings and fresh flowers allows its reputation, nevertheless, to rest (and rest soundly) on the high standard of its cuisine: the best of fresh local ingredients are brought together in imaginative and nutritionally thoughtful menus (the breakfast fare offers everything from freshly squeezed fruit or vegetable juice to home-made spicy apple griddle cakes; bread, of course, is wholemeal and home-baked), while the 3-course evening menu includes a wine recommendation and home-made lemonade!

Open all year. No smoking in the house. Vegetarian, vegan & diabetic diets standard. Licensed. Children: over 12s only. En suite in 5 rooms. Tea/coffee-making & T.V. in all rooms. Credit cards. B. & B. from £20.

Boston House, 4 The Terrace, Windermere, LA23 1AJ (05394) 43654

Boston House is a delightful Victorian Gothic building, dating from 1849, which is peacefully situated in an elevated position on the edge of the village; it has panoramic views of the lake and surrounding fells, yet is just 5 minutes walk from the village centre with its train and coach stop (from which there is free collection by arrangement). The six spacious and comfortable bedrooms have each been tastefully furnished - and one even has an oak half tester bed. The delicious meals are home-prepared from fresh produce and are served in an elegant yet informal dining room: the breakfast menu is very extensive and the delicious evening meal would typically feature Cream of Mushroom Soup with Dill or Wensleydale Fritters with Ginger Preserve; followed by Beefsteak pie cooked in Guiness and Port, and a tempting dessert such as Strawberry, Almond and Redcurrant Tart; after-dinner coffee is served in the pleasant lounge with its interesting collection of books

Open all year. No smoking throughout. Vegetarian and other special diets by arrangement. Licensed. Children welcome. En suite in 3 rooms. Tea/coffee-making & T.V. in all bedrooms. B. & B. from £14.50.

 Braemount House Hotel, Sunny Bank Rd, Windermere, LA23 2EN (05394) 45967

 Braemount House is a small, family-run hotel which was built traditionally of Lakeland stone in 1879 and still retains much of its original, Victorian character and charm; it nestles quietly midway between Bowness and Windermere within easy walking distance of the lake. Accommodation is in six prettily decorated en suite guest rooms, each of which have been well-equipped with a range of helpful amenities including a radio-alarm and direct-dial phone; there is also a comfortable lounge for guests'use. The food is excellent: everything has been home-prepared from fresh, local ingredients (including garden herbs), and a typical 5 course evening menu would consist of Gratin of Avocado and Egg followed by Orange Sorbet, Lamb with Leek and Thyme Sauce, and a mouthwatering dessert uch as Warm Nectarine in Nut Caramel with Fromage Blanc; there is a good selection of wines to accompany the meal, and cheese, coffee and sweetmeats to complete it.   Windermere is an excellent touring centre and affords easy access to all the other parts of Lakeland; there is much to do within the vicinity of the village however, including golf, water sports, riding and, of course, fell-walking.

Open all year. No smoking in the house. Vegetarian & other diets by arrangement. Licensed. Children welcome. En suite, TV & tea/coffee-making in bedrooms. Visa, Mastercard. B. & B. from £22, D. B. & B. from £41.75.

Denehurst, 40 Queens Drive, Windermere (05394) 44710
Traditional 19th C. Lakeland stone guest house. Breakfast only - but with an imaginative and varied menu which changes daily.

Open 50 weeks. No smoking in dining room and all bedrooms. Vegetarian and other special diets as requested. Children welcome. En suite, tea/coffee-making & T.V. in all bedrooms. B. & B. from £15.

 Hazel Bank, Hazel Street, Windermere (05394) 45486
Open all Mar. to Nov. No smoking throughout. Vegetarian by arrangement. Not licensed, but bring your own. No pets. En suite & tea/coffee-making in all rooms. T.V. in lounge. B. & B. from £15.

Hideaway Hotel, Phoenix Way, Windermere, LA23 1DB (09662) 3070
Highly acclaimed small hotel tucked away down quiet country lane just 5 minutes from Windermere Village centre. Imaginative home-cooked cuisine.

Open all year. No smoking in dining room & sitting room. Special diets by arrangement. Licensed. Children welcome. Pets by arrangement. En suite, TV tea/coffee-making in bedrooms. D., B. & B. from around £35.

Kirkwood Guest House, Prince's Road, Windermere, LA23 2DD (05394) 43907
Kirkwood is an attractive stone-built guest house peacefully situated in a quiet area of Windermere yet just a few minutes'walk from the town centre and shops; Lake Windermere is just 1 mile away. Your hosts, Carol and Neil Cox, do all they can to make your stay a happy and memorable one, and you will find that all the bedrooms have been individually furnished and have excellent amenities. The breakfast is first-rate: a range of options are offered - including a menu for vegetarians - and other special diets can be accommodated with a little notice. Kirkwood Guest House is the perfect choice for those seeking to enjoy Lakeland in the uncrowded Autumn, Winter and Spring months, with their clear bright days and welcome absence of traffic!

Open all year. No smoking in dining room. Vegetarian & other diets by arrangement. Children welcome. Pets by arrangement. En suite 4 rooms. Tea-making & T.V. in all bedrooms. Credit cards. B. & B. from £13.

Laurieston, 40 Oak St, Windermere, LA23 1EN (05394) 44253
Open all year. No smoking in the house. Vegetarian by arrangement. Licensed. Disabled access: double ground floor room avail. Children welcome. En suite some rooms. Tea/coffee making & T.V. in all rooms.

Miller Howe Hotel, Rayrigg Road, Windermere, LA23 1EY (05394) 42536
Highly acclaimed hotel and restaurant (by New York - as well as our own - *Times*). Luxuriously appointed. Beautiful lake views.
Open March to Nov. No smoking in restaurant. Licensed. En suite. Room service. Phone/T.V. in bedrooms.

Rockside, Ambleside Road, Windermere, LA23 1AQ (09662) 5343

Rockside is a Lakeland house built in the middle of the last century with slate and stone in the traditional way. Every room is a different size and shape - so each has a different character - and passageways and short flights of steps lead off in all directions, making it a house you want to explore. The 15 centrally heated bedrooms have been well-equipped with TV, radio, clock, telephone and electric blanket - and most have en suite facilities (one is situated on the ground floor). Breakfast is served in a pleasant dining room - and there are 6 choices to choose from; a continental alternative is also available. Rockside is just two minutes'walk from both the train and bus station at Windermere (take the second turn on the left after the Windermere Hotel) and is thus centrally placed and an excellent base from which to enjoy both the attraction of Lakeland's most popular holiday village and the fells, lake and mountains which surround it.
Open all year. No smoking in dining room & 1 bedroom. Vegetarian & vegan standard. Other diets by arrangement. Disabled access: ground floor room. Children welcome. En suite most rooms. Tea/coffee-making & T.V. in all bedrooms. Credit cards. B. & B. from £15.

 Rosemount, Lake Road, Windermere, Cumbria, LA22 2EQ (05394) 43739
Situated midway between Bowness and Windermere, this charmingly hospitable guest house

offers something of a haven for the health-conscious visitor in search of good food and a warm welcome - in smoke-free surroundings! Clean air is not the only health boon at Rosemount for the delicious breakfast menu offers, in addition to traditional fare, a number of healthy alternatives such as fruit, yoghurt, honey and muesli. Packed lunches can be provided on request and accommodation is in comfortably appointed rooms, including two single rooms, (complete with well-stocked tea-trays). Guests in search of good walks will find them just across the road in the peaceful woodlands of Sheriff's Walk.

Open all year. No smoking in the house. Vegetarian and most other special diets by arrangement. Children welcome. En suite, TV & tea/coffee-making in bedrooms. Access, Visa, Mastercard. B. & B. from £19.50

Restaurants

AMBLESIDE

 Harvest Vegetarian Restaurant, Compston Road, Ambleside (05394) 33151/33762
Freshly prepared vegetarian food. Photographic exhibitions of Lakeland Landscapes.
Open weekdays 5 - 9, w/es, 12 - 2.30 & 5 - 9.30. L. around £7. D. around £9. No smoking. Vegetarian, vegan & gluten-free standard. Licensed. Disabled access. Children welcome.

 Sheila's Cottage, The Slack, Ambleside (05394) 33079
Open 11 - 3.30, 7 - 9.30. No smoking. Vegetarian. Licensed. Disabled access. Children welcome.

Wilf's Cafe, 5 Lake Rd, Ambleside, Cumbria, LA22 0AB (05394) 34749
Wholefood café with vegetarian and vegan choices situated above White Mountain.
Open 8.30 a.m. - 8.30 p.m. No smoking. Licensed. Disabled access. Children welcome. Visa, Mastercard.

BASSENTHWAITE LAKE
The Pheasant Inn, Bassenthwaite Lake, Nr Cockermouth, CA13 9YE (07687) 76234
Open 12.30 - 2, 7 - 8.30. No smoking in restaurant. Vegetarian. Wheelchair access. Children welcome.

CARLISLE
Fantails, The Green, Weatherhall, Carlisle (0228) 60239
Open 12 - 2, 6.30 - 9. Separate area for non-smokers. Exclusively vegetarian. Licensed. Children welcome.

 Hudson's Coffee Shop/Restaurant, Treasury Court, Fisher St, Carlisle (0228) 47733
Centrally located café serving wide range of home-made meals and snacks.
90 seats, plus outside seating. Open 9 - 5. L. around £3. No smoking ex. outside seating. Vegetarian. Licensed. Disabled access. Children welcome - children's menu & baby changing facilities. Credit cards.

COCKERMOUTH
Quince and Medlar, 13 Castlegate, Cockermouth, CA13 9EU (0900) 823579
VSUK Best Vegetarian Restaurant '89 & Vegetarian Living Best Vegetarian Restaurant '91.
26 seats. Open Tues. to Sun. from 7. No smoking. Vegetarian standard. Licensed. Children: over 5s only

DENT
The Hop Bine Restaurant, Dent Crafts Centre, Helmside, Dent (05875) 400
The Hop Bine Restaurant is situated in a beautiful converted farm building (which also houses the Dent Crafts Centre) just one and a half miles from Dent village on the Sedbergh Road. The restaurant, which is open throughout the day and in the evening, serves a wide range of delicious home-prepared food, and day-time diners can choose from home-made cakes, pastries and teas as well as a selection of 'International Platters' (various toppings served with generous hunks of bread). The evening menu features a freshly prepared 4-course dinner in which a typical selection might be Italian Hors d'oeuvres followed by Strawberry Sorbet, Lemon Chicken with Grapes and French Bread Pudding (there are some good meat-free options). Musical events are staged each month, and the restaurant makes a perfect venue for private parties and functions.
40 seats. Open 9.30 - 5.30. Set 3-course lunch £7.25, set 4-course dinner £12.95. Smoking banned throughout. Licensed. Disabled access. Children welcome. Access, Visa. Dinner by prior booking only.

HAWKSHEAD
The Minstrels Gallery, The Square, Hawkshead (09666) 423
24 seats. Open 10.30 - 5.30. L. around £2.50. No smoking Disabled access. Children welcome.

KENDAL
Waterside Wholefoods, Kent View, Kendal (0539) 729743
Day-time restaurant & shop serving fresh food; organic ingredients wherever possible.
60 seats. Open 9 - 4. L. around £3.50. No smoking. Exclusively vegetarian. Vegan & some other special diets on request. Disabled access: 'excellent'. Children welcome.

KESWICK
Cottage in the Wood, Whinlatter Pass (059682) 409
For further details please see under the entry in the accommodation section.

Grange Bridge Cottage Tea Shop, Grange in Borrowdale, Nr Keswick (07687) 77201
An 18th C. beamed cottage by the bridge over the River Derwent at Grange in the beautiful Borrowdale Valley. Delicious food - much of it home-prepared.
30 seats. Open April - Oct. 11.30 a.m. to 7 p.m. L. up to £5 (including vegetarian). No smoking throughout. Vegetarian standard. Disabled access. Children welcome.

The Wild Strawberry, 54 Main Street, Keswick (07687) 74399
Friendly, cosy tea room with green slate floors & wooden beams; excellent range of delicious home-made snacks & meals throughout the day; speciality coffees & teas; vegetarian options.
70 seats. Open 10 - 4.45, Tues. - Sat., Sun. 12 - 4.45. (closed Mondays except in summer holidays). No smoking throughout.Vegetarian & other diets. Wheelchair access, but no toilet facilities. Visa, Mastercard.

KIRKBY LONSDALE

Lupton Tower Veg. Guest House & Restaurant, Lupton, Nr Kirkby Lonsdale (044 87) 400
For further details please see under the entry in the accommodation section.

Mews Coffee House, Main Street, Kirby Lonsdale (0468) 71007
Separate dining room for smokers. Vegetarian. Licensed. Disabled access. Children welcome.

KIRKBY STEPHEN

The Old Forge Bistro, 39 North Road, Kirby Stephen, CA17 4RE (07683) 71832
Converted 17th C. smithy specialising in vegetarian & wholefood as well as traditional fare.
No smoking throughout. Vegetarian & wholefood standard. Licensed. Disabled access. Children welcome.

THE LORTON VALE

The Barn, New House Farm, Lorton, Cockermouth, CA13 9UU (0900) 85404
The Barn is situated on the B5289 between Lorton and Loweswater in the beautiful Lorton Vale. It offers a wide range of delicious lunches and teas are served therein.
Open April to Sept., 7 days a week, 12 - 5.30; Oct., Nov., Feb. & Mar., Wed. to Sun., 12 - 4.30. No smoking throughout. L. around £3.25.

MELMERBY

The Village Bakery, Melmerby, CA10 1HE (076 881) 515
Converted 18th C. barn serving home-baked wholefood bread, cakes and pastries.
No smoking throughout. Vegetarian. Licensed. Disabled access. Children welcome. Access, Visa.

PENRITH

Passepartout, 51 Castlegate, Penrith, CA11 7HY (0768) 65852
No smoking. Vegetarian. Other diets on request. Licensed. Disabled access. Children welcome.

Sharrow Bay Hotel, Lake Ullswater, Nr Penrith (07684) 86301
No smoking throughout. Some special diets by arrangement. Licensed.

ULVERSTON

Bay Horse Inn & Bistro, Canal Foot, Ulverston (0229) 53972
No smoking in restaurant. Some special diets. Licensed. Disabled access. Children: over 12s only. Credit cards.

UNDERBARROW

Tullythwaite House, Underbarrow (04488) 397
No smoking. Vegetarian standard. Licensed. Disabled access. Children: over 12s only. Access, Visa.

WORKINGTON

Impressions Restaurant, 173 Vulcans Lane, Workington (0900) 605446
No smoking. Vegetarian standard. Licensed. Disabled access. Children welcome. Access, Visa.

Pubs & Wine Bars

DENT

The Sun Inn, Main St, Dent, Sedbergh (05875) 208
Open pub hours. No smoking in 1 room. Vegetarian meals available. Wheelchair access. Children welcome.

Cheshire
Accommodation

CHESTER

Frogg Manor, Fullers Moor, Nantwich Road, Broxton, Chester, CH3 9JH (0829) 782629
Open all year. Separate room for smokers. Vegetarian by arrangement. Licensed. Children welcome. Pets by arrangement. En suite, TV & tea/coffee-making in bedrooms. Credit cards. B. & B. from £25.

~~Asquith House, 8 Waterloo Road, Chester, CH2 2AL (0244) 380620~~

not listed

ASQUITH HOUSE

Asquith House is an elegant Victorian house which was built in 1895 and was restored to its former glory nearly a century later in 1989 by its present owners; period features have been retained thankfully (iron fireplaces, the fine proportions of the rooms) and, with its proximity to the city centre, it is a perfect base from which to explore the charms of Chester and the surrounding Cheshire countryside. Breakfast is the only meal available at Asquith House but it is a generous meal (English or continental options are available) and there are many excellent restaurants in and around Chester. Accommodation is in very comfortable rooms (all en suite) and the charming sitting room has, its owners tell me, 'No TV!' An asset indeed.
Open all year ex. Xmas. No smoking in the house. Special diets by arrangement only. En suite, tea/coffee-making & T.V. in all bedrooms. B. & B. £25. Single £29.

Stone Villa, 3 Stone Place, Hoole Road, Chester, CH2 3NR (0244) 345014
Open all year. No smoking in bedrooms & dining room. Children welcome. En suite, TV & tea/coffee-making in bedrooms. B. & B. from £18.

CREWE

The Old Hall, Madeley, Nr Crewe, CW3 9DX (0782) 750209
Open all year ex. Xmas. No smoking in dining room, lounge & some bedrooms. 1 room en suite. Tea/coffee-making & T.V. in all bedrooms.

KNUTSFORD

Pickmere House, Park Lane, Pickmere, Knutsford, WA16 0JX (0565) 733433/(0831) 384460
Listed Georgian farmhouse with extensive views of Cheshire countryside; 2m W J19 M6 nr Tatton. Convenient access to Warrington, Runcorn, Chester, Liverpool and Manchester.
Open all year. No smoking in the house. Vegetarian & other diets by arrangement. Children welcome. Pets by arrangement. En suite in most rooms. Tea/coffee-making & T.V. in all bedrooms. B. & B. from £16.50.

Tatton Dale Farm, Ashley Road, Knutsford, WA16 6QJ (0565) 654692
Open all year. No smoking in the house. Vegetarian and most other special diets by arrangement. Disabled access. Children welcome. 1 room en suite . Tea/Coffee-making in bedrooms. T.V. available. B. & B. from £14.

Toft Hotel, Toft Road, Knutsford, WA16 9EH (0565) 3470
Open all year. No smoking in the house. Vegetarian standard. Licensed. Children: over 10s only. En suite in 6 rooms. Tea/coffee-making in all bedrooms. T.V. in 6 bedrooms. Credit cards. B. & B. from £15.

MACCLESFIELD

Chadwick House, 55 Beech Lane, Macclesfield, SK10 2DS (0625) 615558
Open all year. No smoking ex. in T.V. room. Licensed. Children welcome. En suite in 8 rooms. Tea/coffee-making & T.V., including Sky, in bedrooms. Sauna, solarium & exercise room. Access, Visa, Diners. B. & B. from £23.

Goose Green Farm, Oak Road, Mottram St Andrew, Macclesfield, SK10 4RA (0625) 828814
Open all year. No smoking in dining room & bedrooms. Vegetarian and other diets by arrangement.Children welcome. En suite in 1 room. Tea/coffee-making & T.V. in all bedrooms. B. & B. from £16.

MOBBERLEY

 Laburnum Cottage, Knutsford Road, Mobberley, Nr Knutsford, WA16 7PU (0565) 872464
Open all year. No smoking in the house. Vegetarian & other diets by arrangement.Children: over 5s only. No pets. En suite in some rooms. Tea/coffee-making & T.V. in all bedrooms. B. & B. from £20.

NANTWICH

Rookery Hall, Worleston, Nr Nantwich, Cheshire, CW5 6DQ (0270) 610016
Open all year. Smoking banned in dining room & some bedrooms. Vegetarian and other special diets by arrangement. Licensed. Disabled access. Children welcome. No pets. En suite in all rooms. Room service. Satellite T.V. in all bedrooms. Credit cards accepted.

NORTHWICH

 Beechwood House, 206 Wallerscote Road, Weaverham, Northwich, CW8 3LZ (0606) 852123
Open Jan. to Nov. No smoking in the house. Vegetarian and most other special diets by arrangement. Tea/coffee-making & T.V. in sitting room. B. & B. from £12. D. £6.

STOCKPORT

 Mrs Kennington, 35 Corbar Road, Stockport, SK2 6EP (061 483) 4000
Open all year. No smoking in the house. Vegetarian and some other special diets by arrangement. Children by arrangement. Tea/coffee-making facilities. T.V. in lounge. B. & B. from £12.50.

Restaurants

ALTRINCHAM

Debenhams, Altrincham
 Pavilion, a friendly self-service coffee shop serving lunches, snacks and hot & cold drinks.
Open store hours. No smoking. Vegetarian. Disabled access. Children very welcome. Credit/debit cards.

CHESTER

 Abbey Green, 2 Abbey Green, Northgate Street, Chester, CH1 2JH (0244) 313251
No smoking throughout. Exclusively vegetarian. Licensed. Disabled access. Children welcome.

 Browns of Chester, 34-40 Eastgate Row, Chester, CH1 3SB (0244) 350001
The Crypt, waitress service of interesting light lunches & snacks in original 13th C. crypt.
Open store hours. No smoking. Vegetarian. Licensed. Children welcome. Credit/debit cards.
Springles, a friendly self-service restaurant serving lunches, snacks & hot & cold drinks.
Open store hours. No smoking throughout. Vegetarian meals. Licensed. Children welcome. Credit/debit cards.

The Blue Bell Restaurant, 65 Northgate Street, Chester (0244) 317758

The Blue Bell Inn is Chester's only surviving medieval inn and is conveniently situated in the centre of the city. It has a very 'relaxing and unpretentious' atmosphere - perfect for either a quick business lunch or a romantic dinner à deux - and the fact that it is owner-run means that there is an exceptionally high standard of service and a high degree of personal care and attention. The food is excellent: the menu changes regularly and a wide variety of delicious, freshly cooked dishes are offered to guests: a typical lunchtime menu selection might be Smoked Fish Paté with salad leaves followed by Bacon Rarebit and a choice of home-made desserts, while the à la carte evening menu offers a range of tasty and imaginative options such as Baked Somerset Brie with Pimento Coulis followed by Braised Rabbit with Leeks, Tarragon and Cream; there are excellent vegetarian choices on both menus and the accompanying wine list offers a wide selection of international labels.
13 seats. Open 12 - 2.30, 7 - 10. D. around £14.50. No smoking in one room (13-15 seats). Vegetarian and other special diets on request. Licensed. Children welcome. Credit cards.

CREWE
Rockefella's Restaurant, 11 Hightown, Crewe, Cheshire, CW1 3BP (0270) 215668
Popular family restaurant specialising in steaks, hamburgers, etc. Self-serve salad selection.
52 seats. Open 12 - 11.30. L. from £3.35. 50% no-smoking. Vegetarian standard. Licensed. Disabled access. Children welcome. Credit cards.

HASLINGTON
The Fox Beefeater, 58 Crewe Road, Haslington, Cheshire, CW1 1Q2 (0270) 582296
55% no-smoking. Vegetarian standard. Licensed. Disabled access. Children welcome. Credit cards.

MACCLESFIELD
Dukes Coffee House, Dukes Court, Macclesfield (0625) 511453
No smoking in part of café.

NANTWICH
Stapeley Water Gardens & Palms Tropical Oasis, London Rd, Stapeley, Nantwich (0270) 628628
Three separate restaurants in attractive garden settings.
420 seats. Open 11.45 - 3.30. L. around £9. No smoking in 1 restaurant & 40+% ban in other 2. Vegetarian & diabetic by arrangement. Licensed. Disabled: entire site designed for disabled. Children. Access, Visa.

RUNCORN
 Giovanni's Pizza and Pasta, 23 Nantwich Road, CW2 6AF (0270) 500276
Open daily, 12 - 2.30, 6.30 - 11.30. No smoking. Vegetarian. Licensed. Disabled access ex upstairs toilet.

STOCKPORT
 Debenhams, Princes St, Stockport (061) 4774550
Pavilion, a friendly self-service coffee shop serving lunches, snacks and hot & cold drinks.
Open store hours. No smoking. Vegetarian. Disabled access. Children very welcome. Credit and debit cards.

Pubs & Wine Bars

NANTWICH
The Jolly Tar Inn, Wardle, Nantwich, CW5 6BE (0270) 73283
Pleasant canal side pub with large beer garden.
No smoking in 50% of restaurant & 50% of pub. Vegetarian standard. Disabled access. Children welcome.

Greater Manchester
Accommodation & Restaurants

BURY

The Ramsbottom Victuallers Company Ltd, 16-18 Market Place, Ramsbottom, Bury (0706) 825070

Two tiny terraced cottages in the centre of Ramsbottom house two restaurants, a deli and a first-rate wine shop. The award-winning village restaurant has been established for 8 years and is renowned for its 6-course celebration dinners (no choice, but no disappointment either!), while "The Ramsbottom Victuallers Supper Room" provides simple 3-course evening meals with a couple of choices for each course. The cellars are an Aladdin's Cave of rare wines and spirits, mature British cheeses, fine teas and coffees, chocolates, culinary oils, fresh herbs and other delicacies, and much of the produce used and sold is organic (wines purchased in the shop may be drunk in either restaurant for a nominal corkage charge).

Supper Room: open Mon. to Fri. 6 - 10 p.m. 26 seats. Supper £10. Restaurant: open Wed. - Sat. Dinner 8 for 8.30. 16 seats. D. £30. No smoking throughout. Vegetarian & other diets by arrangement. Licensed. Children welcome, "except the very young". Access, Visa.

MANCHESTER

Debenhams, Market St, Manchester (061) 832 8666
A friendly self-service restaurant serving lunches, snacks and range of hot & cold drinks.
Open store hours. No smoking. Vegetarian. Disabled access. Children very welcome. Credit/debit cards.

The Gallery Bistro, Whitworth Art Gallery, Oxford Rd, Manchester (061) 273 5651
No smoking. Vegetarian standard. Licensed. Disabled access. Children welcome.

On the Eighth Day, 109 Oxford Road, Manchester, M1 7DU
No smoking. Vegetarian, vegan & macrobiotic standard. Wheelchair access. Children.

The Greenhouse Vegetarian Restaurant, 331 Gt Western St, Rusholme (061) 224 0730
No smoking. Vegetarian & vegan standard. Wheelchair accesss. Children 'if fully supervised'.

SADDLEWORTH

Woody's Vegetarian Restaurant, 5 King St, Delph, Saddleworth (0457) 871197

The leaflet advertising Woody's Vegetarian Restaurant is frank and outspoken: 'tired of the scrubbed pine and sackcloth image of vegetarianism? Book a candlelit table for the evening at Woody's.' You can see their point - not that there is anything exactly wrong with the anodyne ambience that is so often *de rigueur* in vegetarian restaurants, it's just that vegetarians have sophisticated feelings too, and Woody's panders to them with a charming and elegant atmosphere rarely achieved - or, one wonders, even aspired to - by other meat-free eateries. The food is pretty good, too: everything is home-cooked from fresh ingredients, and a typical meal would feature Apple and Stilton Toast followed by Courgette and Mange Tout Strudel and a selection of imaginative desserts. Woody's has been a 'Vegetarian Restaurant of the Year'finalist in 1989, 1990 and 1991.

30 seats. Open 7.30 - 11. No smoking. Vegetarian & vegan exclusively. Licensed. Disabled access. Access, Visa.

Lancashire Accommodation

BLACKPOOL

 The Birchley Hotel, 64 Holmfield Rd, Blackpool North Shore, FY2 9RT (0253) 54174

 The Birchley is a small, comfortable, licensed hotel where a warm welcome awaits you. Privately owned and manged for 15 seasons by the resident proprietors, it is situated on the select North shore area of Blackpool near to Queen's Promenade, Gynn Leisure Gardens and the boating pool. The Birchley is the perfect choice for those looking for a peaceful relaxing smoke-free hotel. The food served is excellent home-cooking and a choice of menu is offered. The proprietors, Mildred and Ken Robinson, specialise in offering a high standard of accommodation including en suite rooms, a full English breakfast and evening meal. They invite you to join them for one of their "Winter Spring Breaks", "Summer Weeks", "The Dazzling Autumn Illuminations" or the "Festive Season". The entertainment Blackpool has to offer includes theatre shows, Tower World, the Pleasure Beach, fantastic night life or "The Festive Season." Phone the Robinsons (send a stamp please) for a brochure.

Open most of the year. No smoking throughout. Licensed. Children: over 5s only. En suite. Tea/coffee-making & T.V. in all bedrooms. Credit cards. B. & B. from £15.

Chadwick's, 20a Cliff Place, Bispham, Blackpool, FY2 9JT (0253) 54188

Open Mar. to Nov. No smoking in dining room & bedrooms. Vegetarian & other diets by strict prior arrangement. Children welcome. En suite, TV & tea/coffee-making in all rooms. B. & B. from £10.

Imperial Hotel (THF), North Promenade, Blackpool, FY1 2HB (0253) 23971

Open all year. 70% no-smoking dining room & bedrooms. Vegetarian & other diets by arrangement. Licensed. Disabled access. Children welcome. Pets by arrangement. En suite, TV & tea/coffee-making in all rooms.

CARNFORTH

 The Bower, Yealand Conyers, Carnforth, LA5 9SF (0524) 734585

The Bower is a small Georgian country house set at the northernmost tip of Lancashire in the Arnside and Silverdale Area of Outstanding Natural Beauty; it stands in the picturesque and peaceful village of Yealand Conyers, and has  extensive views of Ingleborough and the surrounding hills. It is a private house which has recently been modernised (sympathetically - it retains many original features), and accommodation is in two comfortable guest rooms, each of which has been equipped with a hairdryer and electric blankets. The food is wholesome and delicious (prepared from local or home-grown vegetables wherever possible) and, while the proprietors cater for too small a number to offer a choice, they always consult with guests about likes and dislikes; meals are served in a delightful dining room with French windows opening out onto the garden, and a typical evening meal would feature Stilton Soufflé followed by Chicken Chasseur and a tempting dessert, such as Gooseberry Fool with Amaretti Biscuits. Many beautiful walks may be enjoyed within the vicinity of The Bower - which is also conveniently placed for visiting Leighton Moss RSPB reserve and Morecambe Bay - and entertainment *in situ* may be provided for guests who play bridge (your hosts are keen players) or who sing (they also play the harpsichord and piano)!

Open all year. No smoking in the house. Special diets by arrangement. Children: over 12s only. Pets by arrangement. En suite, TV & tea/coffee-making in bedrooms. B. & B. £21-32, D. £13.50.

Capernwray Country House, Capernwray, Carnforth, LA6 1AE (0524) 732363

Capernwray is a splendid country house which stands in 5½ acres of well-kept grounds, with paddock and orchard (in the Spring they are ablaze with daffodils), in the midst of unspoilt countryside on the Lancastrian/Cumbrian border. Beautifully furnished throughout, each of the en suite bedrooms is centrally heated and has been decorated with tremendous care in colour-co-ordinated fabrics and wall-coverings; each enjoys panoramic views over the Cumbrian and Pennine hills. Breakfast is served in a spacious dining room, and there is also a pleasant lounge - again with views - for guests' use; lots of good pubs and restaurants are within easy reach where you may enjoy an evening meal. A holiday in Carnforth provides the best of several worlds: on the Capernwray doorstep is some of the most peaceful, unspoilt countryside in the realm - yet you are also within easy reach of the historic city of Lancaster, the Lake District, the coast at Morecambe Bay (which lies under the migratory path for tens of thousands of birds) and the Yorkshire Dales.

Open all year. No smoking in the house. Special diets by arrangement. Children welcome. En suite, TV & tea/coffee-making in bedrooms. B. & B. from £19 - 20, Single £15.

Thie-ne-shee, Moor Close Lane, Over Kellet, Carnforth, LA6 1DF (0524) 735882

Hillside bungalow with superb views across to the Lake District and Morecambe Bay. Close to Leighton Moss R.S.P.B. Reserve and Carnforth Steam town. Healthy breakfasts.

Open all year ex. Xmas & New Year. No smoking in the house. Vegetarian and most other special diets by arrangement. Children welcome. Tea/coffee-making: personal service. T.V in lounge. B. & B. from £12.

COLNE

148 Keighley Rd, Colne, Lancs., BB8 0PJ (0282) 862002

Edwardian town house with many original features, including stained glass, panelled doors & cornices. Comfortable bedrooms. Easy access to Pendle, Brönte country & Yorkshire Dales.

Open all year ex. Xmas. No smoking in the house. Vegetarian & special diets by arrangement. TV & tea/coffee-making in bedrooms. B. & B. from £14. ETB Listed and Highly Commended.

KIRKBY LONSDALE

Killington Hall, Killington, Kirkby Lonsdale, via Carnforth, LA6 2HA (05396) 20542

Killington Hall has its origins in the 16th C. when it was home to Sir James Pickering, the second speaker in the House of Commons; for the past 22 years, however, it has been home to the Raw family who have seen many changes in their farming profession over the decades - but few to their lovely old home (it still has a Peile Tower, a priest's hiding hole and a secret passage!). Guests are accommodated in two well-equipped bedrooms - one of which sleeps four in a double bed and bunks, and the other of which has two single beds; there is a shared bathroom and also a cosy lounge, with a wood-burning stove, plenty of books and maps, and a TV with Teletext. The food is wholesome and very much prepared to suit guests' needs: there is a good choice at breakfast (those with lighter appetites are not forced to do battle with bacon and eggs - there are alternatives!), and the evening meal is good, home-cooked fare, prepared from fresh ingredients - no choice but, as your hosts point out, if you are staying for two weeks it is unlikely that you will be served the same dish twice; a bed time drink - with some light refreshment - is served each evening and is included in the price. Killington is probably the smallest village that any guest is likely to have visited - no shop, post office or even pub - just 9 or so dwellings and a village church and hall. All this spells PEACE with, for those keen to travel and tour, the welcome proximity of the Lake District and the Yorkshire Dales.

Open Easter - Oct. No smoking in the house. Special diets by arrangement. Children welcome. Tea/coffee-making in bedrooms. B. & B. £14, D. £10.

LANCASTER

Elsinore House, 76 Scotforth Rd, Lancaster (0524) 65088
Open all year. No smoking ex. lounge. Vegetarian & diets by arrangement. En suite, tea/coffee-making & T.V in all bedrooms. B. & B. from £15.

LYTHAM ST ANNES

Dalmeny Hotel, 19-33 South Promenade, Lytham St Annes, FY8 1LX (0253) 712236
Open all year ex. Xmas. No smoking in dining room & lounge. Vegetarian by arrangement. Licensed. Disabled access. Children welcome. En suite, TV & tea/coffee-making in all rooms. Access, Visa. Room only from £25.

OLDHAM

Hanson House, Grains Rd, Delph, Nr Oldham (0457) 873419
Beautiful Grade II listed building 30 mins from Manchester city centre.
Open all year ex. Xmas. No smoking. Vegetarian. Children: over 5s. only. T.V. B. & B. from £14.

RAMSBOTTOM

Edwardia, 416 Bolton Rd West, Ramsbottom (0204) 888061/(0831) 589750
Beautifully refurbished Edwardian town house on a semi-rural main road.
Open all year. No smoking. Children: over 5s only. Tea/coffee-making & T.V. in all rooms. B. & B. from £15.

SILVERDALE

Lindeth House, Lindeth Rd, Silverdale, Carnforth, LA5 0TX (0524) 701238

Lindeth House is a pleasant country residence wonderfully set in a area of Outstanding Natural Beauty, surrounded by woodland walks, yet just a few minutes'walk from the sea and a short distance from Leighton Moss RSPB Reserve. The house has been attractively decorated and appointed and each of the bedrooms have been individually furnished. The licensed restaurant provides the finest traditional English cuisine which has been prepared from fresh, local produce, and a typical evening meal would feature a range of options from which you might select Smoked Salmon Profiteroles with Lemon Mayonnaise, followed by soup or sorbet, Gressingham Duckling with Sage and Onion Cream, a delicious dessert and cheese, biscuits, a cafetiere of fresh coffee and Chocolate Kendal Mint Cake! The excellent food, combined with the warm and friendly atmosphere, makes Lindeth House an excellent base for a quiet break or touring the Lake District. *Open Feb. to Dec. No smoking in dining room by request & in 1 lounge & bedrooms. Vegetarian by arrangement. Children: over 12s welcome. Licensed. Disabled access. En suite, tea/coffee-making & T.V in all bedrooms. B. & B. from £20.*

SOUTHPORT

Ambassador Private Hotel, 13 Bath St, Southport, PR9 0DP (0704) 543998

The Ambassador Hotel occupies one of the most central positions in Southport adjacent to beautiful Lord Street, with its covered boulevard and elegant shops, and just a short walk from the promenade. The bedrooms have all been very comfortably furnished and well-equipped with a range of helpful amenities including a hair dryer, a hospitality tray, (with drinks and snacks), a shoe cleaner and a mending kit. There is a comfortable bar (not open to non-residents) and in which the resident organist will entertain you during the evening! Your host, Margaret Bennett, is a qualified chef and prepares tasty meals from fresh, seasonal produce: the breakfast menu is tremendous and a wide variety of options are on offer including, in addition to the traditional English bacon, eggs & sausage, cheese on toast, kippers or smoked haddock. There are many interesting places to visit within the vicinity of Southport, including Martin Mere Wildfowl Sanctuary, Formby Red Squirrel Colony & Liverpool's Albert Dock & Maritime Museum.

Open all year ex. Xmas. No smoking in dining room & bedrooms. Vegetarian and most other special diets by arrangement. Licensed. Children: over 5s only. Pets welcome. En suite, tea/coffee-making & T.V in all bedrooms. Credit cards. B. & B. from £23. ETB 3 Crown Commended.

Lynwood Private Hotel, 11a Leicester St, Southport, PR9 0ER (0704) 540794
   Open all year ex. Nov. No smoking. Vegetarian by arrangement. Licensed. Children welcome. Pets by arrangement. Some en suite rooms. Tea/coffee-making & T.V in bedrooms. Credit cards. B. & B. from £14.50.

Restaurants & Pubs

BLACKBURN

Debenhams, Northgate, Blackburn (0254) 63543
Springles, a friendly self-service restaurant serving lunches, snacks and hot and cold drinks.
Open store hours. No smoking. Vegetarian meals. Disabled access. Children welcome. Credit/debit cards.

BOLTON

Debenhams, The Market Place, Bolton (0204) 381511
   Intermission, a friendly self-service coffee shop serving lunches, snacks & hot and cold drinks.
Open store hours. No smoking. Vegetarian meals. Disabled access. Children welcome. Credit/debit cards.

LANCASTER

Libra Wholefood Restaurant, 19 Brock St, Lancaster (0524) 61551
   No smoking. Vegetarian & wholefood exclusively. Licensed. Disabled access. Children welcome.

LYTHAM ST ANNES

Serendipity, Bedford Hotel, 307-311 Clifton Drive South, (0253) 724636
No smoking throughout.

MAWDESLEY

Roberts & Co., Cedar Farm, Mawdesley
   Tea room serving excellent range of home-made and wholesome snacks, teas and full meals.
No smoking throughout.

PRESTON

Eat Fit, 20 Friargate, Preston (0772) 555855
30% no-smoking. Vegetarian. Licensed. Disabled: 'three shallow steps, which do not prohibit wheelchairs'.

SOUTHPORT

Debenhams, 535-563 Lord St, Southport (0704) 36060
   Pavilion, a friendly self-service coffee shop serving lunches, snacks and hot and cold drinks.
Open store hours. No smoking. Vegetarian meals. Disabled access. Children welcome. Credit/debit cards.

TODMORDEN

The Queen Hotel, Rise Lane, Todmorden, OL14 7AA (0706) 812961
Family-run hotel cum pub serving good value bar snacks and imaginative and freshly cooked à la carte meals. 99% home-cooking. Open to non-residents.
No smoking in 1 bar. Vegetarian and most other special diets by arrangement. Licensed.

WIGAN

Debenhams, 17 - 25 Standish St, Wigan (0942) 46231
   A friendly self-service coffee shop serving lunches, snacks and hot and cold drinks.
Open store hours. No smoking. Vegetarian meals. Disabled access. Children welcome. Credit/debit cards.

Merseyside
Accommodation

LIVERPOOL

The Grange Hotel, Holmefield Road, Liverpool, L19 3PG (051) 4272950
Charming 19th C. building standing amidst beautiful well-maintained gardens in a quiet residential area just 3 miles from the centre of Liverpool and 3 miles from the airport. Comfortably furnished en suite bedrooms. Excellent food served in elegant dining room overlooking gardens. Conference and function facilities available.
Open all year. No smoking in dining room & some bedrooms. Vegetarian and most other special diets by arrangement. Licensed. Children welcome. En suite, tea/coffee-making & T.V. in all bedrooms. Credit cards.

NEWTON-LE-WILLOWS

Haydock Post House Hotel, Lodge Lane, Newton-le-Willows, WA12 0JG
Large hotel conveniently close to the junction of the M6 and A580 Liverpool to Manchester road.
Open all year. Separate area of dining room for smokers, and no smoking in 50% bedrooms. Vegetarian and most other special diets by arrangement. Licensed. Disabled access. Children welcome. Pets by arrangement. En suite, tea/coffee-making & T.V. in all bedrooms. Credit cards. B. & B. from £40.

WIRRAL

Ⓝ Riders Hay Guest House, 198 Greasby Road, Greasby, Wirral, L49 2PE (051) 6770682
Small, friendly, family-run guest house in the rural village of Greasby; just 10 minutes from Hilbre Bird Sanctuary and the Wirral Country Park.
Open all year. No smoking throughout. Vegetarian and most other special diets by arrangement. Disabled access. Children welcome. Tea/coffee-making. T.V. in lounge. B. & B. from £14, Single £16.

Restaurants

LIVERPOOL

Everyman Bistro, Everyman Theatre, Hope St (051) 708 9545
A very busy, but friendly, buffet style restaurant in the University/Poly area close to the 2 cathedrals. All food freshly cooked on the premises from fresh produce. Good selection of cask beers.
200 seats. Open noon - 11.30 p.m. No smoking in 1 of 3 rooms before 8 p.m. Vegetarian, vegan and other special diets standard. Licensed.

Pubs & Wine Bars

LIVERPOOL

Everyman Bistro, Everyman Theatre, Hope St (051) 708 9545
One dining/drinking area smoke-free before 8p.m.
For further details please see under the entry in the restaurant section.

Yorkshire and Humberside

North Yorkshire
Accommodation

ARKENGARTHDALE

The White House, Arkle Town, Arkengarthdale, DL11 6RB (0748) 84203

The White House is an 18th C. former farmhouse which stands in the tiny hamlet of Arkle town - a cluster of a dozen or so houses nestling in the banks of Arkle Beck some 3 miles from Reeth in Arkengarthdale. The house was extensively renovated in the 1960s but still retains its old world charm: there are 3 centrally heated bedrooms - two double en suite and one twin - and the visitor's lounge has a welcoming open fire and wonderful views across the dale. Your hosts, Ian and Angela Whitworth, will provide you with a hearty breakfast and a packed lunch to set you up for the day (absolutely necessary with such enticing and energetic walking so close at hand), and at the end of the day you can look forward to a freshly home-cooked meal such as Tomato Soup, Chicken in Barbeque Sauce (with roast potatoes, green beans and home-made coleslaw), a delicious home-made dessert and a choice of three local cheeses (Swaledale, Wensleydale, Coverdale with Chives) plus coffee and mint crisps. *Open Jan. - Nov. No smoking in the house. Vegetarian & other diets by arrangement. Children: over 10s welcome. En suite. Tea/coffee-making in rooms. TV lounge. B. & B. from £15.50, D. £9.50, single supp. £6.*

BEDALE

Hyperion House, 88 South End, Bedale DL8 2DS (0677) 422334

Hyperion House is an attractive well-appointed Victorian house in the charming market town of Bedale, the 'Gateway to the Dales'. It has been comfortably furnished throughout and there are 3 double and one twin-bedded rooms. Smoking is banned throughout the house - so the atmosphere is always clean and fresh - and everything is scrupulously clean. Breakfast is the only meal available at Hyperion House but there are plenty of very nice restaurants in Bedale. *Open all year ex. Xmas & New Year. No smoking in the house. Vegetarian & other diets by arrangement. B. & B. £13.50-15.50.*

The Old Rectory, Patrick Brompton, Bedale, Dl8 1JN (0677) 50343
Open Feb to Nov. No smoking in the house. Vegetarian by arrangement. Licensed. Pets by arrangement. En suite, TV & tea/coffee-making in all rooms. B. & B. from £17. D. £11

'Southfield', 96 Southend, Bedale, DL8 2DS (0677) 423510
Well established 3 bedroomed bed and breakfast establishment.
Open all year ex. Xmas and New Year. No smoking in dining room & upper floor. Vegetarian & most other special diets by arrangement. Children welcome. Tea/coffee-making if requested. B. &. B. from £14.

COXWOLD

Wakendale House, Oldstead Grange, Coxwold, YO6 4BJ (03476) 351
Well-appointed new farmhouse in a peaceful setting with breathtaking views.
Open Feb. - end Nov. No smoking in the house. Vegetarian & other diets by arrangement. Children welcome. T.V. lounge. B. & B. from £14. ETB 2 Crown Commended.

CROPTON

The New Inn & New Inn Restaurant, Cropton, Nr Pickering, YO18 8HH (07515 330)

In spite of its name, the New Inn at Cropton is an old established inn which is peacefully situated close to Cropton Forest and the beautiful unspoilt wilderness of the North York Moors. In addition to offering comfortable accommodation to residential guests (bedrooms are beautifully furnished and have en suite facilities - two specially rated family rooms are available), there is an excellent Victorian restaurant (in which smoking is completely banned), and a first-rate pub (with a smoke-free conservatory); guests preferring a more secluded break can take refuge in the self-catering cottage in the grounds. Guests can dine in the bar/conservatory (on dishes such as home-made Steak and Kidney Pie or Lentil Lasagne) or can choose from an excellent à la carte menu in the elegant restaurant; a typical evening meal would feature King Prawns with Martini followed by Fillet Rossini and a choice of desserts.
Open 11 - 3, 5.30 - 11 (winter opening 12 - 2.30, 7 - 11). Restaurant open 7-9.30. No smoking in restaurant and conservatory. L. around £5, Carvery £4.95, bar meals £3-7, D. £12-£15. Vegetarian, vegan and low-fat available. Wheelchair access. Children welcome. Credit cards.

FILEY

Abbott's Leigh Hotel, 7 Rutland St, Filey YO14 9JA (0723) 513334
Abbot's Leigh is a pleasant Victorian terrace house which is situated in a peaceful residential location close to the beach, gardens and town centre of Filey. The guest bedrooms are all comfortably furnished and have en suite facilities, and one room is on the ground floor. The food is wholesome and nourishing and the 5-course evening meal features a variety of dishes including some good vegetarian options. The proprietors offer reduced terms for weekly bookings and some attractive Spring and Autumn bargain breaks are also available. Filey has 7 miles of golden sands and is ideal for sailing, windsurfing and swimming; additionally you will find that you are ideally placed for touring the Yorkshire Wolds and the North York Moors National Park.
Open all year. No smoking in dining room & bedrooms. Vegetarian/diabetic standard. Licensed. Children: over 3s only. En suite & tea/coffee making in all rooms. T.V. Access, Visa. B. & B. from £16. D. £7.50.

GRASSINGTON

Ashfield House Hotel, Grassington, Nr Skipton, BD23 5AE (0756) 752584
Ashfield House is a secluded 17th century hotel, superbly situated in a quiet backwater near the village square. Family-owned and run, the emphasis is on personal service and comfort: each of the bedrooms has been individually styled and furnished, and welcoming log fires blaze in the entrance and the lounge. All the food is home-cooked on the kitchen Aga and only fresh ingredients (some home-grown) are used; a typical evening meal might feature Cheese-topped Ratatouille, followed by Chicken with Grape and Cider Sauce, and a tempting dessert such as Nutcracker Tart or Burgundy Cream.
Open mid-Jan. to early Nov. No smoking ex. entrance lounge. Vegetarian & other diets by arrangement. Licensed. Children: over 5s only. En suite 6 rooms. Tea/coffee-making & TV in all rooms. B. & B. from £28.

HARROGATE

Alexander Guest House, 88 Franklin Rd, Harrogate, HG1 5EN (0423) 503348
Friendly family-run guest house in tree-lined street close to conference centre & town centre. Beautiful decor, central heating & double glazing. Excellent centre for touring the Dales.
Open all year. No smoking in house. Children welcome. Some en suite available. TV & tea-making in rooms. B. & B. from £16. ETB 2 Crown Highly Commended.

Amadeus Vegetarian Hotel, 115 Franklin Rd, Harrogate, HG1 5EN (0423) 505151
Elegant private hotel on tree-lined road 5 mins. from town centre, exhibition halls and conference centre. Healthy breakfast of natural cereals, fresh fruits, yoghurts, freshly cooked dishes, home made wholewheat toast, honey and preserves. Delicious dinner is equally wholesome!
Exclusively vegetarian/vegan. Open all year ex. Xmas. No smoking in the house. Licensed. Children welcome. En suite in 4 rooms. Tea/coffee-making in bedrooms. T.V. in lounge and 1 bedroom. B. & B. from £22. D. £12.

Hookstone House Farm, Low Lane, Darley, Nr Harrogate, HG3 2QN (0423) 780572
Open all year. No smoking in dining room & bedrooms. Gluten-free standard. Vegetarian by arrangement Children welcome. Pets by arrangement. En suite. Tea-making in rooms. T.V. lounge. B. & B. from £15. D. £7.

 'Rose Garth', 44 Ripon Rd, Killinghall, Harrogate, HG3 2DF (0423) 506469
Rose Garth is a very pleasant smoke-free guest house which stands in a lovely garden just 2 miles from Harrogate and 1¼ miles from Ripley Castle. It has been comfortably furnished and appointed throughout, and there is a ground floor en suite flatlet which is especially suitable for semi-disabled guests (with a helper) and there is parking directly outside this flatlet. Each of the bedrooms has a Sky TV channel and there is parking for 11 cars.
Open all year. No smoking. Vegetarian & other diets by arrangement. Children welcome. En suite. TV & tea/coffee-making in bedrooms. B. & B. from £16.

HAWES

 **Brandymires Guest House, Muker Rd, Hawes, DL8 3PR (0969) 667482**
Brandymires is a lovely 19th C. 3-storey house which stands at the head of Wensleydale just outside the market town of Hawes; it has, as you might imagine, wonderful views from all sides. The house is exceptionally comfortable and welcoming - a necessary requisite for those holidaying in such beautiful but bracing countryside - an open fire blazes in the lounge, and two of the bedrooms have four-poster beds (each room, of course, has lovely views). The food is excellent: everything is home-cooked with imagination and care, and fresh produce is used whenever possible; there is no formal bar but you can enjoy a pre-dinner drink, order a bottle of wine and enjoy a liqueur or a leisurely drink in the lounge - much more civilised. There is much to enjoy within the vicinity of Brandymires: there are several dramatic waterfalls nearby and a number of castles and museums; perhaps the main attraction of the area is the wonderful opportunity for fell-walking (bring gumboots and warm, dry clothes!).
Open Mar. to end Oct. No smoking. Licensed. Pets welcome. No TV. Tea/coffee-making. B. & B. £16.

HELMSLEY

The Pheasant Hotel, Harome, Helmsley, YO6 5JG (0439) 71241/70416
Delightful hotel created from existing village dwellings with a large garden and paddock, overlooking the village pond. Heated indoor swimming pool.
Open March to Nov. No smoking in dining room. Vegetarian & other diets by arrangement. Licensed. Disabled access. Children: over 12s only. En suite, TV & tea/coffee-making in all rooms. D., B. & B. £47 - 58.

HUNMANBY

 Wrangham House Hotel, Stonegate, Hunmanby, YO14 ONS (0723) 891333
Open all year. No smoking in the house. Vegetarian by arrangement. Licensed. Disabled access. En suite, TV & tea/coffee-making in all rooms. Access, Amex, Diners, Visa. B. & B. from £32. D. £13.

INGLETON

Storrs Dale, Hawes Rd, Ingleton, LA6 3AN (0468) 41843
Small guest house specialising in wholesome home cooking.
Open all year. No smoking. Vegetarian by arrangement. Licensed. Children welcome. Tea/coffee-making in all rooms. T.V. on request. B. & B. from £13.

KIRKBYMOORSIDE

Sinnington Common Farm, Kirkbymoorside, York, YO6 6NX (0751) 31719
Open all year. No smoking in dining room & bedrooms. Vegetarian by arrangement. Wheelchair access. Children welcome. Pets by arrangement. En suite, tea/coffee making & T.V. in all rooms.B. & B. from £15. ETB 2 Crowns Commended.

LEYBURN

 Countersett Hall, Countersett, Askrigg, Leyburn, DL8 3DD (0969) 50373

Open Feb. - Oct. No smoking throughout. Vegetarian by arrangement. Licensed. Children: over 8s only. Pets by arrangement. Tea/coffee-making in all bedrooms. T.V. lounge. B. & B. from £15. D. £10.

The Holly Tree, East Witton, Leyburn   (0969) 22383

Open Easter to end Oct. No smoking in dining room, bedrooms, lounge, T.V. room & b'fast room. Vegetarian by arrangement. Licensed. En suite. Tea/coffee-making on request. T.V. lounge. D., B. & B. from £28.

Ivy Dene Guest House, West Witton, Leyburn, Wensleydale,   (0969) 22785

Ivy Dene is a charming 300 year-old Dales farmhouse which stands inside the National Park in the village of West Witton just 4 miles from Aysgarth Falls on the A684, the main route through Wensleydale. It has been renovated with tremendous care and now provides all the comforts you could possibly wish for (it has been awarded a 2 Crown Commended status by the ETB): each of the bedrooms has wonderful views (to the front Wensleydale and the River Ure; to the rear, Pen Hill); additionally there is a welcoming lounge with a beamed ceiling and log fire and, in the hallway, a small but well-stocked bar. The food is wholesome and delicious: everything is home-cooked from fresh ingredients including the bread rolls and puddings, and a typical evening meal would feature home-made soup followed by Pork in Brandy and Cream with fresh vegetables, and a delicious dessert such as Lemon Pudding or Apple Pie with fresh cream.

Open all year. No smoking in the house. Vegetarian by arrangement. Licensed. Children: over 5s welcome. En suite, TV & tea/coffee-making. B. & B. from £18, D. £10, children under 12, £10.

MALTON

Leonard House, 45 Old Maltongate, Malton, YO17 0EH (0653) 697242

Georgian house in attractive market town. Warm welcome. Ideal for touring beautiful Ryedale. Easy access by train or bus. Safe parking in secluded walled garden.

Open all year ex. Xmas. No smoking in the house. Vegetarian & other diets by arrangement. Children: over 4s only. Tea/coffee-making in bedrooms. B. & B. £12.50 - 14.

Newstead Grange Country House Hotel, Norton, Malton, YO17 9PJ (0653) 692502

Elegant Georgian country house with antique furniture & log fire. Home-cooked food. Special breaks at any time of year. Brochure on request. ETB Commended.

Open mid-Feb to Dec. No smoking throughout. Vegetarian by arrangement. Licensed. Children: over 12s only. En suite, tea/coffee-making & T.V. in all rooms. Access, Visa, Mastercard. B. & B. from £25. D. £11.50.

OSMOTHERLEY

Quintana House, Back Lane, Osmotherley, Northallerton, DL6 3BJ (0609) 883258

Although it was only erected in 1978, Quintana House has been designed and constructed on traditional 19th lines of weathered York stone and stands near the crest of the hill in the picturesque village of Osmotherley. Modern construction has its advantages (efficient central heating, for instance) but the timbered ceilings are of a different era and the wonderful moorland views from each of the bedroom windows have a perennial beauty. Your hosts, Dr. and Mrs Bainbridge, have two guest rooms - one twin, one double - and will provide you with a hearty breakfast and a generous packed lunch; you are literally on the edge of the North York Moors at Osmotherley close to the junction of both the Coast to Coast Walk and the Clevelend Way - so stoke up well! On the same subject, the Bainbridges have boot-drying racks in the boiler room for walkers caught in inclement weather. Evening meals are available by arrangement - and delicious repasts they are: a typical menu would feaure Broccoli and Yoghurt Salad followed by marinated Sirloin Steak (with fresh vegetables) and a home-made dessert such as Apricot Layer; there is also a full vegetarian menu, again available on request. *Open all year ex. Xmas. No smoking in the house. Vegetarian on request. Children welcome. Tea/coffee-making & TV in bedrooms. B. & B. £13.*

PATELEY BRIDGE

 Moorhouse Cottage, Pateley Bridge, HG3 5JF (0423) 711123
Open Easter to end Oct. No smoking throughout . Vegetarian by arrangement. Children welcome. No pets. Tea/coffee-making & T.V. in all rooms. B. & B. from £12.

PICKERING

 Bramwood Guest House, 19 Hallgarth, Pickering, YO18 7AW (0751) 74066
18th C. Grade II listed house centrally situated in the historic town of Pickerin.
Open all year. No smoking in the house. Vegetarian by arrangement. Children: over 3s only. Some rooms with private shower. Tea/coffee-making in all rooms. T.V. in lounge. Access, Visa. B. & B. from £12-£17. D. £8.

 Grindale House, 123 Eastgate, Pickering (0751) 76636

 Grindale House is an 18th C. building with the thick stone walls and pan-tiled roof so typical of the area. Situated in tree-lined Eastgate, just a short walk from the centre of Pickering. It was the last town farm and, until recently, large numbers of cattle were kept at the rear (the farmyard is now a car park and garden). The present owners have put a lot of hard work - and flair - into refurbishing their lovely home: there are still many antiques around from their years of antique dealing (they have a small shop next door), and the handsome beamed lounge with its welcoming fire and collection of books is a welcome retreat after a day on the moors; however present day amenities - such as well-equipped bathrooms and colour TVs - are all provided for your comfort as well. Breakfast is a hearty feast prepared on the Aga (free-range eggs, local Cumberland sausages, home-made jams) and there are plenty of good pubs and restaurants within walking distance. Pickering, the terminus for the North York Moors Steam Railway is an ideal base from which to appreciate the beauty of the North York Moors; it is also just 30 minutes' drive from York, Whitby and Scarborough.
Open all year. No smoking in the house. Pets by arrangement. En suite some rooms. Tea/coffee-making & T.V. B. & B. from £14-20.

 Heathcote Guest House, 100 Eastgate, Pickering, YO18 7DW (0751) 76991
Heathcote Guest House is a lovely Victorian former manor house which is centrally situated in the charming town of Pickering at the southern edge of the North York Moors National Park. It has been comfortably furnished and has every modern convenience (including central heating!), but it has retained a number of original features including a magnificent mahogany staircase and a galleried landing. The food is excellent: the 3 course evening meals feature an imaginative variety of dishes and vegetarian cooking is a speciality. You are perfectly placed at Pickering for visiting the North York Moors - which you may explore via the North York Moors Steam Railway which terminates at Pickering and which journeys through beautiful villages & unspoilt countryside.
Open Jan. to Dec. ex. Xmas. No smoking in the house. Vegetarian food a speciality. Other special diets by arrangement. Children welcome. En suite in 2 rooms. Tea/coffee making & TV in all rooms. Credit cards. B. & B. from £13-21, D. £9.

RICHMOND

The Kings Head Hotel, Market Place, Richmond, DL10 4HS (0748) 850220
Open all year. No smoking in dining room & some bedrooms. Vegetarian and vegan standard. Most other special diets by arrangement. Licensed. Disabled access. Children welcome. Pets by arrangement. En suite, tea/coffee-making & T.V. in all rooms. Credit cards. B. & B. from £34.75.

Peat Gate Head, Low Row in Swaledale, Richmond, DL11 6PP (0748) 86388.
Open all year. No smoking in dining room, 1 sitting room & bedrooms. Vegetarian standard. Other diets by arrangement. Licensed. Disabled access: ground floor bedroom . Children: over 5s only. En suite in 3 rooms. Tea/coffee-making in all rooms. T.V. in 1 sitting room. D., B. & B. from £32.50.

The Restaurant on the Green, 5 - 7 Bridge St, Richmond, DL10 4RW (0748) 826229

On the north east corner of the Green beneath the castle ramparts and near to the rushing River Swale you will find the Restaurant on the Green, which was established in July 1989 by the chef/owners, Alan and Helen Bennett, who quickly gained an excellent local reputation for good food, fine wines and efficient service; such was their acclaim that in 1992 they decided to welcome overnight guests who are accommodated in lovely en suite accommodation - taking care of the "who will drive?" decision that mars most evening meals out. The restaurant is an old stone building which was rebuilt in 1689: with two early 18th C. sundials and fine Georgian sash windows, it has plenty of character and the atmosphere therein is intimate and cosy. The food is, its owners tell me, 'bistro' in style (Seafood Crêpes, Spaghetti con i Gamberi alla Marinara, etc.) and the wine selection is eclectic and the owner's personal choice. Good food, good wine and an excellent night's sleep; what more could you want? If it's good walks and fresh air - you're also in the right place: Richmond is on the edge of the Dales (some of the spectacular scenery can be enjoyed from one of bedrooms).
Open all year ex. Xmas. No smoking in the house. Vegetarian & other diets by arrangement. Licensed. Children welcome. En suite, TV & tea/coffee-making in rooms. Credit cards. B. & B. £16.50, single £23, D. around £11.

Ridgeway Guest House, 47 Darlington Rd, Richmond, DL10 7BG (0748) 823801

Ridgeway is a 1920's detached house standing in an acre of lovely gardens, with ample unobstructed parking space. It has been built to a high standard from cut York stone, and stands under a steeply pitched, slated roof and is architecturally interesting both inside and out. A fascinating collection of furniture, clocks and china complement the house - and one bedroom contains a 4-poster bed. Food and service are in the best English tradition and locally grown produce is used where possible in cooking. You are well situated for exploring the cobbled streets of Richmond, with its Norman castle & Georgian theatre.
Open all year. No smoking in the house. Vegetarian & other diets by arrangement. Table licence. Children & pets by arrangement. En suite & tea/coffee-making in all rooms. T.V. in sitting room. B. & B. from £17. D. £10.

ROBIN HOODS BAY

Falconhurst Wholefood Guest House, Mount Pleasant South, Robin Hoods Bay, Nr Whitby, YO22 4RQ (0947) 880582
Open Easter to Sept. No smoking in the house. Vegetarian/wholefood standard. Children and pets by arrangement. Tea/coffee-making in all rooms. TV in lounge. B. & B. from £16. D. £10.

Meadowfield Bed & Breakfast, Mount Pleasant North, Robin Hood's Bay, Nr Whitby, YO22 4RE (0947) 880564
Victorian house; clean and comfortable with plenty of good food. Centrally heated.
Open all year. No smoking in dining room & all public areas. Vegetarian & vegan diets available. Children welcome. One en suite room. Tea/coffee-making facilities. T.V. available. B. & B. from £13.50.

SCARBOROUGH

Amber Lodge, 17 Trinity Rd, Scarborough, YO11 2TD (0723) 369088
Edwardian house of great charm and character, peacefully situated in a conservation area 10 mins walk from South Bay & the town centre. Centrally heated. Fresh ingredients used in cooking. *Open Mar. to Oct. No smoking in the house. Vegetarian standard. Other special diets by arrangement. Children welcome. En suite 5 rooms. Tea/coffee-making & T.V. in all rooms. Credit cards B. & B. from £14. D. £6.*

Derwent House Hotel, 6 Rutland Terrace, Queens Parade, Scarborough, YO12 1JB (0723) 373880
Open all year. No smoking throughout. Vegetarian by arrangement. Licensed. Children welcome. En suite in 6 rooms. Tea/coffee-making & T.V. in all rooms. B. & B. from £16.50. D. £6.

Excelsior Private Hotel, 1 Marlborough St, Scarborough, YO12 7HG (0723) 360716

The Excelsior is a small private hotel beautifully situated on a corner of the North Bay; both the North and South bays can be seen from the hotel; there is a T.V. in the comfortable lounge. Much of the food is home made from fresh ingredients - including the bread, preserves, cakes, soups and sweets. You are well placed at the Excelsior for enjoying cliff and coastal walks, the beaches and parks and many attractions of Scarborough and your hosts, Raymond and Irene Brown, will do everything they can to ensure your stay is a happy and memorable one. Weekly terms and short breaks available. *Open Easter to Oct. No smoking throughout. Vegetarian & other special diets by arrangement, but not vegan. Children welcome.Tea/coffee-making in all bedrooms. T.V. in lounge. B. & B. from £15. D., B. & B. from £18.*

Flower in Hand Hotel, Burr Bank, Scarborough, YO11 1PN (0723) 371471
The Flower in Hand, nestling beneath the castle walls and overlooking the harbour and South Bay, has for 150 years been a much-loved feature of Scarborough's Old Town.
Open all year ex. Xmas/New Year. No smoking in dining room. Vegetarians & other diets. Licensed.Children: over 2s only. En suite in 3 rooms. Tea/coffee-making & T.V. in all rooms. Credit cards. B. & B. from £16.50.

Foxcliffe Tearoom, Station Sq., Ravenscar, Scarborough (0723) 871028
19th C. building which is superbly situated overlooking the countryside. All items freshly prepared including light lunches & afternoon teas. The four spacious letting rooms have sea views. *Open Easter - Sept. No smoking in the house. Vegetarian by arrangement. TV & tea/coffee-making CHildren welcome. B. & B. £13, E.M. £7.*

'The Gypsy', Vegetarian Guesthouse, Church Rd, Ravenscar (0723) 870366
Open all year. No smoking.Vegetarian/wholefood standard. Other diets. Children welcome.

Lea Grae Guest House, Seamer Crossgates, Scarborough, YO12 4ND (0723) 862465
Open all year. No smoking, Vegetarian & vegan. Disabled access. Children welcome. En suite & TV.

Northcote Hotel, 114 Columbus Ravine, Scarborough, YO12 7QZ (0723) 367758
Open May to Oct. No smoking. Children: over 3s welcome. En suite, tea-making & T.V. in all rooms.

Villa Marina, 59 Northstead Manor Drive, Scarborough, YO12 6AF (0723) 361088
The Villa Marina is a superbly appointed detached hotel overlooking Peasholm Park and the Lake, near to the beach and well situated for many of Scarborough's attractions including Kinderland, an indoor pool, Splash World and the Sea-life Centre. The welcome is warm and friendly; bedrooms are light and pleasantly decorated and are equipped with colour T.V. and en suite facilities. Meals are plentiful and varied and are served in the spacious dining room. For the comfort of guests, the Villa Marina is completely smoke-free. Special offers for senior citizens. *Open April to Oct. No smoking throughout. Children: over 3s only. All en suite. Tea/coffee making and T.V. in all rooms. Access, Visa. B. & B. from £18. D., B. & B. from £23.*

Whitestone Farm, Downdale Rd, Staintondale, Scarborough, YO13 OE2 (0723) 870612
Open March to Oct. No smoking in the house. Vegetarian by arrangement. Children welcome. Pets by arrangement. Tea/coffee-making in all bedrooms. T.V. in one lounge. B. & B. from £10. D. £6.50.

Wrea Head House, Wrea Head Farm, Barmoor Lane, Scalby, Scarborough, YO13 0PB (0723) 375844
Open all year. No smoking throughout. Vegetarian by arrangement. Children: over 8s only. En suite, tea/coffee making & T.V. in all rooms. Credit cards. B. & B. from £17.50-£22.

SELBY

Hazeldene Guest House, 32-34 Brook St, Doncaster Rd, Selby, YO8 0AR (0757) 704809
Family-run guest house close to town centre. Private parking. AA listed.
Open all year, ex. Xmas and New Year. No smoking in the house. Special diets by arrangement. Children welcome. Tea/coffee making in all rooms. T.V. in rooms and colour T.V. in lounge. B. & B. from £15-17.

SETTLE

"Halsteads" Bed & Breakfast, 3 Halsteads Terrace, Duke St, BD24 9AP (0729) 822823
A Victorian terraced house with 4 letting rooms, some with private facilities. Conveniently placed between town centre & station. Ideal base for touring Dales, Lakes & Settle-Carlisle Railway. Variety of pubs & restaurants for evening meal.
Open Mar. - Nov. No smoking in the house. Vegetarian by arrangement. Children welcome. Some en suite. TV & tea/coffee-making in bedrooms. B. & B. £16 - 19.50.

Liverpool House, Chapel Square, Settle, BD24 9HR (0729) 822247
Liverpool House, which is situated in a quiet, but central, part of Settle, was built in the 18th C. as a gatehouse for a proposed waterway connecting the town to the Leeds-Liverpool canal. The project was never carried out - but the house is now a comfortable, licensed guest house with bedrooms which have each been decorated and furnished in a manner which complements the architecture and style of this interesting building. Home-cooked food prepared from fresh ingredients is a hallmark of a stay at Liverpool House: in fact advance booking is essential for weekend diners, and menus feature a range of local, as well as traditional, dishes (the home-made soups are a particular speciality). Morning coffee, light lunches, and teas with home-made cakes are available most days, and there are two cosy lounges for guests' use.
Open Feb. 1st to Dec. 22nd incl. No smoking throughout. Vegetarian & other diets by arrangement. Licensed. Children: over 12s only. Tea/coffee making in bedrooms. T.V. in lounge. Visa, Mastercard, Eurocard. B. & B. from £17-19.50.

SKIPTON

Bridge End Farm, Grassington, Threshfield, Skipton, BD23 5NH (0756) 752463
A charming Dales cottage with beams, window seats and a spiral staircase;welcoming log fires; its large gardens run down to the river.
Open all year. No smoking in the house. Vegetarian by arrangement. Children welcome. No pets in house: kennel provided. T.V. in most bedrooms. B. & B. from £18. D. £12.

Devonshire Arms Country House Hotel, Bolton Abbey, Skipton, BD23 6AJ (0756) 710 441

The Devonshire Arms is an historic hotel (hospitality has been offered on this site since the 17th C.) which stands in the heart of the Yorkshire Dales, midway between the east and west coasts. It has been carefully restored and extended, under the personal supervision of the Duchess of Devonshire, to create an hotel of great elegance, character and charm: a stone-flagged reception hall with an open log fire leads into handsome lounges furnished with antiques and family portraits from Chatsworth, and the recently refurbished Burlington restaurant extends into the new, Georgian-style conservatory with its fine views over the lawned gardens to the hills and moors beyond. The food served therein is first-rate: a range of English and Continental dishes are prepared with imagination and flair, and a typical à la carte selection might

feature Mille Feuilles of Smoked Duck and Red Cabbage on a Raspberry Dressing followed by King Prawns Deep Fried in a Cinnamon Batter and Pan Fried Loin of Venison served with a Confit of Cabbage, Bacon and Thyme Spatzle; the desserts are irresistible. The extensive grounds include croquet lawns and a 9-hole putting green, and fly-fishing and clay-pigeon shooting may each be enjoyed locally.
Open all year. No smoking in dining room & bedrooms. Vegetarian by arrangement. Licensed. Disabled access. Children welcome. Pets by arrangement. En suite, tea/coffee-making & TV in all rooms. Access,Visa, Amex, Diners. B. & B. from £85.

Low Skibeden Farm House, Skibeden Rd, Skipton, BD23 6AB (0756) 793849
Low Skibeden is a traditional farm house, with a two-bedroomed holiday cottage nearby, which stands in its own grounds on a livestock smallholding; it has been comfortably furnished throughout and there is a pleasant T.V. lounge for guests' use. Your hosts, Mr and Mrs Simpson, offer tea, coffee and cakes to welcome newly arriving guests and a traditional farmhouse breakfast is served each morning; light refreshments are available each evening at 9.30 p.m.
Open all year. No smoking in the house. Children welcome. En suite in 2 rooms. Tea/coffee-making & T.V. in lounge. B. & B. from £14-16.

WHITBY

Cote Bank Farm, Egton Rd, Aislaby, Whitby (0947) 85314
Cote Bank is a substantial, stone-built 18th C. farmhouse with mullioned windows, log fires and period furniture which stands in a sheltered position amidst a large garden enjoying wonderful country views. The food is wholesome and delicious: fresh produce is used wherever possible and, although this is primarily a bed and breakfast establishment, your hostess, Mrs Howard, will be happy to prepare an evening meal on request. You will find Cote Bank Farm an excellent base for exploring the varied scenery of the North York Moors; Goathland, Robin Hoods Bay and the North York Moors Railway are nearby, while visitors in search of safe, sandy beaches will find them just 5 miles away at historic Whitby with its famous abbey.
Open all year ex. Xmas. No smoking in the house. Vegetarian & other diets by arrangement. Children welcome. H & C, shaver points & tea/coffee-making in all rooms. T.V. in lounge. Amex. B. & B. from £16. D. £9.

'The Low House', Baysdale, Kildale, Nr Whitby, YO21 2SF (0642) 722880
Small 18th C. guest house surrounded by moorland with river nearby; superb views on all sides.
Open Easter to Sept. No smoking in the house. Vegetarian exclusively. Children: over 5s only. B. & B., picnic lunch and dinner from £24.

Grosmont House, Grosmont, Whitby, YO22 5PE (0947) 85539
A Victorian Gentleman's Residence standing in its own extensive grounds.
Open all year. No smoking in the house. Children: over 8s only. Pets by arrangement. T.V. lounge.

1 Well Close Terrace, Whitby, YO21 3AR (0947) 600173
Open most of year but subject to availability. No smoking. Vegetarian standard. B. & B. from £8.50.

Wentworth House, 27 Hudson St, West Cliff, Whitby, YO21 3EP (0947) 602433

Wentworth House is a beautiful 4-storey Victorian house which is conveniently situated just 5 minutes' walk from the harbour, beach and town centre of Whitby. The house is spacious and offers very comfortable centrally heated accommodation in its attractive guest bedrooms, some of which have en suite facilities. The food is wholesome and delicious: everything is freshly prepared (from organic ingredients wherever possible - including free-range eggs) and the proprietors specialise in wholefood vegetarian meals, although non-vegetarian dishes are also available; vegan and other special diets can be accommodated by arrangement and there is a good selection of reasonably priced organic wines. Whitby is a picturesque fishing town with a maze of cobbled streets and houses which huddle on the steep hillsides which sweep down to the harbour; it has much of historical interest to commend it, too, in its ancient abbey, the church of St Mary's & the places which commemorate one of its most famous sons, Cpt. James Cook.

Open all year. No smoking in the house. Vegetarian/wholefood a speciality. Other special diets by arrangement. Licensed. Disabled access: ground floor en suite room with suitable fittings in shower room. Children welcome. En suite in 3 rooms. Tea/coffee-making in all rooms. T.V. lounge. Credit cards. B. & B. from £13. D. £7.50.

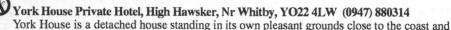 Willow Dale, 17 Carr Hill Lane, Briggswath, Whitby, YO21 1RS (0947) 810525

Open college holidays. No smoking throughout. Vegetarian by arrangement. Disabled access: not easy. Children welcome. En suite, tea/coffee-making & T.V. in all rooms. B. & B. from £16.

York House Private Hotel, High Hawsker, Nr Whitby, YO22 4LW (0947) 880314

 York House is a detached house standing in its own pleasant grounds close to the coast and surrounded by the moorland and farmland of North York Moors National Park, less than 3 miles fom Robin Hood's Bay and Whitby. The en suite bedrooms are tastefully furnished, and each is equipped with a range of helpful amenities including a hairdryer, courtesy tray and colour T.V. The proprietors offer a full English breakfast in the elegant dining room: everything has been home-cooked & an evening meal is available; there is a pleasant lounge and bar for guests' use. **ETB 3 Crown.**

Open Mar.- Oct. inc. No smoking in the house. Special diets by arrangement. Licensed. En suite, tea/coffee making & T.V. in all rooms. B. & B. from £20. D. £10.

YORK

Bowen House, 4 Gladstone St, Huntington Rd, York YO3 7RF (0904) 636881

Late Victorian town house, carefully decorated and furnished with antiques and period furniture. Private car park and close to city centre, restaurants and tourist attractions. Traditional English and vegetarian breakfasts. Reduced winter rates. Brochure available.

Open all year. No smoking throughout. Vegetarian standard. Children welcome. No disabled access. Pets by arrangement. En suite in 2 rooms. Tea/coffee-making & T.V. in bedrooms. Credit cards. B. &. B. from £14.

 *cost; train* £20 *Texi from station   letter of*

City Guest House, 68 Monkgate, York, YO3 7PF (0904) 622483 *conf. £20*

The City Guest House is a lovely Victorian terraced house which is conveniently situated in Monkgate, just a few minutes' walk from the ancient city walls. It is 'comfy, cosy, and a haven for non-smokers', with a choice of single, double or family rooms which have each been decorated and furnished to a very high standard and have en suite facilities; there is a comfortable lounge for guests' use. Breakfast is served in the elegant Victorian dining room (in addition to traditional English there are vegetarian, vegan and continental options available), and there is a wide choice of excellent restaurants within a few minutes' stroll. There is private parking at the City Guest House (essential in York) and you are within walking distance of the Jorvik Centre, York Minster and the Shambles.

Open all year. No smoking. Vegetarian standard. Other diets by arrangement. Children welcome. En suite in most bedrooms. Tea/coffee-making & T.V. in all bedrooms. Credit cards. B. & B. from £14. ETB 2 Crowns.

Claremont Guest House, 18 Claremont Terrace, Gillygate, York, YO3 7EJ (0904) 625158

Claremont Guest House is a small personally-run city centre establishment which is situated in a quiet cul-de-sac of late Victorian terraced houses close to York Minster & within easy walking distance of all the attractions of York. The accommodation is in three attractive guest rooms: there is a Victorian double en suite room which has original stripped pine furniture and fireplace, an old-fashioned high bed (with a modern mattress!), and easy chairs; there are two further double rooms; each room is centrally heated and is equipped with a tea and coffee tray and colour TV. The home-cooked food is served in a pleasant dining room, and a typical evening meal would feature home-made soup followed by Steak and Kidney Pie and Cinnamon Bread and Butter Pudding. *Open all year. No smoking in the house. Vegetarian & other diets by arrangement. 1 room en suite. TV & tea/coffee-making in bedrooms. Children; over 12s only. Credit cards. B. & B. £13 - 20. ETB Commended Listed.*

Dairy Wholefood Guesthouse, 3 Scarcroft Rd, York YO2 1ND (0904) 639367
Open Feb-Dec. No smoking in dining room & sitting room. Vegetarian/wholefood a speciality. Other diets by arrangement. Children welcome. En suite in 2 rooms. Tea/coffee-making & TV in all rooms. B. & B. from £14.

 **The Hazelwood, 24-25 Portland St, Gillygate, York, YO3 7EH Tel & Fax: (0904) 626548**
The Hazelwood was built in 1862 and stands in a quiet residential street in the conservation area of Gillygate, just a short walk from the Minster and the city centre. It has been very attractively furnished and decorated throughout: bedrooms have been equipped with a range of thoughtful little extras - including hair dryer, shoe cleaning equipment and tissues - and most have en suite facilities (three have 4-poster beds); there is also a lounge, with books and games, and a small private walled garden in which to enjoy a quiet drink on a warm summer's evening. Your hosts, Peter and Joy Cox, are very knowledgeable about the area and will do all they can to help you make the most of your stay: they have lots of information about places of interest to be visited nearby - and also the menus of good local restaurants to help you make a choice for your evening meal. *Open all year. No smoking in the house. Vegetarian & other diets by arrangement. Children welcome. En suite, TV & tea/coffee-making in bedrooms. Credit cards. B. & B. £19-25.*

Hobbits Hotel, 9 St Peter's Grove, York, YO3 6AQ (0904) 624538
Comfortable Victorian house with parking in quiet cul-de-sac 10 mins'walk from York centre. *Open all year ex. Xmas. No smoking in dining room & bedrooms. Vegetarian by arrangement. Licensed. Children welcome. Pets by arrangement. En suite, TV & tea-making in rooms. Credit cards. B & B from £22.50.*

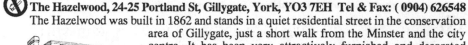 **Holmlea Guest House, 6/7 Southlands Rd, York, YO2 1NP (0904) 621010**
Holmlea is a warm and friendly family-run guest house which is conveniently situated in a quiet position off the main road, with ample street parking. There is a comfortable guests' lounge with colour television and you are just fifteen minutes' walk from the centre of historic York and an hour's drive from both the lovely Yorkshire Dales and the coast. **ETB 3 Crown Commended.** *Open Feb. to end Oct. No smoking in the house. Vegetarian by arrangement. Licensed. Children welcome. Pets by arrangement. En suite in 4 rooms. Tea/coffee-making & T.V. in all bedrooms. B. & B. from £14.*

The Lodge, Earswick Grange, Earswick, York, YO3 9SW (0904) 761387
The Lodge is a modern family home which stands amidst large, well-kept gardens, complete with paddock, free-range hens and apiary (fresh eggs and plenty of honey for breakfast!) in a lovely rural setting near the historic city of York. The house has been very comfortably furnished throughout - there are two spacious bedrooms - and a welcoming open fire burns in the grate on cooler days. You are perfectly situated for visiting both the city of York and for touring the North York Moors & Dales; additionally you are near to Ryedale Sports Stadium & York golf club. *Open all year. No smoking in the house. Vegetarian and other special diets by arrangement. Children welcome. Tea/coffee-making facilities. T.V. in lounge. B. &. B. from £13. ETB 1 Crown.*

Lund House, Main Street, Helperby, Near York, YO6 2NT (0423) 360392
Open all year. No smoking in the house. Vegetarian by arrangement. Disabled access difficult. Children welcome. En suite. Tea/coffee-making in room. T.V. in room. B. & B. from £12.

May Cottage, 44 Main St, Bishopthorpe, York, YO4 4TP (0759) 318846
Self-catering, 2-bedroomed cottage beautifully furnished with antiques. *Open all year No smoking. Children & pets welcome. Colour T.V. £145-£295 p.w.ETB 4 Keys Commended..*

Mulberry Guest House, 124 East Parade, Heworth, York, YO3 7YG (0904) 423468
Mulberry Guest House is a beautifully restored Victorian town house which is situated in a
residential area of York just a short walk from the city centre. Carefully renovated, it retains many
of its original features and has been furnished with care in order to enhance the period charm of
this traditional English home. The care extends to the bedrooms: each has been lovingly furnished
and decorated, and has been equipped with en suite showers, a tea-making tray and a colour TV.
Your hosts serve a traditional English or a Continental breakfast to guests, and there are numerous
places in the city of York in which to enjoy an evening meal (your hosts will help you choose).
Open all year. No smoking in the dining room. Vegetarian & other diets by arrangement. Children welcome.
En suite, TV & tea/coffee-making in all bedrooms. B. & B. £14.50 - 18.50.

Nunmill House, 85 Bishopthorpe Rd, York, YO2 1NX (0904) 634047

Nunmill House is an elegant Victorian residence which has been
lovingly restored by its present owners and now offers
accommodation of an exceptionally high standard to guests: each
of the bedrooms has been furnished and decorated in traditional
style - two rooms have four-posters - and there is a range of helpful
amenities such as tea-making trays and colour TVs (do send for a
colour brochure). Traditional or Continental breakfasts are served
in the elegant dining room, and there are numerous restaurants
nearby where you may enjoy an evening meal. Your hosts, Mr and
Mrs Whitbourn-Hammond, really do everything they can to make
your stay happy and memorable: they are very knowledgeable
about the city and are happy to advise you about its numerous
historic attractions. Having lived in York for 12 years I am biased about its charms, but share the
view that York is a city for everyone: the Minster (Europe's largest medieval cathedral), the Castle
Museum, the city walls appeal historically, aesthetically, architecturally and in every other pleasing
way. A city to enjoy - and to share.
Open Mar. - Oct. No smoking in the dining room & bedrooms. Vegetarian & other diets on request. Children
welcome. En suite, TV & tea/coffee-making in bedrooms. B. & B. from £14.

Papillon, 43 Gillygate, York, YO3 7EA (0904) 636505
Open all year ex. Xmas/New Year. No smoking in the house. Children welcome. En suite in most rooms.
Tea/coffee-making & T.V. in all rooms. B. & B. from £15.

Pond Cottage, Brandsby Rd, Stillington, Nr York, YO6 1NY (0347) 810796
Open Feb to end Nov. No smoking in the house. Vegetarian by arrangement. Children welcome.
Tea/coffee-making in all rooms. T.V. lounge. B. & B. from £12.

Regency House, 7 South Parade, Blossom St, York, YO2 2BA (0904) 633053
Regency House is a Grade II listed building which dates from 1824 and stands in a private
cobbled road within strolling distance of the centre of the city of York, and just 6 minutes' walk
from the railway station. Each of the centrally heated bedrooms has been furnished to a very high
standard and some have en suite facilities; helpful guide books and brochures have been left in
each bedroom to help you plan your stay. The dining room features an old Yorkshire range and a
low beamed ceiling and your hostess, Mrs. Podmore, cooks an excellent breakfast therein (her
Visitors Book bears testament to its popularity); there are numerous good restaurants within easy
walking distance at which you may enjoy an evening meal. There is so much to see and do in the
city of York itself, but visitors are further attracted by the range of other beautiful places within
easy touring distance, such as Whitby, Harrogate, Ripon and the splendours of the North York
Moors National Park.
Open mid-Jan. to mid-Dec. No smoking throughout. Vegetarian & diabetic standard. Children: over 8s only.
Tea/coffee-making & T.V. in all bedrooms. B. & B. from £14.50.

Swallow Hotel, Tadcaster Rd, Dringhouses, York YO2 2QQ (0904) 701000

A member of the Swallow Group, this luxurious and comfortable hotel is surrounded by gardens and overlooks York's scenic Racecourse and the Knavesmire parkland. The Atrium restaurant with its high glass roof and hanging flowers provides a light airy atmosphere and offers first-class cuisine. The Leisure Club has a wide range of free facilities including a fitness section, a relaxation area (with spa bath and sauna), and an indoor heated swimming pool with a separate pool for young children. You are just 5 minutes' drive from the centre of York.

Open all year. No smoking in dining room & part of coffee shop. Vegetarian by arrangement. Licensed. Good disabled access: 2 especially designed bedrooms. Children welcome. Pets by arrangement. En suite, TV & tea/coffee-making in all bedrooms. Access, Visa, Amex, Diners. B. & B. from £47.50. D. £17.95.

Wellgarth House, Wetherby Rd, Rufforth,YO2 3QB (0904) 83592; after Spring '93: (0904) 738592

Detached house in the delightful village of Rufforth, 4 miles from York. Glider flying, microlight flying, museum of mechanical music, car boot sales & clay pigeon shooting, all locally!

Open all year ex. Xmas. No smoking in dining room. Vegetarian & other diets by arrangement. Children welcome. Pets by arrangement. En suite, TV & tea/coffee-making in rooms. Credit cards. B. & B. from £14.

Restaurants

CROPTON

The New Inn & New Inn Restaurant, Cropton, Nr Pickering, YO18 8HH (07515 330)

For further details please see under the entry in the Accommodation section.

GRASSINGTON

 Dales Kitchen Tearooms, 51 Main Street, Grassington, BD23 5AA (0756) 753077

Open 10 - 5. Meals from 12 - 5. No smoking in the restaurant. Licensed. Very good disabled access.

HARROGATE

Betty's Café Tearooms, 1 Parliament St, Harrogate, HG1 2QU (0423) 502746

60% no-smoking. Vegetarian standard. Licensed. Children very welcome Access, Visa.

 Debenhams, 22-30 Parliament St, Harrogate (0423) 68234

Springles, a friendly self-service restaurant serving lunches, snacks and hot & cold drinks.

Open store hours. No smoking throughout. Vegetarian. Disabled access. Children welcome. Credit/debit cards.

Green Park Hotel, Valley Drive, Harrogate, HG2 OJT Tel: (0423) 504681 Fax (0423) 530811

Open 12 - 1.30, 7 - 8.30. No smoking in restaurant. Vegetarian by arrangement. Licensed. Children welcome.

Low Hall Hotel & Coachhouse Restaurant, Ripon Rd, Killinghall, Harrogate. (0423) 508598

Open 12 - 2.30, 6 - 9.30. No smoking in restaurant. Vegetarian and vegan standard. Most other special diets on request, preferably with prior arrangement. Licensed. Disabled access. Access, Visa.

KNARESBOROUGH

 Blenkhorn's Café, 2 Waterside, Knaresborough, HG5 9AZ (0423) 862105

Waterside café and snack bar in the picturesque town of Knaresborough.

 4 Park Place Restaurant, 4 Park Place, Knaresborough, HE5 OGR (0423) 868002

Open from 7.30pm. No smoking. Licensed. Vegetarian by arrangement. Children welcome. Visa.

 Pollyanna's Tea Room, Jockey Lane, High St, Knaresborough (0423) 869208

Open 10 - 5 daily. No smoking. Licensed. Vegetarian standard. Disabled access. Children welcome.

NORTHALLERTON
Bettys Café Tearooms, 188 High St, Northallerton, DL7 8LF (0609) 775154
70% no-smoking. Vegetarian standard. Licensed. Disabled access but no access to toilets. Children welcome.

PICKERING
The Blacksmith's Arms and Restaurant, Aislaby, Pickering, YO18 8PE (0751) 72182
No smoking in restaurant. Vegetarian & vegan standard. Licensed. Disabled access. Children welcome.

RICHMOND
The King's Head Hotel, Richmond, DL10 4HS (0748) 850220
No smoking in restaurant. Vegetarian standard. Licensed. Disabled access. Children welcome. Credit cards.

RIPON
 **The Old Deanery Restaurant, Minster Rd, Ripon, HG4 1QS (0765) 3518**
No smoking throughout. Licensed. Vegetarian & diabetic standard. Disabled access. Children welcome.

SCARBOROUGH
 **Debenhams, Brunswick Pavilion, Vernon Rd, Scarborough (0723) 368181**
Pavilion, a friendly self-service coffee shop serving lunches, snacks and hot and cold drinks.
Open store hours. No smoking. Vegetarian meals. Disabled access. Children welcome. Credit/debit cards.

Foxcliffe Tearoom, Station Sq., Ravenscar, Scarborough (0723) 871028
No smoking. Vegetarian by arrangement. Children welcome. Wheelchair access.

SETTLE
Car and Kitchen, Settle, BD24 9EF (0729) 823638
Family run business established in 1976; snacks and lunches from the finest fresh ingredients.
Open 9.30 - 5, L. 12 - 2.30. No smoking throughout. Vegetarian standard. Children welcome. Credit cards.

Pen-y-ghent Café, Horton-in-Ribblesdale, Nr Settle, BD24 OHE (07296) 333
No smoking throughout. Vegetarian and other special diets by arrangement. Children welcome.

SKIPTON
Dales Teapot, Ropewalk, Albion Square, Skipton (0756) 793416
No smoking throughout. Vegetarian standard. Licensed. Good disabled access.

Devonshire Arms Country House Hotel, Bolton Abbey, Skipton, BD23 6AJ (075671) 441
For further details please see under the entry in the accommodation section.

'Herbs', Healthy Life Natural Food Centre, 10 High St, Skipton (0756) 790619
No smoking throughout. Vegetarian exclusively but other special diets on request. Children's portions.

WHITBY
Magpie Café, 14 Pier Rd, Whitby (0947) 602058
The Magpie Café building dates from the 1750s when it was owned by a whaler. Subsequently it

became a shipping office and then, in the 1930's, a café which is now in the third generation of the McKenzie family. All the food is fresh -notably the fish (including crab, lobster, and salmon) which is landed at the quayside opposite - and the menu offers a choice of over 30 home made desserts as well as cakes, jam and chutney. Children will love the food on their own menu with shortbread elephants, chocolate fish ice cream and jelly baby jelly!

Something for everyone - including those on special diets.
98 seats. Open 11.30 - 6.30. L. from around £6. 50% no-moking.Vegetarian, Weight watchers, diabetic and gluten-free standard. Licensed. Excellent facilities for children, including children's menu. Visa, Mastercard.

YORK

Bettys Café Tearooms, St Helens Square, York (0904) 659142
70% no-smoking. Licensed. Vegetarian. Disabled access but not to toilets. Children very welcome.

The Blake Head Vegetarian Café, 104 Micklegate, York YO1 1JX (0904) 623767
No smoking in restaurant. Disabled access. Children's portions. Access, Visa, Amex.

Debenhams, 5 Coney St, York (0904) 656644
Chinwags, a friendly self-service coffee shop serving lunches, snacks and hot and cold drinks.
Open store hours. No smoking. Vegetarian. Disabled access. Children very welcome. Credit/debit cards.

Four Seasons Restaurant, 45 Goodramgate, York (0904) 633787
15th C. half timbered restaurant - a culinary and architectural treat!
50% no-smoking.Vegetarian standard. Licensed. Children welcome. Credit cards.

Gillygate Wholefood Bakery, Millers Yard, York, YO3 7EB (0904) 610676
Wholefood bakery shop and restaurant. Vegetarian wholefood menu.
No smoking. Vegetarian exclusively. Disabled access. Children welcome.

The Greenhouse Café, 12a Church St, York, YO1 2BB (0904) 629615
No smoking throughout. Vegetarian standard. Licensed. Disabled access. Children welcome.

The Rubicon, 5 Little Stonegate, York (0904) 676076
No smoking throughout. Vegetarian exclusively. Bring your own wine. Children welcome.

Taylors in Stonegate, 46 Stonegate, York, YO1 2AS (0904) 622865
Family run Tea Rooms and Coffee shop founded in 1886. Outstanding variety of teas and coffees offered together with many Yorkshire and Continental specialities.
70% no-smoking. Children's portions. Access, Visa.

Treasurer's House Tea Rooms, Minster Yard, York (0904) 624247/646757
Tastefully furnished tea room in 17th C. Treasurer's House behind York Minster.
Open daily April - Dec. Smoking banned throughout.

The York Arms, High Petergate, York (0904) 624508
No smoking in upstairs dining room (lunchtime). Vegetarian available.

Pubs & Wine Bars

CROPTON

The New Inn & New Inn Restaurant, Cropton, Nr Pickering (07515) 330
No smoking in conservatory which is for drinking and dining.
For further details please see under the entry in the accommodation section.

YORK

Wilde's Wine Bar and Brasserie, Grape Lane, York
Small, intimate wine bar/bistro with pleasant atmosphere and one smoke-free room; imaginative dishes prepared from fresh local produce. Comprehensive wine list. Live jazz on Saturday nights.
Open 11 - 11, Mon. to Sat. Separate no-smoking room (18 seats). Lunch around £3.95. Vegetarian available. Wheelchair access. Children welcome. Access, Visa, Amex.

South Yorkshire
Accommodation

DONCASTER

Canda, Hampole Balk Lane, Skellow, Doncaster (0302) 724028
Open all year. No smoking in the house. Good disabled access: 6 rooms on ground floor. Children: over 9s only. En suite in 6 rooms. Tea/coffee-making facilities. T.V. Credit cards. B. & B. from £17.

SHEFFIELD

Forte Crest Sheffield, Manchester Rd., Broomhill, Sheffield, S10 5DX (0742) 670067
Open all year. No smoking in 50% of bedrooms & 60% dining room. Licensed. Children welcome. Pets by arrangement. En suite & tea-making in all rooms. Credit cards. Room only £70, English Breakfast £8.50.

Parkfield House, 97 Norfolk Rd, Sheffield (0742) 720404
Open all year. Smoking banned throughout house. Vegetarian standard. Most other special diets by arrangement. Tea/coffee-making & T.V. in all bedrooms. B. & B. from £15.

Restaurants & Pubs

DONCASTER

Woolworths plc, 30/36 St Sepulchre's Gate, Doncaster, DN1 1JY (0302) 368486
Woolworth's Tea Bar is a spacious in-store cafe in which you can enjoy breakfast, lunch and a wide range of snacks. The wholesome hot meals feature a good selection of options such as baked potatoes with a variety of fillings, cauliflower cheese, cottage pie, lasagne verdi and chilli con carne; the cold sweet menu varies but would typically include lemon meringue pie, egg custards, double chocolate gateau and blackcurrant cheesecake. Snacks such as granary sandwiches, hoagies and 'doorstep'sandwiches are also available and you can choose from a range of popular fillings such as cheese and tomato, salad mayonnaise, tuna and cucumber, and ham. The Tea Bar is especially welcoming to children and there are baby changing facilities, a bottle-warming service, high chairs and a children's menu. Daily newspapers are provided for customers' enjoyment. The cafe, incidentally, was a 1992 Heartbeat Award winner.
142 seats. Open Mon - Thurs 9 - 5, Fri, Sat 8.30 - 5. L. 11.30 - 2.30. No smoking throughout. Vegetarian and low-fat standard. Disabled access. Children welcome. Credit cards.

SHEFFIELD

Crucible Coffee Shop, Crucible Theatre, Norfolk St, Sheffield, S1 1DA (0742) 760621
Theatre coffee shop. Snacks, baked potatoes, cakes.
Up to 100 seats. Open 10 - 9. L. around £3. Smoking banned in 75% of coffee shop & foyer areas. Vegetarian standard. Disabled access. Children welcome. No credit cards, but luncheon vouchers accepted.

Debenhams, The Moor, Sheffield (0742) 568555
Intermission, a friendly self-service coffee shop serving lunches, snacks and hot and cold drinks.
Open store hours. No smoking. Vegetarian meals. Children very welcome.. Credit/debit cards.

The Fat Cat Pub, 23 Alma St., Sheffield (0742) 728195
Award-winning hostelry with exceptionally wide variety of beverages including draught cider, Old Organic Wines and 10 draught beers (including their own brew!); excellent home-cooked food.
Meals served 12 - 2.30. No smoking in 1 bar (separated from smoking bar by corridor). Vegetarian and vegan standard. Disabled access. Children not allowed in bar by law. Pets welcome.

Frog & Parrot, Division St, Sheffield (0742) 721280
Smoking banned in 2 areas of pub.

West Yorkshire Accommodation

DEWSBURY

Ⓝ Ayton Guest House, 11 Park Rd, Westborough, Dewsbury, WF13 4LQ (0924) 469480
Open all year. No smoking in the house. Vegetarian by arrangement. Children welcome. En suite in 2 rooms.
Tea/coffee-making facilities available. T.V. lounge. B. & B. from £12.50.

HALIFAX

Ⓝ Glenmore Guest House, 19 Savile Park, Halifax, HX1 3EA (0422) 341500
Surrounded by beautiful countryside, Glenmore faces directly onto a tree-lined park and has a welcoming serenity and charm, Spacious en suite bedrooms. Continental or English breakfast. Excellent public transport at door. Trains can be met. *ETB Highly Commended.*
Open Feb. to Dec. No smoking in the house. Vegetarian & other diets by arrangement. Children welcome. En suite, tea/coffee-making facilities & T.V. (including Satellite) in all bedrooms. B. & B. £19.

Ⓝ Wood End, Lighthazels Rd, Ripponden, Sowerby Bridge, HX6 4NP (0422) 824397
Open all year. No smoking in the house. Vegetarian by arrangement. Children welcome. Pets by arrangement.
En suite in 1 room. Tea/coffee-making in both bedrooms. T.V. lounge. B. & B. from £15

HEBDEN BRIDGE

Ⓝ Redacre Mill, Mytholmroyd, Hebden Bridge, HX7 5DQ (0422) 885563

This small, Victorian cotton mill, set in peaceful countryside by the Rochdale Canal, has been delightfully restored and luxuriously furnished to provide accommodation of a very high standard. All meals are prepared from fresh ingredients - including home-grown vegetables - and the evening menu features both traditional and more unusual dishes; meals are served in an airy dining room overlooking the canal. The South Pennines provides excellent walking opportunities - including the Calderdale and Pennine Ways, and Redacrel is within easy reach of "Bronte Country", "Summer Wine Country" & Emmerdale Farm. *ETB 3 Crown Highly Commended.*
Open Feb. to Nov. No smoking in the house. Vegetarian and most other special diets by arrangement. Licensed.
Children welcome. En suite, tea/coffee-making & T.V. in rooms. Access, Visa. B. & B. from £22.50.

HOLMFIRTH

Holme Castle Country Hotel, Holme Village, Holmfirth, HD7 1QG (0484) 686764
Large Victorian house in a mature, walled garden with magnificent views of the surrounding hills & moorland; beautifully furnished; fabulous food with excellent vegetarian choices.
Open all year. No smoking. Vegetarian by arrangement. Licensed. Children welcome. En suite 5 rooms. T.V.,
radio alarm & hairdryer in rooms. Access, Visa. B. & B. from £25 (reduced Fri., Sat. & Sun.) D. £19.

HUDDERSFIELD

Elm Crest Guest House, 2 Queens Rd, Edgerton, Huddersfield, HD2 2AG Tel: (0484) 530990 Fax: (0484) 516227
Elm Crest Guest House is a large detached 8-bedroomed Victorian house which stands amidst its own attractive gardens in a peaceful tree-lined residential street just a few minutes' drive from both the town centre and junction 24 of the M62. It has been very comfortably furnished and appointed (it has 2 Crowns from the English Tourist Board and the Good Room Award), and the proprietors extend a very warm and friendly welcome to guests. With its proximity to the town centre - and its easy access via the M62 to so many of the attractions of both West and North

Yorkshire - the Elm Crest is the perfect choice for both the business traveller and tourists enjoying a short break. *AA 2 "Q" Award. Les Routier. ETB 3 Crown Commended.*
Open Jan. to Dec. No smoking in the house. Licensed. Children: over 5s only.En suite in 5 rooms. T.V. in all rooms. Access, Visa, Amex. B. & B. from £22.

ILKLEY

Beech House, 5 St James Rd, Ilkley, LS29 9PY (0943) 601995
Spacious Victorian house, close to the town centre and public transport. Quiet location within easy walking distance of riverside and moor.
Open all year. No smoking in the house. Vegetarian & other diets by arrangement. Children welcome. Pets by arrangement. Tea/coffee-making in all bedrooms. T.V. in most bedrooms. B. & B. from £12.

LEEDS

Beegee's Guest House, 18 Moor Allerton Drive, Off Street Lane, Moortown, Leeds, LS17 6RZ Tel: (0532) 666221 Fax: (0532) 753300
Guest house with full central heating, personally run by Betty and Bernard Gibbs.
Open Jan. to Dec. No smoking in the house. Vegetarian by arrangement. Ground floor family room. Children welcome. Some rooms en suite. Tea-making & T.V. in rooms. Single £18-22, double £28-32, family on request.

B. & B. Leeds, 118 Grovehall Drive, Leeds, LS11 7ET (0532) 704445
Open all year. No smoking in the house. Children welcome. T.V. available. B. & B. from £12.

The White House, 157 Middleton Park Rd, Leeds, LS10 4LZ (0532) 711231
Smoke-free guest house in South Leeds suburb. Large park and woodland, plus 2 golf courses nearby. 5 mins M1 and M62. Bus from front door. Safe parking. *Non-smokers only.*
Open all year. Non-smokers only. Vegetarian by arrangement. TV & tea/coffee-making in rooms. B. & B. £15.

WAKEFIELD

Cedar Court Hotel, Denby Dale Rd, Calder Grove, Wakefield, WF4 3QZ (0924) 276310
Open all year. No smoking in part of dining room & some bedrooms. Vegetarian by arrangement. Licensed. Disabled access. Children welcome. Pets by arrangement. En suite, tea/coffee-making & T.V. in all bedrooms. Access, Visa, Amex, Diners, Eurocard. B. & B. from £48.50. D. from £21.50

WETHERBY

Glendales, Muddy Lane, Linton, Nr Wetherby, LS22 4HW (0937) 585915
Lovely, large detached house overlooking the village green in Linton near Wetherby; country setting yet just 10 minutes from the A1 and at the half way point between London and Edinburgh.
Open all year. No smoking in the house. Vegetarian & other diets by arrangement. Children: over 12s only. Pets welcome. En suite in 1 room. Tea/coffee-making. T.V. B. & B. from £15.

50 Westgate, Wetherby, LS22 4NJ (0937) 63106
Open all year. No smoking in restaurant and most public areas. Vegetarian by arrangement. Children welcome. Tea/coffee-making facilities in all bedrooms. T.V in lounge. B. & B. from £13.

Wood Hall, Linton, Nr Wetherby, LS22 4JA (0937) 67271
Open all year. No smoking in dining room & bedrooms. Vegetarian standard. Licensed. Disabled access. Children welcome. Pets by arrangement. En suite & T.V. in all bedrooms. Credit cards. B. & B. from £55.

Restaurants

BRIGHOUSE

Brook's Restaurant, 6 Bradford Rd, Brighouse, HD6 1RW (0484) 715284
No smoking in dining room. Vegetarian standard. Licensed. Children welcome (no high chairs).

HUDDERSFIELD

The Blue Rooms, 9 Byram Arcade, Westgate, Huddersfield (0484) 512373

The Blue Rooms are situated in a beautiful, refurbished Victorian arcade in the heart of bustling Huddersfield. The proprietor has worked hard to create just the right kind of ambience - classical music, pleasing decor, an informal, friendly atmosphere - and as a consequence the café is exceedingly popular with a wide cross-section of Huddersfield folk, 'from lawyers to students to shoppers...'Pleasing ambience notwithstanding, the repeat visits are clearly a direct result of the dependably excellent food: everything is home-prepared daily from fresh, additive-free ingredients (including free-range eggs), and the mouth-watering menu features a wide range of tasty options including, in addition to tasty sandwiches, snacks and full meals, some wonderful hot French bread sandwiches, baked potatoes, pancakes and, to follow, delicious wholemeal cakes and puddings; vegan, gluten-free and vegetarian dishes are clearly denoted so on the menu.

69 seats. Open 10 - 5, Mon. to Sat. No smoking in 80% of restaurant. L. around £3. Vegetarian and wholefood standard; vegan and gluten-free options available. Licensed. Children welcome.

ILKLEY

Bettys Café Tea Rooms, 32/34 The Grove, Ilkley, LS29 9EE (0943) 608029
75% no-smoking. Licensed. Disabled access to restaurant but not toilets. Children welcome. Access, Visa.

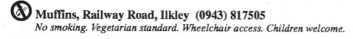

Christchurch Coffee Centre, The Grove, Ilkley, LS29 8LW (0943) 603209
No smoking throughout. Disabled access: ramp. Children welcome.

Muffins, Railway Road, Ilkley (0943) 817505
No smoking. Vegetarian standard. Wheelchair access. Children welcome.

Roman Pergola, 7 Leeds Rd, Ilkley, LS29 8DH (0943) 608639
No smoking throughout. Licensed. Children welcome.

Sweet Indulgence Tearooms, 8 The Grove, Ilkley, LS29 6EG (0943) 816927
No smoking throughout. Children welcome. Credit cards.

LEEDS

Debenham's, 121 Briggate, Leeds LS1 6LX (0532) 435333
Pavilion, a friendly self-service coffee shop serving lunches, snacks and hot and cold drinks.
Open store hours. No smoking. Vegetarian meals. Disabled access. Children welcome. Credit/debit cards.

Lewis's Ltd, The Headrow, Leeds, LS1 (0532) 413131 Ext 17
There are no less than 3 restaurants in the department store at Lewis's in Leeds and each of them has excellent smoke-free facilities. The Rendezvous Restaurant is totally smoke-free and is open from 9 till 5.30, offering a wide selection of reasonably priced salads, sandwiches and cakes. The Dales Restaurant is also open during shopping hours, and has reserved 50% of its seats for non smokers; in addition to offering a wide range of snacks, the Dales Restaurant has a good choice of hot and cold meals for both vegetarians and meat-eaters. Those looking for just a quick pick-me-up cup of coffee would enjoy visiting the Coffee Shop with its 50% smoke-free area; there are lots of tempting cream cakes to choose from, and afternoon tea is also served.
Open 9 - 5.30. Smoke-free facilities in all restaurants.Children welcome. Wheelchair access to all restaurants.

The Queens Hotel, City Square, Leeds, LS1 1PL (0532) 431323
Ridings Roast Room: 98 seats, Clubhouse Restaurant, 46 seats. Smoking banned in up to 75% of Ridings Roast Room (partitions); up to 25% of Clubhouse.. Most special diets catered for, particularly high-fibre, low-fat and gluten-free. Licensed. Excellent disabled access. Children welcome. Credit cards accepted.

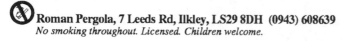

Strawberry Fields Bistro, 159 Woodhouse Lane, Leeds 2 (0532) 431515
Intimate friendly family-run bistro serving a wide variety of vegetarian and meat dishes.
80 seats. Open Mon. - Fri., 11.45 - 2.15, Mon. - Sat. 6 - 11. Main course £4 - £8. Smoking banned in 75% of restaurant. Vegetarian standard. Other special diets available if you phone first. Disabled access, but not to toilets. Children welcome. Access, Visa, Luncheon Vouchers.

WETHERBY

The Penguin Hotel, Leeds Rd, Wetherby, LS22 SHE (0937) 63881
Vegetarian standard. Other special diets require 24hrs notice. Smoking banned in 50% of restaurant. Disabled access. Licensed. Children welcome. Credit cards.

Wood Hall Hotel, Linton, Nr Wetherby, LS22 4JA (0937) 67271
A delightful Georgian house set in its own parkland, sumptuously furnished and with panoramic views; meals prepared from fresh, quality produce.
No smoking in restaurant. Vegetarian on request. Disabled access. Licensed. Children welcome. Credit cards.

Pubs & Wine Bars

BRADFORD
Halfway House, 45 Otley Rd, Baildon, Bradford, BD17 (0274) 584610
No-smoking area.

GUISELEY
The Station, 70 Otley Rd, Guiseley (0943) 872061
No smoking in one area until 6pm.

LEEDS
Fox and Hounds, Tinshill Rd, Cookridge, Leeds, LS16 (0532) 678415
No-smoking area.

Old Griffin Head Inn, Branch End, Gildersome, Leeds, LS27 7ES (0532) 533159
Old world traditional village pub with open fires, oak beams etc.; famous for hot beef and turkey sandwiches!
Serving food 12 - 2.30, 5.30 - 8.30. No smoking in one room. Wheelchair access.

Nags Head, 20 Town St, Chapel Allerton, Leeds LS7 (0532) 624938
Smoking banned in one room.

Punch Clock, Low Rd, Hunslet, Leeds, LS10 (0532) 774165
No-smoking area.

Travellers, Selny Rd, Halton, Leeds, LS15 (0532) 645340
No-smoking area.

Wellington Inn, Wetherby Rd, Leeds, LS17 (0532) 651991
No-smoking area.

Wrens Hotel, 61 New Briggate, Leeds (0532) 458888
No smoking in one room.

SOWERBY BRIDGE
The Moorings, Canal Basin, Sowerby Bridge (0422) 833940
Converted 1790 canal side warehouse, serving range of good reasonably priced food, a large selection of malt whiskies, imported bottled beers and real ales.
Open 11.30 - 3, 5 - 11(from 6 on Sat. & 7 on Mon.) No smoking in family room. Vegetarian standard. Children welcome in family room until 8.30. Wheelchair access.

Humberside
Accommodation

BRIDLINGTON

The Tennyson, 19 Tennyson Ave., Bridlington, YO15 2EU (0262) 604382
A family run hotel with luxurious lounge and comfortable bedrooms close to the beach, leisure world indoor pool and entertainment.
Open all year. No smoking in dining room & bedrooms. Vegetarian standard, most other special diets by arrangement. Licensed. En suite, tea/coffee-making & T.V. in all rooms. B. & B. from £15. D. from £6.

DRIFFIELD

Middleton Wold Cottages, Middleton-on-the-Wolds, Driffield, YO25 9DD (037781) 635
Stone cottage in secluded grounds. Beautifully furnished south facing bedrooms. Home cooking.
Open all year ex. Xmas and New Year. No smoking in the house. Vegetarian & vegan by arrangement. Children welcome. Tea/coffee-making facilities. T.V. in bedrooms. B. & B. from £13.

HULL

Marina Post House Hotel, Castle St, Hull, HU1 2BX (0482) 225221
Open all year. No smoking in part of dining room & some bedrooms. Vegetarian & other diets by arrangement. Licensed. Disabled access. Children welcome. Pets by arrangement. En suite, tea/coffee-making & T.V. in all bedrooms. Credit cards

Restaurants

DRIFFIELD

The Bell Hotel, Market Place, Driffield, YO25 7AP
No smoking in restaurant area. Open 12 - 1.30, 7 - 10. Vegetarian. Disabled access. Pets by arrangement.

HULL

Debenhams, Prospect St, Hull (0482) 25151
Chinwags, a friendly self-service coffee shop serving popular light lunches, snacks and a wide range of hot and cold drinks.
Open store hours. No smoking. Vegetarian meals. Disabled access. Children welcome. Credit/debit cards.

STAMFORD BRIDGE

Three Cups, Stamford Bridge (0759) 71396
Open pub hours. No smoking in restaurant. Children welcome in dining areas until 9pm.

The North East

Cleveland
Accommodation

MIDDLESBOROUGH

The Highfield Hotel, Marton Road, Middlesborough, Cleveland, TS4 2PA (0642) 817638
Built around the turn of the century as a family home & retaining something of its earlier ambience, the Highfield is set in pleasant grounds and, though overlooking the A172, it is reasonably secluded. *Open all year. No smoking in 50% of dining room & in public bar. Vegetarian by arrangement. Licensed. Disabled access. Children welcome. En suite, TV & tea/coffee-making in bedrooms. Credit cards accepted.*

STOCKTON-ON-TEES

Swallow Hotel, John Walker Square, Stockton-on-Tees, TS18 1AQ (0642) 679721
The Swallow Hotel at Stockton on Tees is a modern 4 star hotel right in the heart of the town centre.  50 of the 124 en suite bedrooms are totally smoke-free and each is equipped with a Satellite TV, direct dial phone, hairdryer and iron (trouser presses can also be provided). There are two restaurants: in the Portcullis both table d'hote and a la carte menus are available and, with a less formal atmosphere, the Matchmaker Brasserie (named after John Walker, the Stockton man who first came up with the bright idea of the match!), offers a range of meals and snacks. The Swallow Leisure club has an Egyptian theme and includes a heated pool, jacuzzi, sauna and steam room in addition to a minigym, climbing and cycling machines, rower and sunbeach area. There are conference and banqueting facilities for up to 300 delegates - each conference receives free use of overhead projector, flip charts and notepads - and the professional team can provide any additional equipment that you require.

Open all year. No smoking in over 50% of the brasserie & in some bedrooms. Vegetarian & other diets by arrangement. Licensed. Disabled access. Children welcome. Pets by arrangement. En suite, TV & tea/coffee-making in all bedrooms. Credit cards. B. & B. from £43.

Restaurants

MIDDLESBROUGH

ⓧBarneys, 19 St Barnabas Road, Linthorpe, Middlesborough, TS5 6JR (0642) 826385
Retail shop and café staffed by volunteers from St Barnabas Parish Church; all food cooked fresh on the premises; home-made soup, quiches and savoury dishes such as lasagne, Moussaka, vegetarian loaf, filled potatoes & salads. Sweets include gateaux, cheesecakes, fruit pies, meringues, fruit salad. Shop sells wide range of gifts, books, greeting cards & childrens'clothes. *20 seats. Open 11.30 - 4. L. from £1. No smoking throughout. Vegetarian standard. Disabled access. Children especially welcome (play-pen and playing area provided).*

ⓧDebenhams, The Corner, 1 Newport Rd, Middlesborough (0642) 245201
Springles, a friendly self-service restaurant serving lunches, snacks and hot and cold drinks. *Open store hours. No smoking. Vegetarian. Disabled access. Children welcome. Credit/debit cards.*

STOCKTON-ON-TEES

ⓧ Debenhams, 149 High St, Stockton-on-Tees (0642) 607881
A friendly self-service coffee shop serving lunches, snacks and hot and cold drinks. *Open store hours. No smoking. Vegetarian. Disabled access. Children welcome. Credit/debit cards.*

Co Durham and Tyne & Wear Accommodation

BISHOP AUCKLAND

⊗ Grove House, Hamsterley Forest, Bishop Auckland, DL13 1NL (0388) 88203
Open Jan. to Nov. No smoking throughout. Vegetarian and other special diets by arrangement. Children: over 8s only. Tea/coffee making in all rooms. T.V. in lounge. B. &. B. from £19.

CHESTER-LE-STREET

⊗ 'Crakemarsh' Guest House, Mill Lane, Plawsworth Gate, Chester-le-Street, DH2 3LG (091) 371 2464
This award-winning guest house (just voted '1990 Guest House of the Year' as we went to press) is a lovely country house with panoramic views just 5 minutes from Durham city centre, and 10 minutes from Beamish Museum and the Metro Centre. Several other amenities are close to hand including Durham County Cricket Ground, Lumley Castle and an 18-hole golf course (bookings may be made by arrangement with your hosts). Crakemarsh has been quite beautifully furnished throughout - all rooms have been tastefully designed by the owner - and, although breakfast is the only meal available at Crakemarsh, the local pub, which is a short walk away, does excellent evening meals. It is worth mentioning that Crakemarsh's award, which was sponsored by Makro in conjunction with the National Garden Festival, was based on nominations received by guests! High commendation indeed.
Open all year. No smoking throughout. Vegetarian & other diets by arrangement. Some disabled access. Children welcome, family room available. Tea/coffee making & T.V. in all rooms. B. &. B. from £18 (£22 single, children 3 - 12 half price). ETB listed & Commended.

CONSETT

Bee Cottage Farm, Castleside, Consett, DH8 9HW (0207) 508224

Bee Cottage Farm is a working farm set in peaceful and picturesque surroundings close to the Northumberland/Durham border. It is a very friendly place: visitors are welcome to see the animals - mainly young stock - and children especially are encouraged to participate in the easier (and nicer!) bits of farming life (bottle-feeding baby lambs, perhaps even milking the goat!). The farmhouse itself has been very comfortably decorated - there is a welcoming lounge with an open fire - and smoking is restricted to the two external bungalow-type accommodation areas. Guests may stay as self-caterers or take breakfast if they wish, but most visitors will be tempted by the Tea Room which is open from Easter to September and serves quite delicious cream teas!
Open all year. No smoking in main farmhouse building. Vegetarian & other diets by arrangement. Some disabled access. Some en suite. Tea/coffee making. T.V. in guests' lounge. B. & B. from £16. D. £10.

DURHAM

Acorn Guest House, 5 Mowbray St, Durham, DH1 4BH (091) 386 3108
Pleasantly appointed Victorian town house 5 minutes from bus and rail stations and close to park, woods and the city centre.
Open all year. No smoking in dining room & discouraged throughout house. Vegetarian, diabetic and other special diets standard. Children welcome. Tea/coffee making in all rooms. T.V. in guest lounge.

Bees Cottage Guest House, Bridge St, Durham, DH1 4RT (091) 384 5775
Durham's oldest cottage in a central location close to cathedral and castle. Museums, university, river walks and shops all nearby. Private parking.
Open all year. No smoking in dining room & bedrooms. Vegetarian & other diets by arrangement. Children welcome. En suite, TV & tea/coffee-making in all bedrooms. B. & B. from £19, Single £25.

Colebrick, 21 Crossgate, Durham, DH1 4PS   (091) 384 9585
Open all year. No smoking throughout. Vegetarian by arrangement. Disabled access: 'good'. Children: over 4s only. Tea/coffee making & T.V. in all rooms. B. &. B. from £19.

Ramside Hall Hotel, Carrville, Durham, DH1 1TD   (091) 386 5282

Ramside Hall is a splendid castellated building set in large grounds just off the A1(M)/A690 motor interchange. Formerly the home of the Pemberton family, it was opened as a hotel in 1964 by two businessmen whose families still own it. It has been very luxuriously appointed - there is a pleasing blend of the traditional and the contemporary in the furnishings - and bedrooms are not only individually decorated and styled but are equipped with every modern convenience (free in-house movies, fresh fruit, trouser-presses, the lot); two presidential suites are available offering the ultimate in luxury. Dining is in one of three elegant restaurants - each of them serving a selection of excellent home-made dishes - and a typical evening meal would feature Tuna and Pasta Salad in Raspberrry Vinaigrette, followed by Poached Salmon with Fresh Spinach and Hollandaise Sauce, and a selection of sweets and cheeses; conference and business facilities are first-rate.

Open all year. Smoking banned at breakfast, in part of buffet carvery and in some bedrooms. Vegetarian and other special diets on request. Licensed. Disabled access. Children welcome. Pets by arrangement. En suite, tea/coffee making & T.V. in all rooms. Access, Visa, Amex, Diners. B. & B. from £75.

Royal County Hotel, Old Elvet, Durham, DH1 3JN   (091) 386 6821

The Royal County Hotel is a first-class 150-bedroomed hotel, which has been stylishly appointed and beautifully furnished. The hotel is in the luxury business-class category and therefore has a superb range of leisure amenities including an indoor swimming pool, a spa pool, sauna, steam room, solarium and mini-gym. The bedrooms are very comfortable and have excellent facilities, and a large percentage of smoke-free rooms are available: A wide choice of menu is served in the hotel's restaurants and these, too, have good smoke-free areas.

Open all year. No smoking in part of both restaurants & in some bedrooms. Vegetarian standard. Vegan, diabetic & other diets on request. Licensed. Disabled access. Children welcome. Pets by arrangement. En suite, tea/coffee making & T.V. in all rooms. Credit cards. B. & B. from £85. Special W/E & Summer Breaks available.

NEWCASTLE-ON-TYNE

'Bywell', 54 Holly Avenue, Jesmond, Newcastle-on-Tyne, NE2 2QA   (091) 281 7615
Open all year. No smoking. Vegetarian standard. Children welcome. B.& B. from £16.50.

ROWLANDS GILL

Chopwellwood House B. & B., Chopwell Wood, NE39 1LT   (0207) 542765
Charming detached house in Derwent Valley 1m into a 600 acre Forestry Commission wood & 10 mins from A1; Newcastle, Durham, Hexham, Metro Centre & excellent walks nearby; *Open all year. No smoking. Children welcome. Tea/coffee-making & T.V. in all rooms. B. & B. from £15.*

WESTGATE-IN-WEARDALE

Breckon Hill Country Guest House, Westgate-in-Weardale   (0388) 517228

Breckon Hill is a comfortable, newly restored Dale's house which stands in a large, south-facing walled garden some 1100 feet above sea level commanding breathtaking views of Weardale. The bedrooms have each been comfortably furnished and well-appointed (each has an en suite bathroom), and there is a pleasant lounge and dining room with a welcoming open fire. Food is home-cooked and delicious, and much use is made of garden-grown fruit and vegetables. In Mediaeval times the area between the villages of Eastgate and Westgate formed part of the hunting park of the powerful Prince Bishops of Durham; these days it is scattered with small livestock farms - it is said that there are more sheep than people - and the unspoiled hillsides are ablaze with the bright colours of wild flowers in the Spring. Breckon Hill is close to many public footpaths - including the way-marked Wear Valley and the Weardale Way - and, although the location could not be more peaceful, you are conveniently situated for visiting the cathedral city of Durham, Alston, The Beamish Museum and the bustling city of Newcastle on Tyne.

Open all year. Smoking banned throughout.Vegetarian and other special diets on request. No disabled access. Children welcome. No pets. En suite, tea/coffee making & T.V. in all rooms. B. & B. from £18.

WEARDALE

Pennine Lodge, St John's Chapel, Weardale, DL13 1QX (0388) 537247
Open April to Sept. No smoking in dining room, bedrooms & most public areas. Vegetarian, diabetic and low-fat diets by arrangement. Licensed. Pets by arrangement. En suite in all rooms. B. & B. from £16.50. D. £8.50.

WHITLEY BAY

Lindisfarne Hotel, 11 Holly Avenue, Whitley Bay, NE26 1EB (091) 251 3954
Open all year. No smoking in dining room & some bedrooms. Vegetarian by arrangement. Licensed. Children welcome. En suite in some rooms. Tea/coffee-making & T.V. in all rooms. B. & B. from £15. D. £7.

White Surf Guest House, 8 South Parade, Whitley Bay, NE26 2RG (091) 253 0103
Open all year. No smoking in dining room, bedrooms & most public areas. Vegetarian by arrangement. Children: over 2s only. En suite in some rooms. T.V. in all rooms. B. & B. from £14.50.

WOLSINGHAM

Friarside Farm, Wolsingham, Weardale, DL13 3BH (0388) 527361
No smoking in dining room & bedrooms. Vegetarian and diabetic, but not vegan, by arrangement. Low-fat standard. Children: over 5s only. Pets by arrangement. T.V. in lounge. B. & B. from £14. D. £8.

Restaurants & Pubs

BARNARD CASTLE

Ⓐ **'Priors', 7 The Bank, Barnard Castle, DL12 8PH (0833) 38141**
Excellent wholefood, vegetarian restaurant with organic wine list; craft shop & gallery.
Open Mon. to Fri. 10 - 5, Sat. 10 - 5.30, Sun. 12 - 5.00. No smoking throughout. Vegetarian standard. All special diets on request. Licensed. Some disabled access: 'small step'. Children welcome. Access, Visa, Amex, Diners.

EAST HOWDEN

Duke of Wellington, Northumberland Dock Rd, East Howden (091) 262 3079
No smoking in part of pub.

NEWCASTLE-ON-TYNE

Rupali Restaurant, 6 Bigg Market, Newcastle-on-Tyne, NE1 1UW (091) 232 8629
Exceptionally good restaurant specialising in Indian, Vegetarian, Tandoori and English cuisine.
50% no-smoking. Vegetarian standard. Licensed. Children welcome. Credit cards accepted.

Legendary Yorkshire Heroes, Archbold Terrace, Jesmond, Newcastle-on-Tyne (091) 281 3010
Smoking banned in part of pub.

WILLINGTON

Stile Restaurant, 97 High St, Willington, Nr Crook, DL15 0PE (0388) 746615.
Originally a mine-owner's country cottage and now with two beautiful conservatories overlooking an attractive garden. Excellent home-prepared food from fresh, local ingredients.
42 seats. Open 7 - 9.45. No smoking in dining room (28 seats), allowed in conservatory area. Vegetarian standard, other special diets by arrangement. Licensed. Some disabled access: 'Two steps.'Children welcome. Access, Visa.

Northumberland Accommodation

ALNMOUTH

⊗ The Grange, Northumberland St, Alnmouth, NE66 2RJ (0665) 830401

The Grange is a 200 year-old stone-built house and was formerly used as a granary when Alnmouth was a busy grain shipping port; these days it has been totally refurbished (but with care in order to retain the many period features of the house) and, standing in large landscaped gardens overlooking the River Aln just 2 minutes from the beautiful sandy beach, is a perfect place in a perfect location! All bedrooms are very comfortably furnished - some even have canopied four-posters - and the elegant lounge, with its calming river views, is the ideal place in which to relax after a day's sightseeing. Breakfast is excellent; and there is a good variety of more unusual options including fruit compôte and kippers. It is worth pointing out that the proprietors have the very civilised habit of locking the house at 11.30 p.m. to ensure that everyone gets a good night's rest.

Open Mar. to Nov. Smoking banned throughout the house. Vegetarian by arrangement. Children: over 5s only. En suite in some rooms. Tea/coffee-making & T.V. in all bedrooms. ETB 2 Crown Highly Commended, and holders of Heartbeat Award. B. & B. from £18.

⊗ High Buston Hall, High Buston, Alnmouth, NE66 3QH (0665 830) 341

High Buston Hall is a Grade II listed Georgian house which stands amidst 5 acres of landscaped gardens and paddocks in a commanding position overlooking the Heritage coastline of Northumberland midway between the historic villages of Alnmouth and Warkworth. Traditionally furnished, the house has an atmosphere of elegant informality: there is the welcome opportunity to relax and feel at home, yet the surroundings are gracious enough to make you feel special. The food is excellent: fresh ingredients - some home-grown - are home-cooked and special diets can be accommodated by arrangement. Northumberland abounds with historic houses and castles: the dramatic coastal fortress of Dunstanburgh Castle, home of John of Gaunt, stands 10 miles to the North and can be reached from the tiny fishing port of Craster, famous for its oak-smoked kippers (which are served for breakfast at High Buston Hall).

Open all year. No smoking in the house. Vegetarian & other diets by arrangement. Licensed. Children welcome. En suite, TV & tea/coffee-making in bedrooms. B & B. from £22.50, Single £30.

ALNWICK

⊗ New Moor House, Edlingham, Alnwick, NE66 2BT (066574) 638

This charming stone house was built as a coaching house in the early 1800s and stands amidst the spectacular countryside of the Cheviot Hills halfway between Alnwick and Rothbury and just a few miles from the heritage Northumbrian coast. There are four large, comfortably furnished bedrooms (two can be used as family rooms), and there is a welcoming beamed sitting room with books, games and colour TV; the family takes a keen interest in antiques incidentally - many items around the house have been with them for generations - and the beamed dining room is furnished with pews saved from a local disused church. The food is good-home-cooked country fare; on one evening each week the 3-course dinner is not served which gives guests the opportunity to sample one of the many excellent restaurants in the area.

Open Easter to Oct. inc. No smoking in the house. Some diets by arrangement. Wheelchair access. Children & pets welcome. En suite 1 room. Tea/coffee-making. TV in lounge. B. & B. from £15.50, D., B. & B. from £24.50.

Townfoot Farm, Townfoot, Lesbury, Alnwick, NE66 3AZ (0665) 830755
Open March to Oct. No smoking in dining room and upstairs. Vegetarian by arrangement. Children welcome. Pets by arrangement. Tea/coffee-making in all rooms. T.V. in lounge. B. & B. from £16. D.£9.

BAMBURGH

 Waren House Hotel, Waren Mill, Nr Bamburgh, NE70 7EE (06684) 581
Exceptionally good hotel in 6 acres of grounds situated on the edge of Budle Bay overlooking Holy Island, 2 miles from Bamburgh Castle. Beautifully furnished with antiques. Excellent meals prepared from fresh ingredients. **RAC 3 star & ETB Four Crown Highly Commended.**
Open all year. No smoking ex. library. Vegetarian by arrangement. Licensed. En suite, tea/coffee-making & T.V. in all bedrooms. Visa, Amex, Mastercard, Diners. D., B. & B. from £68 (minimum stay 2 nights).

BARDON MILL

Eldochan Hall, Willimoteswyke, Bardon Mill, NE47 7DB (0434) 344465
Open all year ex. Xmas. No smoking in the house. Vegetarian and other diets by arrangement. Children welcome. Pets by arrangement. En suite & tea/coffee-making in all bedrooms. T.V. in lounge. B. & B. from £14.

BEADNELL

Low Dover, Harbour Rd, Beadnell, NE67 5BH (0665) 720291
Open all year. No smoking in the house. Disabled access. Children: over 5s only. En suite in some rooms. Tea/coffee-making & T.V. in all bedrooms. B. & B. from £15.

BELLINGHAM

Eals Lodge, Tarset, Bellingham, NE48 1LF (0434) 240269
Open all year. No smoking in dining room & bedrooms. Vegetarian & diabetic standard, Licensed. En suite, tea/coffee-making & T.V. in all rooms. B. & B. from £21. ETB 3 Crown Commended.

Ivy Cottage, Lanehead, Bellingham, Nr Hexham, NE48 1NT (0434) 240337
Open all year. No smoking in dining room & bedrooms. Vegetarian & vegan standard. Other diets on request. Children welcome. Pets by arrangement. En suite. Tea-making & T.V. in rooms. B. & B. £13.50-£16. D. £8.

Westfield House, Bellingham, Nr Hexham, NE48 2DP (0434) 220340
This lovely large old country house was built over 100 years ago for a prosperous local grocer and remained in the same family for over 50 years; subsequent changes of ownership threatened to spoil the beauty of this elegant old building (at one time threatening to turn it into flats, heaven forfend!), but 10 years ago it was turned into a guest house, the present incumbents having been in residence since 1988. It is quite beautiful: approached by a tree-lined drive (with glorious views), it stands in lovely gardens and offers a very high standard of accommodation (all rooms have everything you could possibly require - including a rubber duck in the bath!). Breakfast is served in a beautiful dining room and an evening meal may be taken by prior arrangement (this is always prepared from fresh, local and - sometimes - home-grown produce), a typical dinner menu featuring home-made paté followed by Chicken in Cream Tarragon with Peaches and Bread and Butter Pudding.
Open all year. No smoking throughout. Vegetarian and most special diets by arrangement. Not licensed - but bring your own. Children welcome. Pets by arrangement. En suite in some rooms. Tea/coffee-making in all bedrooms. T.V. in lounge. B. & B. from £17. D. £12.

BERWICK-UPON-TWEED

The Old Manse Guest House, 5 Cheviot View, Lowick, TD15 2TY (0289) 88264
Open Mar. to Nov. No smoking in dining room & bedrooms. Vegetarian & diabetic by arrangement. Pets by arrangement. En suite some rooms. Tea/coffee-making in all rooms. T.V. in lounge. B. & B. from £12. D. £8.

'Tree Tops', The Village Green, East Ord, Berwick-upon-Tweed, TD15 2NS (0289) 330679
Open March to Oct. No smoking throughout. Vegetarian standard. Disabled access: 'yes, with helper: single storey accommodation & wide doors'. En suite all rooms. Tea-making. T.V. lounge. B. & B. from £18. D. £11

The Estate House, Ford, Berwick-upon-Tweed, TD15 2QG (089 082) 297

The Estate House is a beautiful Edwardian country house which stands amidst large, well-maintained lawned gardens in the picturesque model village of Ford. Accommodation is in comfortably furnished bedrooms, and there are welcoming open fires in each of the public rooms. The food is wholesome and tasty - everything having been home-cooked from fresh, local ingredients wherever possible. Above all, guests will discover a welcoming, congenial and relaxing atmosphere at the Estate House and will find it a perfect base from which to explore the many impressive castles and abbeys to be found on the English and Scottish borders; walking, cycling, fishing and riding may all be enjoyed locally. *Open April - Oct. 'other times on request'. No smoking in dining room. Vegetarian, gluten-free & other special diets by arrangement. Children: over 5s only. Tea/coffee-making in rooms. T.V. lounge. B. & B. from £14.*

CORNHILL-ON-TWEED

The Coach House at Crookham, Crookham, Cornhill-on-Tweed, TD12 4TD (089 082) 293
Oldest cottage in north Northumberland; for disabled guests all doors are wheelchair-wide.
Open Mar. to Nov. No smoking in dining room & lounge. Vegetarian standard. Licensed. Excellent disabled access. Dogs welcome. En suite in most rooms. Tea/coffee-making in all rooms. Credit cards. B. & B. from £21.

FENWICK

The Manor House, Fenwick, Nr Berwick-upon-Tweed, TD15 2PQ (0289) 81381
Open all year. No smoking in dining room, lounge & bedrooms. Vegetarian standard. Licensed. Children welcome. Pets by arrangement. Tea/coffee-making & T.V. in all bedrooms. B. & B. from £14.50. D. £12.

GREENHEAD-IN-NORTHUMBERLAND

 Holmhead Farm Licensed Guest House and Holiday Flat, Hadrian's Wall, Greenhead in Northumberland, via Carlisle CA6 7HY (06977 47402)

Holmhead Farm is a charming old house, which stands amidst pretty gardens (complete with stream) surrounded by the unspoilt and rugged beauty of the Northumberland countryside. Accommodation is in four cosy and comfortable en suite bedrooms - each with lovely rural views - and there is a separate self-catering cottage for non-smokers in which the range of excellent amenities includes first-class facilities for disabled guests. Perhaps the best thing about a stay at Holmhead is the food: the proprietors boast correctly that their breakfast menu is the longest in the world: I have no reason to doubt them and wish I could do justice to the range of dishes on offer; suffice to say that if you are in Northumberland and wish to dine at 8 a.m. on a choice of English or Scottish porridge followed by Devilled Kidneys, waffles and Raspberry tea - Holmhead Farm would be your best bet. The evening meal lacks choice (most guests doubtless welcome a break from menu-reading) but does not lack quality: fresh, local ingredients are included in the imaginative and tasty 3-course meal, and guests dine together by candlelight at a large, oak table in the cosy beamed dining room. *Winner of Heartbeat Award & Disabled Category 2 by Holiday Care Service.*
Open Jan 6th to Dec. 20th. No smoking throughout. Vegetarian and most other special diets by arrangement. Licensed. Disabled access to holiday flat & ground floor B. & B. (Nov. - Mar. the latter). Children welcome. En suite in all rooms. Tea/coffee-making in lounge. T.V. in lounge. Access, Visa. B. & B. from £19.50. D. £15.50

HALTWHISTLE

 Alde White Craig Farm, Shield Hill, Haltwhistle, NE49 9NW (0434) 320565
17th C. croft-style farmhouse on a working farm; Sympathetically modernised & sitting room has open fireplace & timber ceiling beams; B. & B. plus self-catering cottages
Open all year. No smoking. Vegetarian & other diets by arrangement. Disabled access. Children: over 10s only. En suite, TV & tea/coffee making in rooms. B. & B. from £18.50. Heartbeat Award.

Ashcroft Guest House, Haltwhistle, NE49 ODA (0434) 320213
Victorian vicarage and standing in its own private grounds in quiet market town. Comfortably furnished bedrooms 1 with a 4-poster. Excellent b'fast with lighter option.
Open all year. No smoking throughout. Vegetarian by arrangement. Children welcome. T.V. in lounge. B. & B. from £14. Winners of Heartbeat Award.

HEXHAM

Beggar Bog Farm, Housesteads, Haydon Bridge, Hexham, NE47 6NN (0434) 344320
Acclaimed accommodation 13 miles West of Hexham.
Open all year. No smoking in dining room, lounge & bedrooms. Vegetarian by arrangement. Disabled access. Children welcome. En suite in some rooms. B. & B. from £15.

Crowberry Hall, Allendale, Hexham, NE47 9SR (0434) 683392
Crowberry Hall in Allendale offers a warm welcome to walkers & fabulous food!
Open all year. No smoking throughout. Vegetarian standard. Other special diets by arrangement. Children: over 5s only. Pets by arrangement. Some en suite. T.V. in lounge. B. & B. from £12. D. £5.50.

Dukeslea, 33 Dukes Rd, Hexham (0434) 602947
Tastefully refurbished family home with open country views; centrally heated. 1m to station.
Open all year. No smoking throughout. Vegetarian by arrangement. Children welcome. En-suite shower, radio alarm, tea/coffee-making & T.V. in room. B. & B. from £14. ETB registered, listed.

Geeswood House, Whittis Rd, Haydon Bridge, Nr Hexham (0434) 684220
Open all year. No smoking throughout. Vegetarian, low-fat, gluten-free, diabetic and other special diets by arrangement. Children: over 10s only. Pets by arrangement. T.V. in lounge. B. & B. from £15. D. £8

Middlemarch, Hencotes, Hexham, NE46 2EB (0434) 605003

Middlemarch is the home of Eileen Elliott and her family and is a beautiful listed Georgian house which stands overlooking the Sele and the Abbey in the centre of the delightful market town of Hexham. Accommodation is in very comfortable and spacious centrally heated rooms one of which has en suite facilities and a four poster bed; the breakfast is excellent and accommodation is available throughout the year. You are just a short walk from all the attractions and amenities of this charming little border town, and Hadrian's Wall is just ten minutes' drive away; for those venturing a little further afield, within an hour's drive it is possible to reach the Northumberland Coast, the Lakes or Scotland.
Open all year. No smoking in dining room & bedrooms. Vegetarian & other diets by arrangement. Children: over 10s only. Pets by arrangement. En suite some rooms. Tea/coffee-making & T.V. in rooms. B. & B. £16-£22.

KIELDER WATER

The Pheasant Inn, Stannersburn, Falstone, By Kielder Water, NE48 1DD 90434) 240382

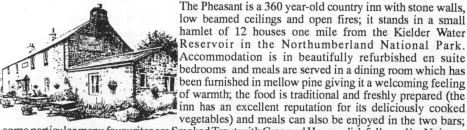

The Pheasant is a 360 year-old country inn with stone walls, low beamed ceilings and open fires; it stands in a small hamlet of 12 houses one mile from the Kielder Water Reservoir in the Northumberland National Park. Accommodation is in beautifully refurbished en suite bedrooms and meals are served in a dining room which has been furnished in mellow pine giving it a welcoming feeling of warmth; the food is traditional and freshly prepared (the inn has an excellent reputation for its deliciously cooked vegetables) and meals can also be enjoyed in the two bars; some particular menu favourites are Smoked Trout with Creamed Horseradish followed by Noisette of Lamb with Apricot and Ginger Sauce and home-made Sticky Toffee Pudding. The Pheasant Inn is very central for visiting all the places of interest in Northumberland: the coast between Alnmouth and the Scottish borders is particularly beautiful and Hadrian's Wall is just to the South of the inn.

A range of water sports may be enjoyed on the reservoir, and bikes may also be hired. Hexham is the nearest market town, with its abbey and historic building, and there are many castles to visit.
Open all year ex. Xmas. No smoking in the dining room & bedrooms. Vegetarian on request. Children welcome. Wheelchair access. En suite, TV & tea/coffee-making in bedrooms. B. & B. from £19, single from £21.

KIRKWHELPINGTON

The Old Vicarage, Kirkwhelpington, NE19 2RT (0830) 40319
Open Apr. to Oct. No smoking in dining room & lounge. Vegetarian & other diets by arrangement. Children welcome. Pets by arrangement. En suite some rooms. Tea-making in rooms. T.V. lounge. B. & B. from £12.50-16.

MORPETH

The Bakers Chest, Hartburn, Morpeth, NE61 4JB (0670) 72214
Beautiful stone-built house in delightful countryside in the charming village of Hartburn; comfortable accommodation and excellent food; many beautiful walks through tranquil woods.
Open Easter to Oct. No smoking in the house. Vegetarian and other special diets by arrangement. No disabled access. Children welcome. Tea/coffee-making. T.V. in lounge. B. & B. from £14.

North Cottage, Birling, Warkworth, Morpeth, NE65 0XS (0665) 711263
300 year-old North Cottage stands in a lovely, large garden just a short stroll from the river and sandy beach on the outskirts of the pretty village of Warkworth, with its historic castle, hermitage and church. Your hosts, Mr and Mrs Howliston, are a particularly welcoming couple - and theirs is a particularly comfortable and welcoming home: afternoon tea is served (free) on arrival, and home-baked cakes and biscuits are served with bedtime cuppas. Bedrooms have been pleasantly furnished and well-equipped with a range of helpful amenities (radios, electric blankets, etc), and there is a large sitting room with colour TV. North Cottage was a recent runner-up in the Northumbria in Bloom competition - and you do not need to travel much further afield to find other delights: Alnwick, Alnmouth and Rothbury are all within easy visiting distance, as are numerous other castles, historic houses and towns. *ETB Highly Commended 2 Crowns. AA Listed QQQ.*
Open all year. No smoking in the house. Vegetarian & other diets by arrangement. En suite, TV & tea'coffee-making in bedrooms. B. & B. from £13.50-15.

ROTHBURY

Thropton Demesne Farmhouse, Thropton, Rothbury, NE65 7LT (0669) 20196
Beautifully situated Victorian stone-built farmhouse in a charming walled garden in the heart of an undiscovered and unspoilt dale; sympathetically renovated and furnished to a very high standard; excellent home-cooked food prepared from fresh, local ingredients.
Open all year. No smoking in the house. Vegetarian and other special diets by arrangement.Children welcome. En suite, TV & tea/coffee making in all rooms. B. & B. from £16.50.

SLALEY

Rye Hill Farm, Slaley, Nr Hexham, NE47 0AH (0434) 673259
300-year-old stone farmhouse in its own 30 acres of working farm in rural Tynedale; self-catering and B. & B. (with dinner by arrangement) available; log fires; good home-cooking.
Open all year. No smoking in dining room & bedrooms. Vegetarian & other diets by arrangement. Licensed. Children welcome. Pets by arrangement. En suite, TV & tea/coffee-making in rooms. B. & B. £16.50. D. £9.

STOCKSFIELD

The Dene, 11 Cade Hill Rd, Stocksfield, NE43 7PB (0661) 842025
Large Edwardian house quietly situated in beautiful garden and woodland.
Open all year. No smoking in dining room & public areas, but allowed in bedrooms. Vegetarian & other diets by arrangement. Children welcome. Pets by arrangement. En suite, TV & tea-making & B. & B. from £16.

WARKWORTH

 Aulden, 9 Watershaugh Rd, Warkworth, NE65 0TT (0665) 711583
Warm, comfortable, friendly guest house situated in the outskirts of the historic village of Warkworth; 1 m from sandy deserted beaches; beautiful riverside walk to hermitage & castle. *Open Mar. to Oct. No smoking in the house. Tea/coffee-making in bedrooms. T.V. in guests' lounge.B. & B. from £13.50. E.T.B 1 Crown Commended.*

WOOLER

Belmont, 15 Glendale Rd, Wooler, NE71 6DN (0668) 81625
Small family home in centre of country town at the base of the Cheviots.
Open Mar. to Oct. No smoking in dining room & bedrooms. Vegetarian and most other special diets by arrangement. Children welcome. Tea/coffee-making in all rooms. T.V. in lounge. B. & B. from £12-£15.

Restaurants

ALNWICK

 Beamish Country House Hotel, Powburn, Alnwick, NE66 4LL (O66578) 266/544
No smoking in restaurant. Vegetarian. Licensed. Some disabled access. Children: over 12s only.

BAMBURGH

 The Copper Kettle Tearooms, 21 Front St, Bamburgh, NE69 7BW (06684) 315

The Copper Kettle Tearooms is one of a row of 18th C. cottages in the picturesque and historically significant village of Bamburgh with its magnificent castle overlooking the sea. The tearooms are full of character and interest: there is a unique set of oak panelling on which are carved various scenes depicting local life, and the original beams are festooned with assorted copperware; the walls are hung with original paintings (most of which are for sale) and there is a fine range of food-orientated products - including preserves, tea, biscuits and pickles - also for sale. With the exception of the bread and teacakes which are provided by a local baker, the owners, Rosemary Christie and David Bates, bake and prepare all the items on their extensive menu using their own recipes and choosing only the finest ingredients: there is a very wide choice of beverages (including six speciality teas and four herbal infusions), and the delicious home-made cakes feature such tempting delights as Walnut and Caramel Fudge with Cream or Border Tart.
28 seats plus 20 in garden. Open March to Oct., 7 days, usually 10.30 - 5.30. Smoking banned throughout interior. Vegetarian often available. Licensed. Limited disabled access. Children welcome. No credit cards.

MORPETH

 Chantry Tearoom, 9 Chantry Place, Morpeth, NE61 1PJ (0670) 514414
Pretty country-style tearoom with views of the old chantry building; all home-baking.
No smoking throughout. Vegetarian standard. Licensed. Some disabled access. Children welcome.

ROTHBURY

 The Vale Milk Bar, High Street, Rothbury, Morpeth (0669) 20461
Café serving morning coffee, light lunches and afternoon tea.
52 seats. Open 10 - 5.30 daily. No smoking throughout. Vegetarian and other special diets by arrangement: ('We serve some vegetarian food and care will be given to anyone with other needs.'). Disabled access: good. Children welcome.

Channel Islands Accommodation

ALDERNEY

Farm Court Guest House, Le Petit Val, Alderney (0481) 822075
Open March to Oct. No smoking throughout. Licensed. Some disabled access. Children welcome. En suite, TV & tea/coffee-making in all rooms. B. & B. from £20.

GUERNSEY

Hotel Hougue du Pommier, Castel, Guernsey Tel: (0481) 56531 Fax: (0481) 56260

Originally a farmhouse dating back to 1712, Hougue du Pommier literally means Apple Tree Hill and it derives its name from the days when apples from the farm orchard were used in the preparation of local cider. These days it has been beautifully converted into an elegant hotel, although the original charm of the house and the 10 acres of grounds are relatively unchanged and there is thus a peace and tranquillity about the place which recalls a vanished era. This makes it a wonderful place to spend a relaxing holiday: the food is excellent and is served in a dining room in which the six original rooms of which it is comprised have retained the names which denote their original purpose (the Parlour, the Bakery, etc). Bedrooms are very comfortable and have a wide range of facilities (direct dial phone, baby alarm, etc.) and there is a fully licensed bar complete with inglenook fireplace and low-beamed ceilings. The proprietors have provided a tremendous range of leisure activities for you to enjoy *in situ*: there is a solar-heated pool, a sauna, a solarium and a games room; laundry services are also available as well as a courtesy coach to and from St Peter Port. You are just 10 minutes' walk from the sandy beaches and adjacent to an 18-hole pitch and putt golf course and the Guernsey Indoor Lawn Bowls Centre.
Open all year. No smoking in 50% of dining room & some bedrooms. Vegetarian & other diets by arrangement. Children welcome. Licensed. Wheelchair access to ground floor rooms. Credit cards. D., B. & B. £31-43.

La Favorita Hotel, Fermain Bay, Guernsey (0481) 35666

La Favorita is an attractive white-painted building set amidst pleasant gardens in the beautiful wooded valley which leads down to Fermain Bay. It used to be a privately owned country house and, although these days it has been considerably extended and modernised, it retains the character (and of course magnificent sea views!) of its former life; from the elegant drawing room with its open fire to the intimate dining room with its lovely garden views, everywhere there is an atmosphere of peaceful tranquility and guests are encouraged to relax, unwind and enjoy. The food is excellent: the menu, which changes daily, is based around traditional English cooking (with some imaginative Continental culinary excursions) and a typical evening meal would feature Baked Blue Brie with Mushroom Sauce, followed by Cream of Chicken Soup, Baked Sea Bream with Tomato, and a delicious dessert, such as Coupe Mandarine; there is a good vegetarian option on each evening menu. A recent successful addition to La Favorita is its pleasant Coffee Shop, overlooking the garden, in which light meals are served during the day, & an indoor heated pool, spa & sauna.
Open March to Nov. No smoking in dining room. Vegetarian standard. Other diets on request. Licensed. Disabled: 1 bedroom purpose-equipped for disabled guests. Children welcome (nappy-changing room). En suite, TV & tea/coffee-making in all rooms. Visa, Amex, Mastercard. B. & B. from £36.

Midhurst House, Candie Rd, St Peter Port, Guernsey (0481) 724391
Open Easter to Oct. No smoking in dining room. Vegetarian, diabetic, low-fat, coeliac, allergy-free diets by arrangement. Licensed. Children: over 8s only. En suite, TV & tea/coffee-making in all rooms. D., B. & B. from £32.

Sunnydale Guest House, Braye Rd, Vale, Guernsey (0481) 47916
Open all year. No smoking. Vegetarian by arrangement. En suite, TV & tea-making in all rooms.

JERSEY

 Hinchcliffe Guest House, Victoria Ave, First Tower, St Helier, Jersey (0534) 21574
Open Mar. to Oct. No smoking throughout. Diets by arrangement. Tea-making in all rooms. T.V. lounge.

La Bonne Vie Guest House, Roseville St, St Helier, Jersey (0534) 35955 Fax: (0534) 33357
La Bonne Vie Guest House is a beautiful Victorian house which retains many original period features; it has been tastefully furnished throughout - some bedrooms have antique brass beds or hand-made French four-posters - and there is an inviting open fire in the lounge and dining room in winter; there is even a library for guests' use, and games - such as Trivial Pursuit and backgammon - are available for your enjoyment. La Bonne Vie is very conveniently situated just a minute's walk from the beach and five minutes' walk from the town centre.
Open March to Nov. inc. No smoking in dining room & discouraged in bedrooms. Special diets by arrangement. Children: over 8s only. En suite, tea/coffee-making & T.V. in all rooms. Credit cards. B. & B. from £15.50.

SARK

 Beauvoir Guest House and Tea Shop, Sark (0481) 832352 Fax: (0481) 832551
 Situated at the centre of the island close to the Seigneurie, Beauvoir is a charming granite-built house, built at the turn of the century. It has recently undergone extensive renovations and now offers exceptionally comfortable accommodation and very good food; there is a charming tea garden (and indoor tea shop for those not inclined to al fresco dining) which specialises in home-baking and dishes prepared from organically home-grown fruit and vegetables. Resident guests at Beauvoir are really in for a treat: all meals have been home-cooked from fresh ingredients and the imaginative 5-course evening menu features such delights as home-made Smoked Mackerel Paté, followed by Orange Sorbet, home-made Brie and Herb Quiche and an irresistible dessert, such as home-made Chocolate Gateau; guests may also enjoy the benefits of a quiet lounge and a separate residents' bar. Sark is the smallest and, thankfully, the least developed of the Channel Islands: there are no street lights (bring a torch) and the beautiful sandy beaches are all reached by many steps or steep paths; this, combined with the fact that there is a short walk from the ferry to the guest house (although your luggage is taken by carrier) means that a holiday on Sark is best suited to those who find it easy to get about.
Open all year. No smoking in the house. Vegetarian, diabetic, low-cal., gluten-free & some other diets by arrangement. Licensed. Disabled access; ground-floor rooms with ramped access. Children: over 10s only. En suite, tea/coffee-making, central heating & T.V. in all bedrooms. Credit cards. B. & B. from £20, D., B. & B. from £30.

Hotel Petit Champ, Sark (0481) 832046
Charming hotel in unrivalled position on the west coast of the unique island of Sark. Restaurant renowned for good cuisine. Solar-heated swimming pool.
Open Apr. to Oct. No smoking in dining room & 1 lounge/library. Vegetarian and other diets by arrangement. Licensed. Children: over 7s only. En suite in all rooms. Credit cards accepted. Half Board from £35-£46.

Restaurants

GUERNSEY

Rocquaine Bistro, Rocquaine Bay, West Side of the Island (0481) 63149
Open daily April to Oct. Smoking banned in part of restaurant.

Beauvoir Guest House and Tea Shop, Sark (0481) 832352
Tea shop serving speciality and herb teas and light meals, including vegetarian options
Open 10.30 - 5. No smoking throughout. Vegetarian standard. Restaurant licence. Children welcome.

Northern Ireland Accommodation

CO ANTRIM

 Ahimsa, 243 Whitepark Rd, Bushmills (026 57) 31383
Beautifully renovated 200-year-old cottage in peaceful setting close to the Giant's Causeway.
Open all year. No smoking in the house. Vegetarian exclusively. Children welcome. Pets welcome. Tea/coffee making available. B. & B. from £9.

CO FERMANAGH

 Brindley, Tully, Killadeas, Enniskillen, Co Fermanagh (03656) 28065
Standing in an extensive garden with panoramic views of Lower Lough Erne & islands.
Open all year. No smoking in the house. Vegetarian & other diets by arrangement. Disabled access. Children welcome. En suite in most rooms. Tea/coffee making in conservatory. T.V. in all bedrooms. B. & B. from £15.

Glen House, 212 Crawfordsburn Rd, Crawfordsburn, BT19 1HY (0247) 852229

 Glen House is a home of great character and charm which is quietly situated amidst large grounds just a short walk from the beach at Crawdordsburn. A first-rate breakfast is served to guests (your host, Noreen Harte, is a winner of the Galtee Irish Breakfast Award) and vegetarians can be accommodated by arrangement. Glen House is an excellent choice for both business travellers and those seeking a family or a golfing holiday: a number of restaurants and pubs are close by and you are within walking distance of the bus and train stops. Private parking is available.

Open all year. No smoking in the dining room, most bedrooms & lounge. Vegetarian by arrangment. En suite, TV & tea/coffee-making in bedrooms. Children welcome. Credit cards. B. & B. from £20.

Restaurants

BELFAST

Debenhams, Unit 34, Castle Court, Royal Ave, belfast (0232) 439777
Pavilion, a friendly self-service coffee shop serving lunches, snacks and hot and cold drinks.
Open store hours. No smoking. Vegetarian meals. Disabled access. Children welcome. Credit/debit cards.

The Mortar Board, 3 Fitzwilliam Street, Belfast (0232) 332277
Coffee house very near the university & museum area of Belfast; good, home-cooked snacks.
Open 9 - 7. L. around £3. No smoking throughout. Vegetarian standard. Children welcome.

CO DOWN

Pat's Restaurant, 88 Castlewellan Rd, Lenish, Ratheriland, Co Down (08206) 38121
Open evenings from Tues. to Sun. No smoking.Vegetarian on request. Licensed. Disabled access.

The Red Fox Coffee Shop, 6 Main Street, Hillsborough, Co Down (0846) 682586
Small coffee shop with a relaxed atmosphere.
Open 10.30 - 2, 3 - 5. No smoking. Vegetarian standard. Other diets on request. Disabled access.

CO FERMANAGH

Florence Court, Enniskillen, Co Fermanagh (036 582) 249
Charming National Trust Tea Room, situated in the grounds of the beautiful 18th C. house and pleasure gardens, a leisurely two hour drive from Belfast. Treat yourself from their array of delicious home-cooked snacks - such as baked potatoes with a variety of fillings - or sample a Cream Tea or (Savoury Tea) with home-baked cakes, & relax in the surroundings of a bygone era.
40 seats. Open June to Sept. 12 - 6. April, May, Sept., weekends & Bank Holidays only, 12 - 6. L. from £3. Smoking banned in 50% of restaurant. Vegetarian on request. Disabled access. Children welcome. Credit cards.

Scotland

Borders
Accommodation

DENHOLM

⊗ **Barnhills Farmhouse, Nr Denholm, Roxburghshire, TD9 8SH (045 087) 577**
Beautiful ex-farmhouse set in a wild garden with orchard and vegetables.
Open all year. No smoking. Vegan wholefood only. Children welcome. Tea/coffee making. B. & B. from £12.

HAWICK

Whitchester Christian Guest House & Retreat Centre, Borthaugh, Hawick, Roxburghshire, TD9 7LN (0450) 77477
Mid 19th C. manor standing in 3 acres of lawned grounds and offering 'a place of rest, rehabilitation and peace' within a Christian context; beautifully furnished throughout.
Open Feb. to Dec. No smoking in the house ex. in T.V. lounge. Vegetarian standard. Most other special diets by arrangement. Disabled access. Children welcome. Pets by arrangement. En suite in 5 out of 10 rooms. Tea/coffee making in bedrooms. T.V. in lounge. B. & B. from £13.20.

JEDBURGH

Froylehurst, Friars, Jedburgh, Roxburghshire TD8 6BN (0835) 62477
Detached late Victorian house with lovely garden offering comfortable accommodation in tastefully decorated rooms; full Scottish breakfast.
Open Apr. to Oct. No smoking in dining room. Vegetarian breakfasts available. Children: over 5s only. Tea/coffee making & T.V. in all bedrooms. B. & B. from £13.

⊗ **Harrietsfield House, Ancrum, by Jedburgh, Roxburghshire, TD8 6TZ (08353) 327**

 Harrietsfield House is a spacious and comfortable ex-farmhouse with a lovely garden set in beautiful countryside just 5 miles from Jedburgh. Breakfast is the only meal which is usually available at Harrietsfield (a vegetarian evening meal may be booked by prior arrangement), but all food is prepared from wholefoods and, when possible, organically home-grown produce. Accommodation is in warm, comfortable rooms and there is an inviting lounge with a log fire in the evening as well as a cup of tea and home-baking. You are centrally situated in this part of the world for visiting all the Border towns and are just 44 miles from Edinburgh; golf, riding and fishing may all be enjoyed locally.
Open Easter/Apr. to Oct. No smoking in the house. Vegetarian standard. Other diets by arrangement. One downstairs bedroom. Children welcome (but at full tariff). Pets by arrangement. En suite in two rooms. Tea served in lounge 9.30 pm. T.V. in lounge. B. & B. from £13.

KELSO

Duncan House, Chalkheugh Terrace, Kelso, Roxburghshire, TD5 7DX (0573) 25682
Lovely listed Georgian house in a beautiful elevated position overlooking the River Tweed.
Open Mar. to Oct. No smoking in the house, ex. some bedrooms. Vegetarian by arrangement. Disabled access. Children welcome. Pets by arrangement. En suite. Tea-making & T.V. in all bedrooms. B. & B. from £11.50.

MELROSE

⊗ **Collingwood, Waverley Road, Melrose, Roxburghshire TD6 9AA (0896 82) 2670**
Detached Victorian house with large garden quietly situated one mile from Melrose & minutes from the River Tweed; splendid views of Eildon Hills; family home of Jack & Angela Sugden.
Open most of the year. No smoking in the house. Vegetarian and most other special diets by arrangement. Children by arrangement. En suite & tea/coffee making in bedrooms. T.V. in lounge. B. & B. from £17.

Priory View, 15 Priors Walk, Melrose (0896 82) 2087
Open all year. No smoking in the house. Vegetarian & diabetic diets by arrangement. Children welcome. Tea/coffee making in bedrooms. T.V. B. & B. from £12.

PEEBLES

 Drummore, Venlaw High Road, Peebles, EH45 8RL (0721) 20336
Open Easter to Oct. inc. No smoking in the house. Vegetarian and low-fat diets by arrangement. Children by arrangement. Tea/coffee making in bedrooms. T.V. in lounge. B. & B. from £12.

Kingsmuir Hotel, Springhill Rd, Peebles, EH45 9EP Tel: (0721) 720151 Fax: (0721) 721795

 Kingsmuir is a charming century old country house which stands amidst leafy grounds on the quiet, South side of Peebles looking across parkland to the River Tweed; indeed it is just 5 minutes' walk through the park to the High Street. It is a family-run hotel and as such offers friendly, efficient service: the bedrooms are exceptionally comfortable and there is a stylish new lounge for guests' use; the modern refurbishments and additions have been sympathetically undertaken, but the original character of the building is still clearly in evidence in the other comfortable lounge and in the dining room. The food is excellent: everything is prepared from fresh, local produce, and in addition to an imaginative evening à la carte menu, there are some good choices for children and vegetarians on separate menus; the Kingsmuir Hotel is "Taste of Scotland Recommended", incidentally. Peebles is a Royal and Ancient Borough just 40 mnutes' drive South of Edinburgh; there are many fine shops in the city and in addition you are close to many stately homes and castles of great historic interest.
Open all year ex. Xmas day. No smoking in dining room & lounge. Vegetarian standard. Licensed. Children & dogs welcome. En suite, TV & tea/coffee-making in bedrooms. Credit cards. B. & B. £27-31, single £31-37.

Tweed Valley Hotel & Restaurant, Walkerburn, by Peebles, EH43 6AA (089687) 636
Edwardian country house standing in its own grounds; beautifully furnished; fresh food and home-grown herbs used in cooking; activity courses and holidays arranged throughout the year.
Open all year. No smoking in dining room. Vegetarian & other diets by arrangement. Licensed. Children welcome. Pets by arrangement. En suite, TV & tea/coffee making in rooms. Credit cards. D., B. & B. from £43.

Mrs Julia Wilding, 10 Gallow Hill, Peebles, EH45 9BG (0721) 20372
Open all year. No smoking in the house. Vegetarian & most other special diets by arrangement. Children welcome. Pets by arrangement. Tea/coffee making in bedrooms. T.V. in lounge. B. & B. from £12.50.

Restaurants, Pubs & Wine Bars

PEEBLES

Tweed Valley Hotel & Restaurant, Walkerburn, by Peebles, EH43 6AA (089687) 636
45 seats. D. around £18. No smoking in restaurant. Vegetarian and other special diets on request. Licensed. Children welcome. Access, Visa, Allied Credit.

SELKIRK

Tibbie Shiels Inn, St Mary's Loch, Selkirk TD7 5NE (0750) 42231
Old inn in lovely location on the shore of beautiful St. Mary's loch, one of the most tranquil spots in southern Scotland; serving excellent food with good vegetarian options, real ale and malt whiskies.
Open Mar. - Oct., 11 - 11, closed Mon. Serving food 12 - 2. 30, 3.30 - 8.30. No smoking in 16 seats (sep. room). Extensive vegetarian menu. Children welcome. Disabled access.
For further details please see under the entry in the accommodation section.

SWINTON

The Wheatsheaf Hotel, Main St, Swinton (089 086) 257
No smoking in conservatory.

Dumfries and Galloway Accommodation

CASTLE DOUGLAS

Airieland House, Gelston, Castle Douglas, DG7 1SS (055) 668 375

Airieland House is a listed Victorian mansion which stands in a secluded 3 acre woodland garden amidst beautiful unspoilt Galloway coutnryside; in Spring and Summer the garden is ablaze with daffodils, rhododendrons and wild flowers. Your hosts, John and Josephine Herbertson, purchased this lovely house in 1988 and since that time have refurbished it to a very high standard: the original features of the building have been retained - including the fine wood carvings, cornices and stained glass - and the furnishings are traditional and sympathetic; there are panoramic views from all the windows. Each of the guest bedrooms has been luxuriously appointed (one is en suite, one has a private bath), and central heating supplements the open fire in the lounge. The food is delicious and wholesome: everything is home-cooked from fresh produce and a typical evening meal would feature Scotch Broth followed by Steak Bengairn (strips of Scottish sirloin in a whisky sauce), and a choice of Scottish desserts (perhaps Atholl Brose - cream, oatmeal, honey and whisky!); local cheese and biscuits would complete the meal. Airieland House is a perfect holiday base for those in search of unspoilt countryside and wonderful walks; you are, however, within easy motoring distance of both Edinburgh and Glasgow. *STB Highly Commended.*
Open Mar. - Sept. inc. No smoking in the house. Children: over 12s welcome. En suite/private bath & tea/coffee-making in bedrooms. TV in lounge. B. & B. around £30, D. £15.

Blairinnie Farm, Blairinnie, Parton, Castle Douglas, Kirkcudbright (0556) 67268
Open May. to Sept. No smoking in the house. Vegetarian and most other special diets by arrangement. Children welcome. Tea/coffee making in bedrooms. T.V. in lounge. B & B from £10.

Cairnraws, New Galloway, Castle Douglas, Kirkcudbrightshire DG7 3SB (06442) 293
Cairnraws stands one mile from New Galloway commanding panoramic views over Loch Ken. Idealspot for birdwatchers, naturalists, hill walkers.
Open all year ex. Xmas. No smoking in the house. Vegetarian and most other special diets by arrangement. Children: over 12s only. Tea/coffee made on request. B. & B. from £12.50.

The Imperial Hotel, 35 King Street, Castle Douglas, DG7 1AA (0556) 2086/3009
Former coaching inn and listed building, this family-run 2 star hotel has been tastefully decorated with both antique and modern furnishings; good quality home-cooking using fresh, local produce. Ideal as base to tour countryside or to use excellent nearby golf courses. Special 3-day breaks.
Open all year. No smoking in bedrooms and 25% of dining room. Vegetarian standard. Licensed. Disabled access. Children & pets welcome. En suite, tea/coffee making & TV in rooms. Access, Visa. B & B from £25.

Windywalls, Upper Drumwall, Gatehouse of Fleet, Castle Douglas (0557) 814249
Open all year. No smoking in the house. Vegetarian and most other special diets. Children welcome. Pets by arrangement. Tea/coffee making in bedrooms. T.V. in lounge. B & B from £12.

CRAWFORD

"Field End" Guest House, Crawford, Lanarkshire, ML12 6TN (08642) 276
Attractive stone-built villa situated on a quiet, private road opposite the church. Ideal halfway house and touring centre. *Private parking. ETB 2 Crowns, RAC & AA Acclaimed. Recommended world-wide.*
Open all year ex. Xmas & New Year days. No smoking. Vegetarian by arrangement. Children welcome. En suite in 2 rooms. Tea-making & TV in rooms. Credit cards. B. & B. from £12. red. children & senior citizens.

DALBEATTIE

Torbay Farmhouse, Rockcliffe, by Dalbeattie, Kirkcudbrightshire, DG5 4QE (055663) 403

Open Easter to Oct. No smoking in the house. Vegetarian by arrangement. Disabled access. Children welcome. Pets by arrangement. En suite & tea/coffee making in bedrooms. T.V. in lounge. B & B from £14.

DUMFRIES

Lochenlee, 32 Ardwall Rd, Dumfries, DG1 3AQ (0387) 65153

Large semi-detached sandstone family home in a quiet residential street 10 mins' walk from the restaurants in the centre of Dumfries & 5 mins'walk from the railway station. Near to lovely forest walks, & with green bowling, swimming and golf locally.

Open all year. No smoking in the house. Vegetarian & diabetic with notice. Children welcome. Tea/coffee making & T.V. in all rooms. B. & B. from £12-£14.

GRETNA

The Beeches, Loanwath Road, Gretna, via Carlisle, CA6 5EP (0461) 37448

The Beeches is an attractive 19th C. former farmhouse which is peacefully situated in a quiet area half a mile from the A74 at Gretna. A very high standard of accommodation is offered to guests - indeed the proprietors have been awarded a 2 Crown Commended status by the Scottish Tourist Board. There are two charming bedrooms, each of which have panoramic views of the Solway Firth and Lakeland Hills, and there is a comfortable lounge with a colour T.V. for guests' use. Breakfast is the only meal to be served at The Beeches, but there is a good choice of restaurants nearby. *STB 2 Crown Commended & QQQ AA Listed.*

Open Jan. to Nov. No smoking in the house. Vegetarian by arrangement. Children: over 12s only. En suite & tea/coffee making in all rooms. TV on request. B & B from £15.

KIRKCUDBRIGHT

Millburn House, Millburn Street, Kirkcudbright, DG6 4ED (0557) 30926

Charming 19th C. white-painted, stone-built house of traditional design with lovely conservatory breakfast room; breakfast only.

Open all year. No smoking in the house. Vegetarian and most other special diets by arrangement. Children welcome at full tariff. En suite & tea/coffee making in bedrooms. T.V. in lounge. B & B from £18.

SANQUHAR

Nithsdale Guest House, Glasgow Road, Sanquhar (0659) 50288

Charming stone-built house set in lovely gardens overlooking picnic area, loch and golf course.

Open all year. No smoking in dining room and bedrooms. Vegetarian and most other special diets by arrangement. Children welcome. Tea/coffee making in bedrooms. T.V. in lounge. B & B from £13.

STRANRAER

 Fernlea Guest House, Lewis Street, Stranraer, Wigtownshire, DG9 7AQ (0776) 3037

 Fernlea is a lovely large detached Victorian villa standing in a private garden close to the town centre. It is pleasantly furnished throughout and, under the personal supervision of the proprietor, everything is done to make your stay a welcome and happy one. The cuisine is of the traditional variety with a high proportion of home-cooking; a typical evening menu would feature home-made Chicken Broth, followed by Lamb with Mint Sauce (and all the trimmings) and a filling dessert, such as Apple Pie with fresh cream. Stranraer, because of its ferry service, is known as the gateway to Ireland - it has much to commend it to those who decide to linger awhile, however: warmed by the Gulf Stream, this is the mildest corner of Scotland, and the mountain & coast scenery is tremendous.

Open all year. No smoking in the house. Vegetarian and most other special diets by arrangement. Children by arrangement. En suite in 2 rooms. Tea/coffee making & T.V. in all bedrooms. B & B from £12.50.

Restaurants

GATEHOUSE OF FLEET

 Bobbin Coffee Shop, 36 High St, Gatehouse of Fleet (05574) 229
No smoking throughout.

MOFFAT

 Well View Hotel, Ballplay Road, Moffat, Dumfriesshire, DG10 9JU (0683) 20184
24 seats. Open 7 - 8.30. No smoking throughout. Vegetarian and some other special diets on request. Licensed. Children welcome. Access, Visa.

NEW ABBEY

 Abbey Cottage Coffees & Crafts, 26 Main Street, New Abbey, Dumfries, DG2 8BY (038 785) 377

Country restaurant in a charming setting next to Sweetheart Abbey, serving home-made meals; good vegetarian selection.

40 seats. Open 10 - 5. L. around £3. No smoking throughout. Vegetarian standard. Some other special diets on request. Licensed. Disabled access: 'wide doors, ramp, disabled loo'. Children welcome.

Edinburgh Accommodation

EDINBURGH

Adam Guest House, 2 Hartington Gardens, Edinburgh, EH10 4LD (031 229) 8664

Adam House is a family-run guest house which is situated in a quiet cul-de-sac (free from parking restrictions), just fifteen minutes' walk from the city centre and close to bus routes, shops, theatres and restaurants; Bruntsfield Links and The Meadows public parks are just a short walk away. The house has recently been completely refurbished by the present owners and all the rooms are now bright, comfortable and well-equipped with a T.V., hot drink facilities and wash hand basin; some have en suite facilities. The proprietors and staff offer warm hospitality and a very friendly service, and families and children are particularly welcome with reduced rates being available throughout the year.

Open all year. No smoking in the house. Vegetarian & other diets by arrangement. Children welcome. Pets by arrangement. Some rooms en suite. Tea/coffee making & T.V. in all bedrooms. B. & B. from £15 per person.

Camore Guest House, 7 Links Gardens, Edinburgh, EH6 7JH (031 554) 7897

Original Georgian listed house with panoramic views over Leith Links. 10-15 mins from city centre on main bus route. 5 mins walk from local restaurants and Leith's new Waterworld.

Open all year. Smoking banned in dining room. Vegetarian by arrangement. Licensed. Children welcome. Pets by arrangement. T.V. with Satellite channels & tea/coffee making in all bedrooms. B. & B. from £14.

Highfield Guest House, 83 Mayfield Road, Edinburgh, EH9 3AE (031 667) 8717

Highfield is a small, friendly, guest house only ten minutes' drive from the centre of Edinburgh. The rooms are clean and comfortable, all with wash basins and centrally heated. Tuck into the full cooked breakfast and help yourself to cereals, oatcakes, yoghurt, toast, etc. Home-made porridge is also available. A cot, high chair and toys are provided for visiting children. Room notes and menu are available in braille for the use of blind guests and personal attention is assured at all times. The house is well situated for the university and King's Buildings and within walking distance of Arthur's Seat and Blackford Hill. STB Commended.

Open all year. No smoking in the house. Vegetarian and most other special diets by arrangement. Disabled access: Ground-floor bedroom & shower/room/WC. Children welcome. Guide dogs by arrangement. Tea/coffee making in bedrooms. T.V. in lounge. B. & B. from £13.

Cost / from train

Hopetoun Guest House, 15 Mayfield Road, Edinburgh, EH9 2NG (031 667) 7691

Hopetoun is a small, friendly, family-run guest house which is conveniently situated close to the university and just one and a half miles to the south of Princes Street. A pleasant 25-minute walk through quiet suburban streets will bring you to the Castle and Royal Mile in the historic heart of Edinburgh's Old Town. The proprietors offer very comfortable accommodation in a completely smoke-free environment and there is a friendly, informal atmosphere. The Hopetoun Guest House has been awarded a 2 Crowns Commended status by the STB for 1993, and is also a member of Edinburgh Marketing and the Edinburgh Hotel and Guest House Association, the two city organisations which promote high standards in the accommodation industry.

Open all year. No smoking in the house. Vegetarian and other special diets by arrangement. Children welcome. Tea/coffee making & TV in bedrooms. Central heating. Off-street parking. B. & B. from £14.

Mrs C A King, 103 Willowbrae Avenue, Edinburgh (031 661) 2852

Open May to Sept. No smoking in the house. Vegetarian by arrangement. Children welcome. Tea/coffee making & T.V. in all bedrooms. B & B from £12.

Six Mary's Place, Guest House, Raeburn Place, Stockbridge, EH4 1JH Tel & Fax: (031) 332 8965
Beautiful Georgian guest house, restored to its original splendour, offering peaceful accommodation and good food - mainly vegetarian. Run under auspices of Edinburgh's Community Trust to help & employ people who have had mental health problems.
Open 4 Jan. - 24 Dec. No smoking in the house. Vegetarian standard. Other diets by arrangement. Children welcome. 1 room en suite. Tea/coffee-making in bedrooms. B. & B. £20, full board £28.

Studio Bed & Breakfast, 173 Bruntsfield Place, Edinburgh, EH10 4DG (031 229) 2746
Open all year. No smoking in the house. Vegetarian and most other special diets by arrangement. Children welcome. Tea/coffee making avail. B. & B. from £12.

Teviotdale House, 53 Grange Loan, Edinburgh, EH9 2ER (031 667) 4376
Elegant, stone-built Victorian town house in a beautiful tree-lined street; *fabulous* food!
Open all year. No smoking in the house. Vegetarian and most other special diets by arrangement. Children welcome. En suite, tea/coffee making & T.V. in all bedrooms. Credit cards (surcharge). B. & B. from £19.50.

The Town House Guest House, 65 Gilmore Place, Edinburgh, EH3 9NU (031 229) 1985
Charming 3-storey Victorian town house, beautifully renovated. Breakfast only.
Open all year. No smoking throughout. Vegetarian by arrangement. Children welcome. En suite in some rooms. tea/coffee making & T.V. in all bedrooms. B. & B. from £14.50.

10A Dean Terrace, Edinburgh, EH4 1ND (031 332) 0403
Garden flat of Georgian building overlooking the Water of Leith; B. & B. or self-catering.
Open all year. No smoking. Vegetarian by arrangement. Children welcome. T.V. B. & B. from £14.

Restaurants

Alp-Horn Restaurant, 167 Rose Street, Off Charlotte Square, Edinburgh, EH2 4LS (031 225) 4787
The Alp-horn is a chalet-style restaurant, owned by the Denzlers, which stands just 2 minutes from Princes Street in the heart of Edinburgh. It specialises in serving delicious Swiss cuisine - but with a French basis - and diners may feast on such house specialities as Bündnerfleisch (air-dried beef and ham from the Swiss mountains), Veal Zürichoise and Rösti, Venison and Spätzli and Apfel Strudel, and those feeling less adventurous may dine on a freshly prepared soup followed by Rump Steak Toreador (garnished with diced mushrooms and peppers on tomato sauce). The extensive wine list includes Swiss Fendant and Dôle, and there are some tempting desserts.
64 seats. Open 12 - 2, 6.30 - 10. L. around £10, D. around £17. Smoking banned in one dining room. Vegetarian on request. Licensed. No disabled access. Children welcome. Access, Visa, Amex.

Chapter One, 57 George Street, Edinburgh, EH2 2JQ (031 225) 4495
Café located in general bookshop/newsagents in the centre of the city.
75% no-smoking. Vegetarian standard. Children welcome.

Cornerstone Café, St John's Church, Princes Street, Edinburgh, EH2 4BJ (031 229) 0212
Vegetarian/vegan/wholefood cafe serving hot food, salads, snacks, cakes, etc.
No smoking throughout. Disabled access 'difficult, but there is a ramp & toilet has wheelchair access'.

Crawfords Country Kitchens, 26/27 St James Centre, Edinburgh (031 556) 3098
No smoking on upper floor. Vegetarian and other special diets on request. Disabled access. Children welcome.

Debenhams, 109 Princes St, Edinburgh (031) 225 1320
Freebodys Restaurant overlooking Princes St with a splendid view of the castle. Self-service restaurant serving popular light lunches, snacks and a wide range of hot and cold drinks.
Open store hours. No smoking throughout. Vegetarian meals. Disabled access. Children very welcome. Credit and debit cards accepted.

Helios Fountain, 7 Grassmarket, Edinburgh, EH1 2HY (031 229) 7884
Excellent vegetarian/wholefood cafe with friendly atmosphere at the rear of book shop.
No smoking throughout. Vegetarian, vegan, sugar-free standard.Disabled access. Children welcome.

The Indian Cavalry Club, 3 Atholl Place, Edinburgh, EH3 8HP (031 228) 3282

The Indian Cavalry Club is not a club, of course, but a wonderful restaurant which won itself so many friends that it soon began to feel like a real club. It serves the kind of modern Indian cuisine favoured by the most exclusive circles of Delhi and Bombay and especially at the banquets for which the officers' mess of the Cavalry Regiment is famous (hence their name). These dishes are lighter and less fiery than traditional fare and rely on the finest, freshest ingredients. The main courses range from exquisitely prepared meat and poultry to seafood and vegetarian delicacies. However you don't have to be a maharajah, tycoon or field marshal to eat here! The à la carte selection is very reasonably priced and there are some splendid set banquets which are most economical, particularly for families or parties.

20 seats. Open 12 - 2.30, 5.30 - 11.30. L. around £10. 25% no-smoking. Vegetarian & other diets on request. Licensed. Disabled access. Children welcome. Credit cards.

 **The Kalpna Restaurant, 2-3 St Patrick Square, Edinburgh, EH8 9EZ**

The Kalpna is a widely recommended, award-winning Indian vegetarian restaurant, which is rated amongst the best in Britain and specialises in Indian vegetarian wholefood cuisine from the Gujarat region of India. The name Kalpna denotes a combination of 'imagination' and 'creation'- an apt way to describe the culinary procedures in the Kalpna kitchen in which only freshly ground spices are used in cooking and the speciality dishes surprise the palate with their delicious invention and flair. The proprietors are further to be commended for having adopted a non-smoking policy when they opened ten years ago - something of a pioneering attitude at the time - and for the wit in their choice of logo, the elephant, which reminds diners that you do not have to eat meat to be big, strong and intelligent.

Open 12 - 2, 5.30 - 11. No smoking throughout. Children welcome. Wheelchair access. Access, Visa, Amex.

"Parrots", 3-5 Viewforth, Edinburgh, EH10 4JD (031 229) 3252
Very popular restaurant - parrots abound - serving a wide range of dishes ranging from good vegetarian options to wonderful meat pies; excellent cooking; booking virtually essential.
40 seats. Open Fri. & Sat. 5 - 10.30 p.m. (last orders), Sun. - Thurs. 6 - 10.30 p.m. D. around £11. No smoking. Vegetarian on request. Licensed. Disabled access. Children welcome Fri. & Sat. 5 pm and at lunchtimes.

Pizza Hut (UK) Ltd, 34-36 Hanover Street, Edinburgh, EH2 2DR (031 226) 3652
66% no-smoking. Vegetarian and vegan. Licensed. Disabled access, 'but not to washrooms'. Children welcome.

The Potting Shed Restaurant, Bruntsfield Hotel, 69 Bruntsfield Place (031 229) 1393
No smoking in conservatory area. Vegetarian standard. Licensed. Disabled access. Children welcome.

The Queen's Hall, Clerk Street, Edinburgh Tel: (031 668) 3456 Fax: (031) 668 2656
Excellent wholefood restaurant.
150 seats. Open 10 - 5. Smoking banned in 70% of restaurant. Vegetarian/wholefood standard. Licensed. Disabled access: 'ramp/toilets etc.' Children welcome.

"Reeds" Restaurant & Coffee Shop, 124 Princes Street, Edinburgh EH2 3AA (031 225) 6703
50% no-smoking. Vegetarian standard. Licensed. Disabled access. Children welcome.

 Seeds Wholefood Café, 53 West Nicolson St, Edinburgh, EH8 9DB (031) 667 8673
No smoking throughout the restaurant. Children welcome.

"The Stedding", 118 Biggar Road, Edinburgh, EH10 7DH (031 445) 1128
50% no-smoking. Vegetarian standard. Licensed. Disabled access. Children 'limited'. Access, Visa.

Fife
Accommodation

ABERDOUR

Hawkcraig House, Hawkcraig Point, Aberdour, Fife, KY3 0TZ (0383) 860335
Beautiful old white-painted ferryman's house dramatically situated overlooking the sea.
Open Feb. to Nov. No smoking in the house. Vegetarian by arrangement. Bring your own wine. Children: over 8s only. En suite & TV in both rooms. Tea/coffee on request.B. & B. from £16. STB 2 Crown Highly Commended.

The Woodside Hotel, High St, Aberdour, Fife, KY3 0SW (0383) 860920
The Woodside Hotel was built in 1873 by the Greig brothers of Inverkeithing - one of whom became one of Catherine the Great's admirals; these days the house has been spendidly converted into what can only be described as one of the most attractive and appealing hotels in the area. Under the personal supervision of its resident owners, Nancy and Peter Austen, the hotel has 21 bedrooms, each of which have been decorated and furnished with style and flair - one has a private sitting room. The public rooms are quite unique: the Clipper Bar is certainly one of the most unusual in Scotland, and features the splendid stained glass and wood panelling from the Orient Line vessel, Orontes; the Woodside Restaurant is an elegant venue in which to enjoy the wide variety of different foods - including the far eastern dishes which reflect Nancy's Singapore origins; everything is prepared from fresh, local produce. You are within walking distance of the station, Aberdour Castle and the picturesque harbour.
Open all year. No smoking in part of the dining room & the Earlsgate bar. Vegetarian & other diets by arrangement. Wheelchair access. Children & pets welcome. Licensed. En suite, TV & tea/coffee-making in bedrooms. Credit cards. B. & B. from £24, D., B. & B. from £39.50.

ANSTRUTHER

Cornceres Farm, Anstruther, Fife (0333) 310337
Open all year except Dec. No smoking in the house. Vegetarian by arrangement.Children welcome. Tea/coffee making in lounge. T.V. in lounge. B. & B. from £12.50.

CULROSS

Woodhead Farm, Culross, Fife, KY12 8ET (0383) 880270
Open all year. No smoking in the house. Vegetarian and most other special diets by arrangement. Children welcome. Tea/coffee making & T.V. in all bedrooms. B. & B. from £15.

CUPAR

Greigston Farmhouse, Peat Inn, Cupar, Fife, KY15 5LF (033 484) 284
Typical 16th/17th C. Scottish Laird's house with light, airy and spacious south-facing rooms.
Open Mar. to Nov. No smoking throughout. Vegetarian by arrangement. Disabled access. Children welcome. Pets by arrangement. En suite & tea/coffee making in bedrooms. T.V. in lounge. B. & B. from £13.

FREUCHIE

Lomond Hills Hotel, Lomond Road, Freuchie, KY7 7EY (0337) 57329
White-painted 25-bedroomed hotel in the picturesque village of Freuchie.
Open all year. No smoking in restaurant & 4 bedrooms. Vegetarian standard. Licensed. Disabled: "restaurant & 1 bedroom on ground floor". Children welcome. En suite, tea/coffee making & T.V. in all bedrooms.

PITTENWEEM

Victoria Cottage, 11 Viewforth Place, Pittenweem, Fife, KY10 2PZ (0333) 311998
Charming cottage in a small but active fishing village within the East Neuk of Fife.
Open all year. No smoking in the house. Vegetarian and most other special diets by arrangement. Children welcome. Pets by arrangement. Tea/coffee making & T.V. in all bedrooms. B. & B. from £11.

ST ANDREWS

 Edenside House, Edenside, by St Andrews, KY16 9SQ (0334) 838108
Beautiful 19th C. farmhouse set back from the A91 on the Eden Estuary nature reserve.
Open all year. No smoking in the house. Vegetarian standard and other special diets by arrangement. Disabled access good: some ground floor rooms available. Children welcome. En suite, tea/coffee making & T.V.

 Mrs Sally McGilchrist, 3 Dempster Terrace, St Andrews (0334) 72504
Well-appointed Edwardian terraced house overlooking duck-filled burn 4 mins from town.
Open Apr. to Nov. No smoking in the house. Vegetarian by arrangement. Tea-making in rooms. B. & B. £12-13.

St Andrews Golf Hotel, 40 The Scores, St Andrews (0334) 72611

Situated on the cliffs overlooking St Andrews Bay and links, and 200 metres from the 'old course', St Andrews Hotel is a tastefully modernised, listed Victorian building with comfortable bedrooms and elegant public rooms (including a charming oak-panelled restaurant). The food is excellent: everything is prepared from fresh, local sea-food, game and meats, and is complemented by a first-rate choice of wines; meals are served by candlelight in the aforementioned dining room or, if you prefer a more informal atmosphere, you could dine in Ma Bells basement bar and restaurant with its vast array of foreign and local beers. The hotel is owned and run by the Hughes family and specialises in providing golfing holidays for individuals and small groups.
Open all year. No smoking in restaurant. Vegetarian & other diets by arrangement. Licensed. Children welcome. Pets by arrangement. En suite, tea/coffee making & T.V. in all bedrooms. Credit cards.

 Number Ten, Hope Street, St Andrew's, KY16 9HJ (0334) 74601
10-bedroomed guest house offering B. & B. close to the city centre and golf courses.
Open Jan. to Nov. No smoking in the house. Vegetarian and most other special diets by arrangement.Disabled access: "Ground floor entrance & bedrooms available". Children welcome. Pets by arrangement. En suite , TV & tea/coffee making in bedrooms.B. & B. from £17.

 West Park House, 5 St Mary's Place, St Andrews (0334) 75933
Beautiful Georgian house in centre of historic town near to university, beach and golf courses.
Open Mar. to Nov. No smoking in the house. Vegetarian & other diets by arrangement. Children welcome. En suite in most rooms. Tea/coffee making & T.V. in bedrooms. B. & B. from £16.50.

Restaurants

ABERDOUR

Hawkcraig House, Hawkcraig Point, Aberdour, Fife, KY3 0TZ (0383) 860335
10 seats. Meals served by arrangement. Prices D. £13 (£16.50 non-residents). No smoking throughout. Vegetarian and diabetic on request. Children: over 8s only.
For further details please see under the entry in the accommodation section.

FREUCHIE

Lomond Hills Hotel, Lomond Road, Freuchie, KY7 7EY (0337) 57329
Open 12.30 - 2, 7 - 9.15. D. £12.25. No smoking in restaurant. Vegetarian standard. Other diets by arrangement. Licensed. Disabled access: 'Restaurant on ground floor'. Children welcome. Access, Visa, Amex, Diners.
For further details please see under the entry in the accommodation section.

Glasgow & Central
Accommodation

DOLLAR

Strathdevon House, Harviestoun Road, Dollar, FK14 7PT (0259) 42320
Open all year. No smoking in the house. Vegetarian and most other special diets by arrangement. Children welcome. En suite in all rooms. Tea/coffee making on request. T.V. in lounge. Credit cards B & B from £12.

FALKIRK

turn so it's on my left

"Chez-Nous", Sunnyside Road, Brightons, Falkirk (0342) 715953
Open Feb. to Nov. No smoking in the house. Vegetarian by arrangement. Disabled access. Children welcome. En suite in 1 room. Tea/coffee making in bedrooms. T.V. in lounge. B & B from £13. *left again —*

GLASGOW

corner of Tantallon st. Carment Dr. *2nd on rt. 1st house on left hand.*

The Copthorne Glasgow, George Square, Glasgow, G2 1DS (041) 332 6711
Open all year. No smoking in some bedrooms & 50% of restaurant. Vegetarian by arrangement. Licensed. Children welcome (under 16s free). En suite, tea-making & T.V. in rooms. Credit cards. B. & B. from £47. *stairs*

off train, see ... footbr ... down left possible st.

Alison Couston, 13 Carment Drive, Shawlands, Glasgow, G41 3PP (041) 632 0193
#2 Victorian house in quiet street close to the shops and restaurants; traditional and pleasantly decorated rooms; friendly atmosphere. *£16 Pollock Shaws East (P'shawsE)*
Open Apr. to Sept. or by arrangement. No smoking in the house. Vegetarian by arrangement. Children welcome. Pets by arrangement. Tea/coffee making in bedrooms. T.V. in lounge. B. & B. from £12. *from 1/2 hr.*

Mrs J Freebairn-Smith, 14 Prospect Avenue, Cambuslang, Glasgow (041) 641 5055 *from 5 past*
Large Victorian villa standing in half an acre of lovely gardens. *to the hour 20* *Cath cart of or Newton*
Open all year. No smoking in public rooms & some bedrooms. Vegetarian by arrangement. Children welcome. Pets by arrangement. Tea/coffee making & T.V. in all bedrooms. B & B from £11.

Regent Guest House, 44 Regent Park Sq., Strathbungo, Glasgow, G41 2AG (041) 422 1199

#1 4233143 4231855

The Regent Guest House is a charming 'B' listed Victorian terraced house at the quiet end of a busy street just 2 miles south of Glasgow city centre (and, even more conveniently, just 1 mile north of the splendid Burrell Collection which is one of Glasgow's principle attractions). The guest house has been exceptionally well-appointed: the welcome-trays in the bedrooms, for instance, do not just contain the usual tea and coffee, but also have Perrier, hot chocolate, Horlicks and shortbread. Likewise the breakfast menu features not just the usual platter of cooked fare but also offers some healthy options such as fresh fruit and yoghurt. Breakfast and evening meals are available at the Regent Guest house and there is also a good selection of restaurants at the other end of the street offering a wide range of culinary choices including Greek, Italian and Indian.

Open all year. No smoking in the house ex. 3 bedrooms. Vegetarian & other diets by arrangement. Children welcome. Pets by arrangement. Tea/coffee making & T.V. in all bedrooms. Credit cards. B. & B. from £20.

STIRLING

Mrs Thelma Harper, 67 Burnhead Road, Larbert, Stirling, FK5 4BD (0324) 553168
Open all year. No smoking in the house. Vegetarian and most other special diets by arrangement. Children welcome. Tea/coffee making in bedrooms. T.V. on request. B & B from £14.50.

Mr and Mrs D McLaren, "Allandale", 98 Causewayhead Rd, Stirling (0786) 65643
Open all year. No smoking in the house. Vegetarian by arrangement. Children welcome. Tea/coffee. T.V. in lounge. B & B from £12.

Mrs J Colville, 12 Argyll Avenue, Riverside, Stirling, FK8 1UL (0786) 62632
Open all year. No smoking in the house. Choice of breakfasts. Children welcome. Tea/coffee avail. on request at any time. T.V. in lounge. B & B from £10.

Restaurants

DRYMEN

 Drymen Pottery Tearoom, The Square, Drymen (0360) 60458
Open daily 9.30 - 5.30. No smoking throughout tearoom.

 Burnbank Hotel, 67/85 West Princes Street, Glasgow (041) 332 4400
30 seats. Open 12 - 2.30, 7 - 10. No smoking throughout. Vegetarian and some other special diets on request. Licensed. Disabled access. Children welcome. Credit cards accepted.

GLASGOW

 Café JJ, 180 Dumbarton Road, Glasgow, G11 6XE (041) 357 1881
Small, family-run café offering a wide selection of home-made food at reasonable prices.
36 seats. Open 10.30 - 7 (Mon.-Wed.), 10.30 - 10 (Thurs. - Sat.), 12 - 6.30 (Sun). L. around £3, D. around £7. No smoking throughout. Vegetarian & other diets on request. Licensed. Children welcome.

 The Coach House, Balmore, Torrance, Glasgow, G64 4AE (0360) 20742
Interesting charitable enterprise offering home-baked snacks & cakes together with shop selling crafts and gifts.
10 seats. Open 11 - 5. L. around £2. No smoking throughout. Vegetarian standard. Children welcome.

The Copthorne Glasgow, George Square, Glasgow, G2 1DS (041) 332 6711
60 seats. Open 12 - 2.30, 7 - 10. No smoking in approx. 50% of dining room. Vegetarian and some other special diets on request. Licensed. Children welcome. Credit cards.

Debenhams, Glasgow
Two self-service restaurants and a coffee shop serve this premium store in Glasgow. Somewhere to suit everyone with a family restaurant at the top of the shop..
Open store hours. Smoking banned throughout. Vegetarian meals. No disabled access. Not licensed. Children very welcome. Credit and debit cards accepted.

Shish Mahal Restaurant, 45-47 Gibson Street, Glasgow (041) 334 7899
'Opened in 1964 there has been a queue outside from 1964 onwards!'Now into its 3rd generation of owners this excellent restaurant serves Western and Indian food.
110 seats. Open midday - 11.30. L. from £7. Smoking banned in well-ventilated section of restaurant. Vegetarian standard. Licensed. Disabled access. Children welcome. Credit cards accepted.

STIRLING

Broughton's Restaurant, Blair Drummond, Stirling, FK9 4XE (0786) 841897
No smoking in restaurant. Vegetarian standard. Licensed. Disabled access. Children lunchtime only.

Grampian Accommodation

ABERDEEN

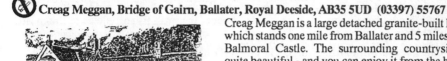 St Elmo, 64 Hilton Drive, Aberdeen, AB2 2NP (0224) 483065
Open all year. No smoking. Children welcome. Tea-making & T.V. in all bedrooms. B. & B. from £10.

BALLATER

Craigendarroch Guest House, 36 Braemar Road, Ballater, AB35 5RQ (03397) 55369
*Open all year. No smoking ex. in 1 bedroom. Vegetarian by arrangement. Disabled access: "Ground floor."
Children welcome. Pets by arrangement. En suite, TV & tea/coffee making in bedrooms. B. & B. from £14.*

 **Creag Meggan, Bridge of Gairn, Ballater, Royal Deeside, AB35 5UD (03397) 55767**

Creag Meggan is a large detached granite-built house which stands one mile from Ballater and 5 miles from Balmoral Castle. The surrounding countryside is quite beautiful - and you can enjoy it from the house: all the bedrooms have lovely views. Your hostess, Mrs Marilyn Johnson, will do everything she can to make your stay happy and memorable: the bedrooms are clean and comfortable, and the excellent food has all been home-cooked from fresh, local produce. Royal Deeside has plenty to offer its visitors: there are numerous country walks to be enjoyed, and salmon fishing and golf are both available locally; for the more energetic there are mountain bikes to be hired or hill walking, and there is, of course, the castle trail to follow, which includes Balmoral.
Open May - Sept. No smoking in the house. Children: over 12s only. TV & tea/coffee-making in bedrooms. B. & B. £14, D. £8.

The Green Inn, 9 Victoria Road, Ballater, AB3 5QQ (03397) 55701
The Green Inn is a granite-built former temperance hotel which overlooks Ballater village green. All the food has been prepared on the premises and maximum use is made of local, fresh produce. Traditional Scottish specialities are a regular feature of the menu and a set vegetarian menu is also available. There are some wonderful dishes to choose from: as an appetiser you might try a bisque of West Coast Langoustines served with Lochnagar Whisky, or Cream of Wood Pigeon with Morrels, Mushrooms and Pearl Barley; as a main course you might be tempted by roast loin of Scotch Lamb with a light curry, mango and banana sauce garnished with grilled scallops - or perhaps a Fricassée of locally caught Seafood and Shellfish served with a Lime and Avocado Salad. For dessert there is Sticky Toffee Pudding served with Citrus Fruits and a Whisky Butterscotch Sauce, or 'Crowdie Cake'- a blend of Crowdie Cheese, lemon and buttermilk served with Blairgowrie Fruit and Berries in a raspberry and red wine sauce. The Green Inn has a very extensive wine list with bottles representing every region from Alsace to Australia and from Champagne to Chile, as well as a good choice of traditional beers. Service in the dining room is informal and friendly.
Open all year. No smoking in dining room. Vegetarian standard. Other diets by arrangement. Licensed. Disabled access. Children welcome. Pets by arrangement. En suite, TV & tea/coffee making in bedrooms. Access, Visa. B. & B. from £18.50.

Pannanich Wells Hotel, South Deeside Road, Ballater, AB3 5SJ (03397) 55018
Open all year. No smoking ex. in bar & residents' lounge. Vegetarian standard. Other diets by arrangement. Licensed. Disabled access. Pets by arrangement. En suite, tea/coffee making & T.V. in all bedrooms. Access, Visa. B. & B. from £35.

ELGIN

Ⓧ **'Carronvale', 18 South Guildry Street, Elgin, Moray, IV30 1QN   (0343) 546864**
Beautiful stone-built Victorian town house within walking distance of the town & stations.
Open all year ex. Oct. No smoking in the house. Vegetarian by arrangement. Children welcome. Tea/coffee making in bedrooms. T.V. in lounge. B. & B. from £12.

Ⓧ **Non Smokers Haven, 63 Moss Street, Elgin, Moray, IV30 1LT   (0343) 541993**
South-facing   19th C. town house with walled garden; guests enjoy the quiet central position, comfort & personal attention; private parking; ideal for golfers, ornithologists. STB Commended.
Open all year. No smoking. Children welcome. Tea/coffee making & T.V. in rooms. B. & B. from £11.

MORAY

Ⓧ **Seaview B & B, 82 Granary Street, Burghead, Moray, IV30 2UA** (0343) 830034
Commended guest house situated on the harbour front of the small fishing village of Burghead.
Open all year. No smoking in the house. Vegetarian by arrangement. Disabled: '1 ground floor bedroom'. Children welcome. Pets by arrangement. Tea/coffee making & T.V. in all bedrooms. B. & B. from £11.

MUIR OF ORD

The Dower House, Muir of Ord, Ross-shire, IV6 7XN   Tel & Fax: (0463) 870090
The Dower House offers exceptionally comfortable accommodation and award-winning food.
Open all year. No smoking in dining room & some bedrooms. Vegetarian by arrangement. Licensed. Disabled access. Children welcome. Dogs by arrangement. En suite & T.V. in rooms. Credit cards. B. & B. from £45.

FORRES

Ⓧ **Parkmount House Hotel, St Leonard's Road, Forres, IV36 0DW   (0309) 73312**
Open all year. No smoking in the house. Vegetarian by arrangement. Licensed. Children welcome. Pets by arrangement. En suite, TV & tea/coffee making in bedrooms. Access, Mastercard. B. & B. from £29.

GLENLIVET

Minmore House Hotel, Glenlivet, Ballandalloch, AB3 9DB   (08073) 378
Open May to Nov. No smoking ex. in bar & some bedrooms. Vegetarian by arrangement. Licensed. Children welcome. Pets by arrangement. En suite & tea/coffee making in bedrooms. B. & B. from £28.

HUNTLY

Faich-Hill Farmhouse Holidays, Gartly, Huntly, Aberdeenshire, AB54 4RR   (046688) 240
Open all year. No smoking ex. sun lounge. Vegetarian by arrangement. Children: over 4s only. En suite in one bedroom. Tea/coffee making. T.V. lounge. B. & B. from £12. Twice Scottish 'Farmhouse of the year' Winner.

KEITH

The Haughs Farm Guest House, Keith   (05422) 2238
Comfortable farmhouse with lovely large southfacing dining room overlooking the pretty garden
Open 1 Apr. to 15 Oct. No smoking in dining room & bedrooms. Vegetarian & diabetic diets by arrangement. Disabled access. Children welcome. En suite in 3 rooms. Tea-making & T.V. in rooms. B. & B. from £12.50.

Restaurants

ABERDEEN

Ⓧ **Charles Michie Chemists, 391 Union Street, Aberdeen   (0224) 585312**
Charles Michie's is a beautiful store at the top of Union Street in of which you'll find a fresh and pretty coffee shop. The delicious food has all been home-prepared - including the Scottish scones and bakeries, and fragrant, fresh coffee - and the proprietors tell me that even smokers enjoy the fact that the coffee shop is smoke-free "everything smells and tastes that bit nicer somehow". The coffee shop is open for morning coffee, lunches and afternoon tea - and, as you leave, you can enjoy browsing through the selection of gifts, cards, stationery and perfumes in the store.
Open shop hours. No smoking. Vegetarian & diabetic standard. Disabled: 'Staff help with wheelchairs'.

Highlands
Accommodation

ACHARACLE

Glencripesdale House, Acharacle, Argyll, PH36 4JH (096 785) 263

Glencripesdale House is a beautifully renovated 18th C. farmhouse overlooking Loch Sunart and the peak of Ben Laga in Ardnamurchan; it is very remotely situated in Morvern, a peninsula on the south shore of the Loch which is frequently by-passed by visitors and is consequently an isolated and unspoilt wilderness, rich in flora and fauna. The proprietors of Glencripesdale House are well aware that most of their guests come to appreciate the peace, tranquility and richness of natural beauty that the region surrounding their home has to offer; consequently they have made their home into a haven of rest and a place to escape from the cares and worries of the 20th C. The rooms are all beautifully decorated and furnished and meals are stupendous - almost everything having been prepared from fresh ingredients (the remoteness of Glencripesdale makes it necessary for the proprietors to freeze some of their own produce - but nothing has ever been commercially frozen); a typical evening menu would feature home-made Vegetable Soup followed by Lochy Trout in White Wine and Fennel, and Bramble and Apple Crumble with Bramble Cordial. *Open Mar. to Oct. & Xmas & New Year. No smoking in dining room. Vegetarian & other diets by arrangement. Licensed. Children welcome. En suite in all rooms. Tea/coffee making in hall. Full board from £55 daily.*

AULTBEA

Cartmel G.H., Birchburn Road, Aultbea, Achnasheen, W. Ross (0445) 731375
Open Mar. to Oct. No smoking. Vegetarian by arrangement. 'Good' disabled access. Children welcome. Pets by arrangement. 1 room en suite. Tea/coffee making. T.V. lounge. B. & B. with dinner from £18.

Oran Na Mara, Drumchork, Aultbea, Ross-shire, IV22 2HU (0445) 731394
Spacious, comfortable hill side guest house with stunning views from all rooms. Two STB Highly Commended self-catering apartments.
Open Easter to end Oct. No smoking in the house., Vegetarian & vegan standard. Disabled: 'all on ground floor'. Children: over 8s welcome. Pets by arrangement. Wash-handbasin, tea/coffee making & T.V. in all bedrooms. B. & B. from £13.

"Sandale", 5 Pier Road, Aultbea, Ross-shire, IV22 2JQ (0445 731) 336
Modern house standing in colourful gardens in the little croft and fishing village of Aultbea. Spectacular views of Loch Ewe from the guest lounge. Evening meals prepared from fresh, local produce. Home-baking. Inverewe gardens 6 miles.
Open Mar. to Oct. No smoking in the house. Vegetarian and most other special diets by arrangement. Children welcome. Tea/coffee making in bedrooms. T.V. in lounge. B. & B. from £12.

AVIEMORE

Aviemore Self Catering, 17 Craig-na-Gower Avenue, Aviemore, Inverness-shire, PH22 1RW (0479) 810031 (24 hrs)
Number seventeen is a comfortable family home where a warm welcome awaits you. Enjoy open views to the hills - and on chilly days have your cup of tea in comfort before a peat fire! There is safe off-road parking and self catering accommodation is also available in pine lodges or bungalows. The standard of accommodation and service at 17 Craig-na-Gower is very high indeed and the proprietors have been awarded a 2 and 4 Crowns Commended status for their holiday provision.
Open all year. No smoking in the house. Vegetarian by arrangement. Children welcome. En suite in all rooms. Tea/coffee on request. T.V. in lounge. B. & B. from £12.50. STB 2 & 4 Crown Commended.

BOAT OF GARTEN

Avingormack Guest House, Boat of Garten, Invernessshire PH24 3BT. (047983) 614
Avingormack is a converted croft which is situated in a beautiful rural location with magnificent, uninterrupted views of the Cairngorm mountains, yet just 4 miles from the tourist centre at Aviemore and convenient for all the sites and activities at Strathspey. The bedrooms are large and tastefully appointed, and the central heating and double glazing are welcome additions on cooler days! Your hosts Jan and Matthew Ferguson provide plentiful and delicious Scottish and vegetarian cuisine, which has all been prepared from fresh, local produce (organic and homegrown wherever possible); a typical evening menu might feature Courgette and Mint Soup with home-baked wholemeal bread, followed by poached fresh salmon with lobster butter (served with new minted potatoes and a salad of garden vegetables and edible flowers), followed by a dessert of plum and almond tart with cream. Matthew is a qualified ski instructor who will be happy to teach you to ski in either winter or summer on the local plastic slope or on the Cairngorm Mountains; golf, fishing and canoeing can all be enjoyed nearby and mountain bikes are available for hire.
Open all year. No smoking in the house. Vegetarian & traditional cooking standard. Other diets by arrangement. Children welcome. En suite some rooms. Tea/coffee making & T.V. in rooms. T.V. lounge. B. & B. from £13.

Heathbank House, Boat of Garten, Inverness-shire, PH24 3BD (0479) 83234
Open Dec. to Oct. No smoking in dining room & bedrooms. Vegetarian by arrangement. Licensed. Children accepted. En suite some rooms. Tea-making in bedrooms. T.V. lounge. B. & B. from £16, D.,B. & B. £28.

BRORA

Ard Beag, Badnellan, Brora, Sutherland, KW9 6NQ (0408) 621398
Small, comfortable former croft house in a pleasant south-facing garden with fine views.
Open May to Sept. No smoking in dining room & bedrooms. Vegetarian by arrangement. Children welcome. Tea/coffee making in bedrooms. B. & B. from £11.

Carrol Guest House, Golf Road, Brora, Sutherland, KW9 6QS (0408) 21065
Open May to Sept. No smoking in the house. Vegetarian by arrangement. Children welcome. En suite in 2 rooms. Tea/coffee making & T.V. in all bedrooms. B. & B. from £18.

Sumundar Villa, Harbour Road, Brora, Sutherland, KW9 6QF (0408) 21717
Open Feb. to Nov. No smoking in the house. Vegetarian and diabetic standard. Disabled access. Children welcome. Tea/coffee making & T.V. in all bedrooms. B. & B. from £13.

Tigh Fada (Non-Smokers Haven), Golf Road, Brora, KW9 6QS (0408) 621332
Spacious detached house peacefully situated in its own pleasant gardens with fine, uninterrupted views of the sea and hills.
Open all year. No smoking in the house. Vegetarian by arrangement. Children welcome, 'not toddlers'. Pets by arrangement. Tea/coffee making in rooms. B. & B. from £12.50-£15.50, with reduced price for 2+ nights.

CARRBRIDGE

Kinchyle Guest House, Carrbridge, Inverness-shire, PH23 3AA (047984) 243
Open all year. No smoking in the house. Vegetarian and low-fat diets by arrangement. Children welcome. Tea/coffee making in bedrooms. T.V. in lounge. B. & B. from £12.

DRUMBEG

Drumbeg House, Drumbeg, Nr Lochinver, Sutherland, IV27 4NW (05713) 209
Charming Victorian house standing amidst 3 acres of garden beside water lily loch. Good home-cooking, delicious desserts; coal fire. Centrally heated throughout.
Open all year. No smoking in the house. Vegetarian and most other special diets by arrangement. Children: over 10s only. En suite & tea/coffee making in bedrooms. T.V. in lounge. B. & B. from £20. D. from £10.

DULNAIN BRIDGE

Auchendean Lodge Hotel, Dulnain Bridge, Inverness-shire, PH26 3LU (047) 985347

Visitors to Auchendean Lodge Hotel will feel that they have stepped back into another era: beautifully appointed throughout with period antiques, furnishings and paintings which have been chosen to complement the building's many original Edwardian features, Auchendean Lodge has outstanding views across the River Spey and over the Abernethy Forest to the Cairngorm Mountains. Its owners, Eric Hart and Ian Kirk, have created an ambience of comfort, style and good service, which prevails in an atmosphere of informality and great friendliness; both owners share the cooking and specialize in an imaginative cuisine (and some traditional Scottish dishes), which have been prepared not only from local and home-grown produce but from ingredients culled from the moors and woods (such as the wild mushrooms which Eric picks daily in late summer and autumn). Staying at Auchendean Lodge is an enjoyable and unique experience - and whether your strongest memories will be of the house, the food or the magnificent surroundings will be for you to decide.

Open all year. No smoking in dining room & sitting room. Vegetarian, vegan and most other special diets by arrangement. Licensed. Disabled access. Children welcome. Pets by arrangement. En suite in most bedrooms. Tea/coffee making & T.V. in all rooms. B. & B. from £20.

DURNESS

 Port-na-Con House, Port-na-Con, Loch Eriboll, By Altnaharra, Lairg, Sutherland, IV27 4UN (0971) 511367

Port-na-Con stands on the west side of Loch Eriboll, 6 miles east of Durness, and was built 200 years ago as a Custom House and harbour store. Completely renovated in 1984, it is now a comfortable, centrally heated guest house in which all bedrooms overlook the loch: the first floor lounge and balcony have particularly impressive views and here guests can enjoy not only the scenery, but also the varied wild life, including seals, otters and birds. The food is the very best of Scottish fare: all dishes are home-cooked from fresh, local ingredients and a typical evening meal would feature Salmon and Crab Terrine with home-made bread, followed by Roast Beef with fresh vegetables, and a delicious dessert, such as Chocolate & Orange Cheesecake.

Open April - Oct. inc. No smoking in the house. Vegetarian & other diets by arrangement. Licensed. Children & well-behaved dogs welcome. Tea/coffee-making in bedrooms. Access & Visa. D., B. & B. £26, single £32.

FORT WILLIAM

 Mrs B Grieve, 'Nevis View', 14 Farrow Drive, Corpach, Fort William, Inverness-shire, PH33 7JW Tel: (0397) 772447 Fax (0397) 772800

Open all year. No smoking in the house. Vegetarian standard. Vegan by arrangement. Children welcome. Pets by arrangement. Tea/coffee making & T.V. in all bedrooms. B & B from £11.50. D. £6.

Taransay, Seafield Gardens, Fort William, Inverness-shire, PH33 6RJ (0397) 703303
Taransay is a comfortable, modern family home which is situated in a quiet residential area just off the A82 and close to the town centre. It has panoramic views over Loch Linnhe and the Ardgour Hills, and you are perfectly placed for visiting Ben Nevis or enjoying the skiing on Aonach Mor. Families are made very welcome, and skiers will find themselves particularly well catered for, as there are storage and drying facilities within the house. Breakfasts are delicious - and served in generous portions - and packed lunches can be prepared on request. Your host will be happy to recommend local restaurants for dining in the evening, and to help you plan your sightseeing trips.

Open Jan. to Oct. No smoking in the house. Vegetarian standard. Other diets by arrangement. Children welcome. En suite available. Tea/coffee making in rooms. T.V. lounge. B. & B. from £12.50. 2 Crowns Commended.

GLENFINNAN
The Stage House, Glenfinnan, Inverness-shire, PH37 4LT   (0397 83) 246

This beautiful 17th C. coaching inn is superbly situated in one of Scotland's most picturesque glens at the head of Loch Shiel; it has been beautifully renovated over the years, and all rooms are comfortably furnished and well-appointed. The excellent à la carte menu offers some imaginative dishes which have been prepared from fresh, local produce - including venison, salmon and seafood - and a typical evening menu would feature Creamed Stilton and Onion Soup followed by Supreme of Duck with a rich plum sauce (and a selection of vegetables) and a Scottish dessert such as Cranachan and fresh raspberries. The Stage House owns extensive fishing rights on Loch Shiel, with no less than 4 boats and outboard motors being available for guests' use; mountain bikes are also available for hire. Additionally there is much else to enjoy in this area which is both steeped in history and rich in beautiful scenery (the peaks of Glencoe and Ben Nevis are within easy reach - so to speak).
Open Mar. to Jan. No smoking ex. 2 bars. Vegetarian standard. Diabetic by arrangement. Licensed. Children: over 5s only. Pets by arrangement. En suite, TV & tea-making in rooms. Access, Visa. B. & B. from £25.95.

GRANTOWN-ON-SPEY

 Kinross House, Woodside Avenue, Grantown-on-Spey, Morayshire, PH26 3JR   (0479) 2042

Peacefully situated in the delightful country town of Grantown-on-Spey, Kinross House is an attractive Victorian villa which has been beautifully decorated and furnished throughout. David and Katherine Elder, your Scottish hosts, have established a well-deserved reputation for the warmth of their hospitality and their excellent home-prepared food. David will be wearing his MacIntosh tartan kilt when he serves your evening meal which, typically, might feature Stilton and Leek Soup followed by Baked Trout (with fresh vegetables) and an imaginative dessert such as Oranges in Cointreau with Orange Sorbet; a good mature Scottish cheddar with biscuits and oatcakes, followed by fresh coffee and mints, would complete the meal. The Kinross House brochure will tell you more about the lovely surrounding area in which you can visit Balmoral and Braemar, Loch Ness and Inverness, Cawdor Castle, Culloden Battlefield as well as numerous woollen mills and whisky distilleries.
Open Mar. to Nov. No smoking. Vegetarian by arrangement. Sorry, no dinner on Weds. Licensed. Children: over 7s only. En suite most rooms. Tea-making & T.V. in rooms. B. & B.   £16-22 (en suite), £13-19 (no en suite).

 Stonefield Cottage, 28 The Square, Grantown-on-Spey, Moray, PH26 3HF   (0479) 3000
Open Easter to end Oct. No smoking. Vegetarian and most other special diets by arrangement. Children welcome. Tea/coffee making in bedrooms. B. & B. from £12.

INVERNESS
Ardmuir House Hotel, 16 Ness Bank, Inverness, IV2 4SF   (0463) 231151
Ardmuir House is a charming stone-built Georgian house of character, set on the east bank of the River Ness just a few minutes' walk from both the town centre and the Ness Islands. The delicious home-cooked food is prepared from fresh ingredients and features some imaginative dishes, as well as more traditional Scottish fare; a typical evening menu might feature Haggis with Onion Sauce followed by Lemon Baked Chicken with Vegetables and a tempting dessert such as Pineapple Upside-down Cake. You are perfectly placed for exploring the whole of the Highlands and are within easy reach of Loch Ness, Balmoral and Royal Deeside, Glen Affric, The Spey Valley, Ullapool and the West Coast, Fort William and Ben Nevis. Your hosts Jean and Tony Gatcombe will be happy to provide information about nature reserves and other areas of special historical or

architectural interest. 0463-230-228 (17, 18, 19)

Open all year. No smoking in dining room. Vegetarian & other diets by arrangement. Licensed. Disabled access. Children welcome. Pets by arrangement. En suite & hairdryers in all bedrooms. Tea/coffee making. T.V. (5) COST? 450

Borlum Farmhouse B. & B., Drumnadrochit, Inverness, IV3 6XN Tel & Fax: (045) 62358
This early 18th C. farmhouse has a unique position overlooking Loch Ness, with commanding views of the surrounding hills; comfortably furnished throughout with antiques, fabrics and furnishings that are pleasing to the eye, the house is centrally heated and offers a choice of double twin or family rooms (there is also a further suite which sleeps five and a choice of self-catering cottages). In the colder months a wood-stove burns in the sitting room, while in the summer the conservatory is used as the sitting room so guests can enjoy the panoramic views of Loch Ness and the Glen. Your hosts, Captain and Mrs MacDonald-Haig, also have a farm with Highland Cattle, and a BHS approved Riding Centre which caringly caters for all ages and stages; the immediate area offers a wide variety of outdoor activities including, fishing, hill-walking, golf, curling and bowls, and you are on the main bus route to (and just 20 mins'drive from) Inverness.

Open all year. No smoking in the house. Children & pets welcome. Some rooms en suite. TV in sitting room. Credit cards. B. & B. around £19. (4) Single?

'Clach Mhuilinn', 7 Harris Road, Inverness, IV2 3LS (0463) 237059 (1) full
Spacious modern detached house with beautiful garden in quiet residential area 1m. S. of city. Bar meals nearby. Excellent touring base. STB 2 Crown Highly Commended. B.& B. only.
Open Mar. to Nov. No smoking in the house. Special diets by arrangement. Children: over 10s welcome. Tea/coffee making in bedrooms. T.V. in lounge. B. & B. from £15.

Darnaway House, 5 Darnaway Road, Inverness, IV2 3LF (0463) 234002 (3) not ringing
Open Mar. to Oct. No smoking in the house. 2 public bathrooms. Tea/coffee making. T.V. in all bedrooms. B. & B. from £15. Parking available.

Glencairn Guest House, 19 Ardross Street, Inverness, IV3 5NS (0463) 232965 (2)
B. & B. in quiet residential street close to town centre, theatre, cathedral and River Ness. Loch Ness 5 mins by car.
Open all year. Smoking banned throughout the house. Vegetarian & other diets by arrangement. Children welcome. En suite in two bedrooms. Tea/coffee making in hall. T.V. in lounge. B. & B. from £14-£20. £20

Glendruidh House, Old Edinburgh Road, Inverness, IV1 2AA Tel: (0463) 226499 Fax: (0463) 710745

Glendruidh House is a charming and unusual building standing in its own pleasant grounds overlooking Inverness, the Moray Firth and the Black Isle. Its design is extraordinary: with its interesting tower over the entrance hall, the many dormer windows and an amazing circular drawing room which has beautiful garden views; its rare peace and tranquillity bely the fact that it is just 2 miles from the centre of Inverness. The cuisine reflects a largely traditional menu and offers home-cooked dishes which have been superbly prepared from fresh local produce. A typical table d'hote dinner selection might be Cream of Potato and Chives Soup or Chicken Liver Paté with cranberries, followed by Poached Fresh Wild Salmon with Parsley and Lemon Butter or Roast Leg of Chicken Stuffed with Raisins and Nuts (and fresh vegetable accompaniments); dessert might be Toffee Apple Sponge or Poached Victoria Plums in Port. Whilst many small hotels are totally smoke-free, Glendruidh House is unusual in that it has a small luxurious bar open to the public which is also smoke-free. The Glendruidh House brochure rightly eulogises the Highlands as a place for all seasons: spring is the time of endless days (blue skies at midnight!) and autumn is the time when heather purples the mountains; winter is not just when the

skiers repair to Aviemore, but is the season when the cognoscenti come to appreciate Scotland's beautiful frozen lochs and to see waterfalls hanging like crystal from the mountains.
Open all year. No smoking in the house. Vegetarian and most other special diets by arrangement. Licensed. Disabled access: 'with assistance; ground floor rooms & wide doors'. Children welcome. En suite , tea/coffee making & T.V. in all bedrooms. Credit cards. B. & B. from £29

Ness Bank Guest House, 7 Ness Bank, Inverness, IV2 4SF (0463) 232939
Ness Bank Guest House is a comfortable Victorian guest house in a superb location on the banks of the River Ness overlooking the cathedral and within a few minutes' walk of the town centre. There are many scenic riverside walks to be enjoyed through the Ness islands as well as in the nearby public parks and gardens. Inverness is a town of great architectural and historic interest; surrounded by magnificent countryside, it is a perfect base from which to visit Loch Ness, Culloden Battlefield and the nearby castles and gardens. Ther area has many facilities for outdoor pursuits such as hill-walking, climbing, skiing, golf, fishing, watersports, tennis & pony-trekking.
Open all year. No smoking in the house. Vegetarian and some other special diets by arrangement. Tea/coffee making & T.V. in all bedrooms. B. & B. from £15.

Rose Lodge, 6 Kenneth Street, Inverness, IV2 5NR (0463) 233434
Open all year. No smoking in the house. 2 rooms en suite. Tea-making. T.V. lounge. B. & B. from £10.

Sky House, Upper Cullernie, Balloch, Inverness IV1 2HU (0463) 792582
Spacious, modern home in beautiful open countryside yet 5 mins drive from the highland capital and its airport. Magnificent views across the Moray Firth. Wholesome and healthy b'fast.
Open all year. No smoking throughout. Vegetarian by arrangement. Pets by arrangement. En suite in some rooms. Tea/coffee making & T.V. in all rooms. Access, Visa. B. & B. from £18.

KINGUSSIE

Cornerways, Newtonmore Road, Kingussie, PH21 1HE (0540) 661446
Modern detached house in attractive flower-filled gardens in Kingussie. B'fast only.
Open Mar. to Oct. No smoking in the house. Vegetarian by arrangement. Children: over 6s only. En suite in one room. Tea/coffee making in bedrooms. T.V. in lounge. B. & B. from £13.50.

Homewood Lodge, Newtonmore Road, Kingussie, PH21 1HD (0540) 661507
Charming country house offering excellent accommodation; log fires and delicious dinners; home-made bread, scones and icecreams. Vegetarian meals always available.
Open all year ex. Xmas. No smoking in the house. Vegetarian standard. Licensed. Children welcome. Pets by arrangement. En suite & tea/coffee making in bedrooms. T.V. in lounge. B. & B. from £19.

The Royal Hotel, 29 High Street, Kingussie, Inverness-shire, PH21 1HX (0540) 661898
Family-owned & run hotel in the quiet village of Kingussie; excellent cuisine prepared from fresh, local produce.
Open all year. No smoking in dining room, part of bar & reception. Vegetarian and most other special diets by arrangement. Licensed. Disabled access. Children welcome. Pets by arrangement. En suite , TV & tea/coffee making in bedrooms. Credit cards. B. & B. from £26 D. £12.

KYLE OF LOCHALSH

Culag, Carr Brae, Dornie, Kyle, Ross-shire, IV40 8HA (059 985) 341
Open Mar. to Nov. No smoking in the house. Exclusively vegetarian & vegan. Children welcome. Tea/coffee making in bedrooms. B. & B. from £12. D. £7.50.

The Retreat, Main Street, Kyle, Ross-shire, IV40 8BY (0599) 4308
Open all year. Smoking banned throughout the house. Vegetarian and most other special diets by arrangement. Restricted licence. Children: over 14s only. Tea/coffee making in bedrooms. T.V. in lounge.B. & B. from £13.

Tigh Tasgaidh, Bank House, Dornie, Kyle of Lochalsh, Ross-shire (059 985) 242
Open Mar. to Nov. No smoking. En suite & tea-making in bedrooms. T.V. lounge. B. & B. from £14.

17, 18, 19

KYLESKU

 Linne Mhuirich, Unapool Croft Road, Kylesku, via Lairg, Sutherland, IV27 4HW (0971) 502227

Fiona and Diarmid MacAulay welcome up to 6 non-smoking guests to their modern croft house, which is superbly situated on a hillside leading down to the rocky shore of Loch Glencoul; its quiet, peaceful, yet accessible position makes it an excellent base for exploring the north-west Highlands. Many guests return annually for the comfort and attention, peace and the delicious food (which is 'Taste of Scotland' recommended). Everything has been home-made from fresh and local ingredients, and Fiona specializes in preparing local fish and seafood dishes; quiches, pâtés, tasty casseroles, delicious vegetarian dishes and tempting desserts also feature on her menus (although there are also low-calorie choices for those with an eye on the waistline!). There is no T.V. reception here - so nothing can interfere with after dinner conversation or just sitting back and enjoying the spectacular views from the comfort of the lounge (or perhaps browsing through the MacAulays' extensive collection of books).

Open May to Oct. No smoking in the house. Vegetarian, low-fat, high-fibre diets by arrangement. Bring your own wine. Children welcome. Pets by arrangement. 1 room with private bathroom. Tea/coffee making in bedrooms. B. & B. from £16.50, D. £9.50. STB 2 crowns commended. "Taste of Scotland" recommended.

LAIRG

Gneiss House, Invershin, by Lairg, Sutherland, IV17 4ET (054 982) 282
Attractive bungalow in pretty garden amidst the glorious unspoilt Sutherland countryside.
Open all year. No smoking in the house. Vegetarian and most other special diets by arrangement. Pets by arrangement. En suite & tea/coffee making in bedrooms. T.V. in lounge. B. & B. from £13.

LOCHCARRON

Ladytrek Scotland, 'Foxgloves', Leacanashie, Lochcarron, W. Ross (05202) 238
Open Easter - Oct. No smoking. Vegetarian by arrangement. Tea-making. Incl. walking hol. price.

LOCHINVER

'Polcraig', Lochinver, Sutherland, IV27 4LD (05714) 429
Open Apr. to Sept. No smoking. Tea/coffee making in bedrooms. T.V. lounge. B. & B. from £12.50.

LOCHNESS-SIDE

The Foyers Hotel, Lochness-side, Inverness, IV1 2XT (04563) 216
Open all year. No smoking in the hotel. Vegetarian standard. Vegan & other diets by arrangement. Licensed. Children welcome. En suite some rooms. T.V. lounge. Credit cards. B. & B. from £27.50.

NETHYBRIDGE

Talisker, Dell Road, Nethybridge, Inverness-shire, PH25 3DG (047982) 624
Open all year. No smoking in the house. Diabetic diets by arrangement. Children: over 8s only. Pets by arrangement. Tea/coffee making facilities. T.V. in lounge. B. & B. from £11.50.

NEWTONMORE

Craigellachie House, Main Street, Newtonmore, Inverness-shire (0540) 673360
Comfortable family home built in the 1800s and thought to be the oldest house in Newtonmore. Excellent breakfast with lots of options. Evening meals by arrangement.
Open all year ex. Xmas. No smoking in the house. Vegetarian & vegan standard. Other diets by arrangement. Children welcome. Pets by arrangement. Tea/coffee making in bedrooms. T.V. in lounge. B. & B. from £14.

The Pines Hotel, Station Road, Newtonmore, Inverness-shire (05403) 271
Country house set in secluded pine wooded gardens; log fire in the lounge; excellent food.
Ideal for touring and birdwatching.
Open April to Oct. No smoking in the house. Most diets by arrangement. Licensed. Children: over 6s only. No pets. En suite in all bedrooms. Tea/coffee making facilities. T.V. in lounge. B. & B. from £21.

REAY

 Askival, Reay, Caithness, KW14 7RE (084 781) 470
Angling holidays run from angling school and resource centre situated in attractive village.
Open Mar. to Nov. No smoking Vegetarian by arrangement. Children welcome. T.V. in lounge.

SPEAN BRIDGE

Invergloy Halt, By Spean Bridge, Inverness-shire, PH34 4DY (039781) 621
Modern single-storey house peacefully situated on the site of a former railway halt.
Open Mar. to Oct.; other times by arrangement. No smoking in the house. Vegetarian standard. Disabled access. Children: over 14s only. Pets by arrangement. Tea/coffee making in bedrooms. T.V. lounge.

Old Pines, Gairlochy Road, Spean Bridge, Inverness-shire, PH34 4EG (039) 781324
Old Pines is a happy family home of great character, built in Scandinavian style, which stands

in 30 peaceful acres of land and commanding breathtaking views of Aonach Mor and Ben Nevis. The bedrooms are comfortable and prettily decorated, and fresh flowers, interesting books and log fires all help to create a relaxing, informal atmosphere and a restful holiday! The cooking is excellent: delicious meals are imaginatively prepared from the best of fresh local ingredients, and a typical dinner menu would include cheese and fruit Salad with raspberry vinegar
dressing followed by Trout stuffed with Leeks, Garlic and Orange or Pheasant with Black Grapes
and Fresh Herbs and, for dessert, a Rhubarb and Banana Brulée. Old Pines is a perfect base from
which to tour Scotland's West Highlands, and there is winter skiing 6 miles away at Aonach Mor.
Open all year. No smoking indoors. Vegetarian & other diets by arrangement. Not licensed, but guests welcome to bring own. Disabled access: 'Completely accessible; 3 specially adapted ground floor bedrooms.' Children welcome. Pets by arrangement. En suite in most rooms. Tea/coffee on request. T.V. in lounge. Access, Visa, Mastercard. D., B. & B. from £30. STB 3 Crowns Commended. The Taste of Scotland Member.

STRATHPEFFER

Gardenside Guest House, Strathpeffer, Ross and Cromarty, IV14 9BJ (0997) 421242
Charming 19th C. house in a splendid situation surrounded by woodland and fields.
Open 1 Mar. to 4 Jan. No smoking in the house. Vegetarian by arrangement. Licensed. Disabled: ground floor rooms avail. Children welcome. En suite. Tea-making in bedrooms. T.V. lounge. B. & B. from £13.50.

TONGUE

Ben Loyal Hotel, Tongue, Sutherland, IV27 4XE (0847 55) 216

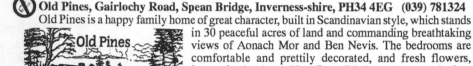

The Ben Loyal Hotel is a white-painted building standing in a quite splendid location overlooking the waters of the Kyle of Tongue and the peaks of the mountain after which it has been named. The hotel has been designed with the seemingly sole intention of enabling guests to enjoy these quite stunning panoramas in almost every room: from the comfortably furnished lounge with its picture window to the beautifully appointed bedrooms (pine furniture, pretty fabrics, fourposters). Perhaps the best views can be had from the dining room, however - although here you will find that your loyalties are torn between relishing the view and savouring the food: only fresh, local produce - some of it
home-grown - is used in the preparation of a largely traditional menu and the table d'hote meal
could well feature home-made Lentil Soup followed by Supreme of Salmon in a Seafood Sauce
(served with fresh vegetables) and a selection of good old-fashioned puddings, such as Bread and

Butter Pudding. Ben Loyal is, as I have indicated, surrounded by quite breathtaking countryside; there are lots of lovely sandy beaches to wander along and the wildlife flourishes in abundance. *Open all year. No smoking in dining room. Vegetarian and most other special diets by arrangement. Licensed. Disabled access: 'partial, with assistance'. Children welcome. Pets by arrangement. En suite in most rooms. Tea/coffee making in bedrooms. T.V. on request. Access, Visa. D., B. & B. from £35.50 - 44.50 (discounts for stays of 3 or more nights).*

ULLAPOOL

Altnaharrie Inn, Ullapool, IV26 2SS (085 483) 230
Beautiful old house standing on the south shores of Loch Broom; can only be reached by launch (6 trips daily)! & has an atmosphere of great tranquillity;outstanding cuisine (chef rated among top few in Britain).
Open Easter to late Oct. No smoking in the house. Vegetarian & other diets by arrangement. Licensed. Children: over 8s only. Pets by arrangement. En suite in all rooms. Tea/coffee avail. D., B & B from £105.

The Old Manse, Clachan, Lochbroom, By Ullapool, Ross-shire (0854) 85264
Open Apr. to Oct. No smoking in the house. Vegetarian breakfast standard. Children welcome. Tea/coffee making in bedrooms. B. & B. from £12.50.

Tigh-Na-Mara (House by the Sea), The Shore, Ardindrean, Nr Ullapool, Loch Broom, Wester-Ross, IV23 2SE (0854 85) 282
A special guest house for special people! Tony and Shan invite you to share their secluded

and idyllic home, a beautiful old house with lots of character and breathtaking views overlooking Loch Broom. The 30 foot lounge/dining room is warmed by a wood-burning stove and has a spiral stair leading up to just two romantic bedrooms and a wood-panelled bathroom (there is a new Honeymoon suite in the boatshed!). Tony and Shan serve gourmet Scottish vegetarian and vegan dishes which have been cooked on the range, and a typical evening meal might feature avocado in a kiwi and yogurt sauce, vegetarian game pie (including vegetarian haggis, and served with roast potatoes, oranged carrots, broccoli and rich thyme gravy), and for dessert, a heady dose of Flumery (Drambuie, cream, honey and lemon on a toasted oatmeal base); full board is available but breakfast is enormous, packed lunches can be prepared on request, and the 4-course evening meal will satisfy the stoutest of appetites. You are blissfuly isolated at Tigh-na-Mara, so bring your own wine and wellies (Ullapool is 20 minutes' drive away and Inverness train, bus and air services an hour's drive), but your hosts have thought of everything to keep you happy in situ, including providing a babysitting service, transfers from Inverness (by helicopter if you so wish), and free use of boats, bikes and windsurfers.
Open all year. No smoking in the house. Vegetarian & most other meat-free special diets standard. Children welcome. Tea/coffee making in bedrooms. D., B. & B. from £23.

Restaurants

ARDESIER

The Old Bakehouse, 73 High St, Ardesier (0667) 62920
Open daily 10 - 6, May to Oct. Smoking banned throughout.

DORNOCH

Dornoch Castle Hotel, Castle Street, Dornoch, Sutherland, IV25 3SD (0862) 810216
No smoking in restaurant. Vegetarian standard. Licensed. Disabled access. Children welcome.

GLENFINNAN

The Stage House, Glenfinnan, Inverness-shire, PH37 4LT (0397 83) 246
No smoking ex. in 2 bars. Vegetarian standard. Diabetic by arrangement. Licensed. Children: over 5s only.

KINGUSSIE

The Cross, 25/27 High Street, Kingussie, PH21 1HX (0540) 661166
No smoking throughout. Vegetarian by arrangement. Licensed. Access, Visa.

KYLE OF LOCHALSH

Wholefood Café, Highland Design Works, Plockton Road, Kyle of Lochalsh, IV40 8DA (0599) 4388/4702
Open 12.30 - 3, 6.30 - 8.30. D. around £11. No smoking throughout. Vegetarian, vegan, diabetic and gluten-free standard. Licensed. Disabled access. Children welcome. Access, Visa.

LOCHINVER

Acmins Bookshop and Coffee Shop, Inverkirkaig, Lochinver (05714) 262
Small coffee shop attached to book shop; open seasonally.
Open 10 - 5. No smoking. Vegetarian dishes often available. Disabled access. Children welcome.

NAIRN

Cawdor Castle Restaurant, Cawdor Castle, Nairn, IV12 5RP (06677) 615
Pleasant café/restaurant serving a wide range of snacks & teas prepared in the castle kitchens.
Open May 1st to Oct. 4th, 11 a.m. - 5 p.m. L. around £3. No smoking throughout. Vegetarian standard. Some other special diets on request. Table licence. Disabled access. Children welcome. Credit cards accepted.

NETHYBRIDGE

Pollyanna's, Nethybridge, Inverness-shire, PH25 3DA (0479) 87342
Open 9.30 - 5. ex. Mondays from Mar. to Oct. No smoking throughout. Vegetarian and some other special diets by arrangement. Disabled access. Children welcome. Access, Visa.

NEWTONMORE

The Tea Cosy, Main St, Newtonmore (0540) 673315
No smoking throughout.

STRATHPEFFER

Gardenside Guest House, Strathpeffer, Ross and Cromarty, IV14 9BJ (0997) 21242
Open 6.30 pm. No smoking throughout. Vegetarian and some other special diets by arrangement. Licensed. Disabled access. Children welcome.

ULLAPOOL

Altnaharrie Inn, Ullapool, IV26 2SS (085 483) 230
For further details please see under entry in accomodation section.

Ceilidh Place, West Argyle St, Ullapool (0854) 2103
Pleasant café-bar, serving good range of vegetarian options.
Open 11 - 2.30, 5 - 11 (12.30 - 2.30, 6.30 -11 Sun.) Serving food 10 - 10 (until 6 in winter). Restaurant closed Sun. lunchtime. No smoking in restaurant. Vegetarian standard. Children welcome in dining areas only.

Pubs & Wine Bars

INVERNESS

Glendruidh House, Old Edinburgh Road, Inverness, IV1 2AA (0463) 226499
Charming building of unusual design, standing in its own pleasant grounds overlooking Inverness, small, luxurious smoke-free bar open to the public.
Open weekdays 5 - 11 p.m., Sat. 11 a.m. - 2.30 p.m.., 5 - 11 p.m., Sun. 12.30 - 2.30 p.m., 6.30 - 11 p.m. Bar meals available. Wheelchair access with assistance.

Lothian
Accommodation & Restaurants

DALKEITH

⊗ **Belmont, 47 Eskbank Road, Dalkeith, Midlothian, EH22 3BH (031 663) 8676**
Large, Victorian house with many original period features; conservatory and garden; easy access to Edinburgh including excellent bus service.
Open all year. No smoking in the house. Special diets by arrangement. Children and pets welcome. En suite in 1 room. Tea/coffee available. B. & B. from £14.

DUNBAR

St Helen's Guest House, Queen's Road, Dunbar, EH42 1LN (0368) 63716
Open Jan. to Oct. No smoking ex. T.V. lounge. Vegetarian standard. Children welcome. Pets welcome. En suite in 1 room. Tea/coffee making in bedrooms. T.V. in lounge. B. & B. from £12.

EAST CALDER

⊗ **Whitecroft Farm, East Calder, Near Edinburgh, EH53 0ET (0506) 881810**
Open all year. No smoking. Vegetarian by arrangement. Children welcome. Tea/coffee making & T.V. all rooms.

HADDINGTON

⊗ **Peter Potter Gallery, 10 The Sands, off Church St, Haddington (062082) 2080**
No smoking throughout.

NORTH BERWICK

⊗ **Harding's Restaurant, 2 Station Road, North Berwick, EH39 4AU (0620) 4737**
Specialises in dishes prepared from fresh, local produce; extensive Australian wine list.
24 seats. Open 12.30 - 2.00 & 7.30 - 9.00 Wed. - Sat. D. around £19.75. L around £10. No smoking. Vegetarian & other diets on request. Licensed. Disabled access: 'ramped entry; wide entry WC'. Children welcome.

Orkneys & Shetlands
Accommodation & Restaurants

KIRKWALL

Briar Lea, 10 Dundas Crescent, Kirkwall, Orkney (0856) 2747
B & B offering healthy breakfast options such as home-made yoghurt and stewed fruit.
Open all year. No smoking in dining room and bedrooms. Vegetarian and vegan standard. Some other special diets by arrangement. Children welcome. Tea/coffee making in bedrooms. T.V. in lounge. B. & B. from £13.

⊗ **2 Dundas Crescent, Kirkwall, Orkney, KW15 1JQ (0856) 2465**
Open all year. No smoking in the house. Vegetarian by arrangement. Children welcome. Tea/coffee making in lounge. T.V. in lounge. B. & B. from £9.50.

PAPA STOUR

⊗ **Mrs S Holt-Brook, North House, Papa Stour, Shetland, ZE2 9PW (059 573) 238**
Stone-built house. Working croft on small island on West of Shetland. Own boat to visit caves and spectacular coastline. Home-made bread cakes. Local crab and fresh, croft produce.
Open Apr. to Sept. No smoking in the house. Vegetarian by arrangement. Disabled: 'ground floor bedroom'. Children welcome. Pets by arrangement. 1 en suite. Tea-making. T.V. in lounge. B. & B. from £11. D. £5.

LERWICK

⊗ **Puffins, Puffin House, Mounthooly Street, Lerwick (0595) 5065**
'Alternative' shop with cafe serving home-made soups and home-baked snacks and cakes.
20 seats. Open all day. No smoking throughout. Children welcome.

Strathclyde
Accommodation

AYR

Brenalder Lodge, 39 Dunure Road, Doonfoot, Ayr, KA7 4HR (0292) 43939

Brenalder Lodge is a beautiful, large, modern bungalow superbly situated overlooking the Firth of Clyde with panoramic views of the Carrick Hills. It has been quite exceptionally well-furnished and appointed throughout: bedrooms are light, airy and spacious and the conservatory-type dining room sets the scene for the delicious meals which have all been cooked on the premises from fresh ingredients. The four-course breakfast is a generous and healthy treat, while the evening meal reflects a largely traditional menu, and would typically feature home-made soup followed by home-made Steak Pie (with fresh vegetables) and a good old-fashioned dessert, such as Apple Pie. The Lodge is an ideal base for exploring 'Burns Country' and the world famous golf courses of Turnberry and Royal Troon are nearby.

Open all year. No smoking in the house ex. T.V. lounge. Disabled access. Children: over 7s; younger by arrangement. Pets by arrangement. En suite, tea-making & T.V. in rooms. B. & B. from £25. D. £16.

The Tweeds, 6 Montgomerie Terrace, Ayr, KA7 1JL (0292) 264556

Open all year. No smoking in the house. Vegetarian by arrangement. Children welcome. Pets by arrangement. Tea/coffee making & T.V. in all bedrooms. B. & B. from £12.

BIGGAR

Candybank Farm, Biggar, Lanarkshire, ML12 6QY (0899) 20422

Open Apr. to Oct. No smoking throughout. Vegetarian by arrangement. Disabled access 'to ground floor bedroom'. Children welcome. Pets by arrangement. Tea/coffee making & T.V. in all rooms. B. & B. from £11.

CRAWFORD

Field End Guest House, Crawford, Lanarkshire, ML12 6TN *(off A74/M74)* **(08642) 276**

Attractive stone-built villa on quiet, private road opposite Crawford church. Ideal halfway house and touring centre. *STB 2 Crowns. AA & RAC Acclaimed*. World-wide commendations. Parking.

Open all year ex. Xmas & New Year days. No smoking in the house. Vegetarian & other diets to order. Children welcome. En suite 2 rooms. Tea/coffee making & TV. Credit cards. B. & B. from £14. (red. children & sen. cits.)

GALSTON

Auchencloigh Farm, Galston, Ayrshire, KA4 8NP (0563) 820567

Auchencloigh Farm is a family-run farm which has been in the same family for 5 generations. It dates from the 18th C. and stands amidst large shrubbed gardens in 240 acres of Ayrshire countryside. The house is furnished in traditional style, and an open fire supplements the central heating. The accommodation consists of one double and one family room (cot available), and meals are served in a pleasant lounge/dining room - with the aforementioned open fire. The food is wholesome farmhouse fare and everything is home-cooked from fresh ingredients - some home-grown. The area abounds with natural and unspoilt beauty and there are numerous walks to be enjoyed: additionally there is a noticeboard of information about local events & attractions.

Open Easter - Oct. No smoking in the house. Special diets by arrangement. Children welcome. TV & tea/coffee-making in bedrooms. B. & B. from £14.

HAMILTON

RoadChef Hamilton Motorway Service Area, M74 Northbound, Hamilton, Lanarkshire, ML3 6JW (0698) 282176

Hamilton is the site of RoadChef's first 36 bedroom Lodge in Scotland. Each of the bedrooms have been comfortably furnished and well-appointed with a trouser press, hairdryer and tea and coffee

making facilities in addition to other amenities. The self-service Orchards restaurants have good smoke-free areas (50 of the 140 seats are smoke-free), and serve a wide selection of popular meals. There is always a vegetarian option on the menu and baby foods are also available (there is a changing room). Other facilities include a tourist information centre, a fully equipped conference room, totally refurbished shopping and forecourt facilities.

Open all year ex. Xmas day. No smoking in part of restaurant & some bedrooms. Vegetarian. Wheelchair access. Children welcome. En suite, TV & tea/coffee. Credit cards. B. & B. from £36.

HELENSBURGH

Thorndean, 64 Colquhoun St., Helensburgh, Dumbartonshire, G84 9JP (0436) 74922
Friendly Scottish welcome in spacious 19th C. house standing in extensive gardens; lovely sea views. Private parking. Your hosts organise barbeques, sailing in 31'cruiser & hill-walking.
Open all year. No smoking in the house. Vegetarian and other diets by arrangement. Children welcome. Most rooms en suite. Tea/coffee making in bedrooms. B. & B. from £16.

LARGS

South Whittlieburn Farm, Brisbane Glen, Largs, Ayrshire, KA30 8SN (0475) 675881
Attractive farmhouse on working sheep farm 2m NE Largs. 2 Crown Commended. Golf, horse-riding, sailing, fishing, diving & hill-walking. Ferries to Arran, Cumbrae and Bute nearby.
Open all year. No smoking in dining room & some bedrooms. Vegetarian & other diets by arrangement. Children welcome. En suite 1 room. TV & tea/coffee-making in bedrooms. B. & B. from £14.50.

OBAN

Ardlonan, Drummore Road, Oban, Argyll, PA34 4JL (0631) 62529
Open Mar. to Oct. No smoking in the house. Vegetarian by arrangement. Disabled access: 'ground floor rooms'. En suite, TV & tea/coffee making in bedrooms. B. & B. from £13.

Asknish Cottage, Arduaine, by Oban, Argyll, PA34 4XQ (085 22) 247
Asknish Cottage is a small, modern detached house which stands on a hillside with wonderful views across the sea to the nearby islands of Jura, Scarba, Shuna and Luing; swimming and fishing may both be enjoyed just 100 yards away at the small sandy beach with its pier. Bedrooms are comfortable - each has a wash hand basin and can take an extra bed or cot for a child at a reduced rate - and, although breakfast is the only meal to be served at Asknish, there are a several restaurants locally which offer a variety of good, freshly-prepared meals. Guests at Asknish Cottage are made to feel very much at home and to come and go as they please; your hostess, Elspeth Campbell, is very knowledgeable about the area however, and will gladly help you plan your itinerary if you wish. You are midway between Lochgilphead and Oban, and horseriding, boating, birdwatching and hillwalking can all be enjoyed locally.
Open all year. No smoking in the house. Vegetarian and most other special diets by arrangement. Children and pets welcome. Tea/coffee making in bedrooms. T.V. in lounge. B. & B. from £13.

PAISLEY

Myfarrclan Guest House, 146 Corsebar Road, Paisley, Renfrewshire, PA2 9NA. Proprietors: Keith & Brenda Farr (041) 884 8285
STB 2 Crowns Highly Commended guest house in quiet residential area, convenient for Glasgow airport, Loch Lomond, Ayrshire & city centre. Quiet, safe garden with childrens'play area.
Open all year. No smoking in the house (permitted in garden if you must!). Vegetarian & low-fat diets by arrangement. Children welcome. En suite/private facilities in most rooms. Tea/coffee making, trouser presses, T.V., video & Satellite in all bedrooms. Luxury sun & guest lounges. B. & B. from £21.

SEAMILL

 Spottiswoode Guest House, Sandy Rd, Seamill, W. Kilbride, Ayrshire, KA23 9NN (0294) 823131

Built in 1896, Spottiswoode is a spacious Victorian home which has been tastefully decorated and traditionally appointed by its present owners who have taken care to retain the house's original charm and character. It stands just feet away from the Firth of Clyde - the beautiful sea and island views can be appreciated from the dining room and bedrooms - and the surrounding countryside is both rich in natural wildlife and also an ideal base from which to explore Ayrshire and the nearby islands (Glasgow is just 45 minutes away by train or car). Your hosts at Spottiswoode, Christine and Jim Ondersma, are thoroughly committed to quality and guest satisfaction: each of the guest bedrooms have been decorated to a very high standard and are equipped with fluffy towels, reading materials, well-lit mirrors and other thoughtful touches. The breakfast menu is another example of the Ondersmas' attention to detail: prepared with minimum fat and salt, both Scottish and American specialities are offered, including locally-made, additive-free sausages, free-range eggs, and home-made bread and yoghurts; evening meals are creative and freshly prepared (24 hours notice, please). There is much to enjoy *in situ* - a soak in the deep Victorian bath, afternoon tea on the lawn, games and music at the fireside ... There is no reason at all to move from base except, perhaps, to enjoy a ramble in the magnificent surrounding countryside or the lovely walks along the shore coast; golf can also be arranged.
Open all year. Non-smokers only. Vegetarian a speciality & other diets by arrangement. Children: over 10s only. En suite, TV, tea/coffee-making & hairdryer in bedrooms. Credit cards. B. & B. from £16, D. from £9.50.

ST CATHERINE'S

 Arnish Cottage Lochside G. House, Poll Bay, St Catherine's, Argyll, PA25 8BA (0499) 2405
Lovely house in conservation area midway between St Catherine's & Strachur. A truly idyllic spot on a private road 20 ft from the lochside. A wealth of wildlife & peace; walks from the doorstep.
Open all year. No smoking in the house. Vegetarian & other diets by arrangement. En suite & tea/coffee-making in bedrooms. TV in lounge. B. & B. from £17, D. £11.

Restaurants

AYR

Brenalder Lodge, 39 Dunure Road, Doonfoot, Ayr, KA7 4HR (0292) 43939
For further details please see under the entry in the accommodation section.

BRIDGE OF ORCHY

Bridge of Orchy Hotel, Bridge of Orchy, Argyll, PA36 4AD (08384) 208
No smoking in restaurant. Vegetarian, diabetic and vegan standard. Licensed. Children welcome. Credit cards.

LOCHGILPHEAD

The Smiddy, Smithy Lane, Lochgilphead, Argyll, PA31 8TE (0546) 3606
Vegetarian and seafood restaurant.
No smoking throughout. Vegetarian exclusively. Children welcome. Access, Visa.

PAISLEY

Paisley Arts Centre, New Street, Paisley, PA1 1EZ (041 887) 1010
Limited smoking tables. Vegetarian standard. Licensed. Disabled access. Children welcome. Access, Visa.

TAYNUILT

Shore Cottage Tearoom, beside Loch Etive, Taynuilt (08662) 654
Open Easter to Oct. No smoking throughout. Good disabled access.

Tayside
Accommodation

BLAIRGOWRIE

🚭 **Dryfesands Guest House, Burnhead Road, Blairgowrie, PH10 6SY (0250) 3417**
Spacious white-painted bungalow in pretty gardens on a hillside overlooking Blairgowrie.
Open all year. No smoking. Children: over 10s only. En suite & tea-making. T.V. lounge. B & B from £17.

BRECHIN

🚭 **Blibberhill Farmhouse, Brechin, Angus, DD9 6TH (030 783) 225**
Open all year. No smoking. Vegetarian by arrangement. En suite & tea/coffee making. B & B from £12.50.

BROUGHTY FERRY

🚭 **Invermark Hotel, 23 Monifieth Road, Broughty Ferry, Dundee, DD5 2RN (0382) 739430**

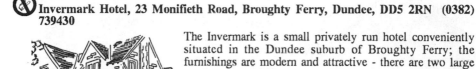

The Invermark is a small privately run hotel conveniently situated in the Dundee suburb of Broughty Ferry; the furnishings are modern and attractive - there are two large public rooms which can comfortably host small functions, such as weddings or birthday parties - and all bedrooms have been tastefully furnished and appointed. The food is exceptionally good: only fresh produce is used in the cooking and, while breakfast is the only meal which is usually available at Invermark, evening meals may be taken on request. Originally a fishing village, Broughty Ferry is now a bustling, residential city suburb; it still has lots of character, though: the seafront is guarded by a 15th C. castle, and the high street is full of interesting craft shops.
Open all year. No smoking in the house. Vegetarian & other diets by arrangement. Restricted licence. Children welcome. En suite in some rooms. Tea/coffee making & T.V. in all bedrooms. B & B from £17.50.

CALLANDER

🚭 **Brook Linn Country House, Leny Feus, Callander, FK17 8AU (0877) 30103**
Open Easter to Oct. No smoking in the house. Vegetarian by arrangement. Licensed. Children welcome. Pets by arrangement. En suite, TV & tea/coffee making in bedrooms. B & B from £16.

🚭 **Arran Lodge, Leny Rd, Callander, Perthshire, FK17 8AJ (0786) 50976**
Arran Lodge is a delightful period riverside bungalow which has been luxuriously appointed

and stands on Callander's Western outskirts. Guests may enjoy a stroll through the tranquil garden down to the river and, if they fish successfully therein, their host will prepare their catch for them. Guests who allow the owner-chef to provide his own ingredients for the evening meal may look forward to delicious food prepared with care and flair, a typical evening meal featuring such main courses as salmon cooked with butter, garlic, parsley and mushrooms or saddle of venison chops with port and brandy sauce. Arran Lodge has received the highest possible grading in a number of awards including STB 3 Crown De Luxe, AA Selected QQQQ and RAC Highly Acclaimed. Clearly a very, very special place.
Open Mar. - Nov. inc. No smoking in the house. Vegetarian by arrangement. En suite, remote control TV, radio & tea/coffee-making. Bring your own wine. B. & B. around £25. D. £13.

The Lubnaig Hotel, Leny Feus, Callander, FK17 8AS (0877) 30376
Open Mar. to Nov. No smoking ex. in bar. Vegetarian by arrangement. Licensed. Children: over 7s only. Pets by arrangement. En suite, TV & tea/coffee making in bedrooms. D., B & B from £34.

Orchardlea House, Main Street, Callander, FK17 8BG (0877) 30798
Open May. to Oct. No smoking in the house. Vegetarian by arrangement. Disabled access: limited, ground floor bedrooms. En suite in most rooms. Tea/coffee making on request. T.V. in all bedrooms. B & B from £15.

Roslin Cottage Guest House, Lagrannoch, Callander, Perthshire, FK17 8LE (0877) 30638
Open all year. No smoking ex. lounge. Vegetarian by arrangement. Children welcome. Pets welcome. Tea/coffee making in bedrooms. T.V. in lounge. B & B from £11.

CRIANLARICH
Portnellan Lodge Hotel, by Crianlarich, FK20 8QS (08383) 284 Fax (08383) 332

Portnellan House dates from the mid 19th C., and stands in the wooded grounds of a private estate overlooking Glen Dochart; it was originally built as a shooting lodge by the Marquis of Breadalbane, but these days it has been substantially extended and sympathetically modernised to provide spacious, warm and comfortable accommodation while retaining its original Victorian character. The en suite bedrooms have each been tastefully decorated, and the public rooms have book and music collections for guests' use; central heating supplements the cosy wood-burning stove in the lounge. The delicious home-cooked food is prepared from fresh, local ingredients and, with sufficient advance notice, special requests can be undertaken (lunch boxes can also be prepared on request); a good selection of malt whiskies and wines are available from the bar (which is, incidentally, the only room at Portnellan where smokong is permitted). Glen Dochart is rich in wild life: an abundant hunting territory for eagle, buzzard and osprey and a grazing ground for the red deer which may be seen wandering through the grounds. Private fishing and clay pigeon shooting are also available and some challenging golf courses can be reached within a short drive.
Open all year. No smoking in bedrooms, dining room & drawing room. Vegetarian and most other special diets by arrangement. Licensed. Children under 10 years and pets accommodated in the lodge suites but not in the main house. En suite in all rooms. Tea/coffee making, T.V., video, radio, trouser press & hairdryer in all bedrooms. Access, Visa, Eurocard. B. & B. from £20. D. from £12.

CRIEFF
Cairnleith, North Forr, Crieff, PH7 3RT (0764) 2080
Open all year. No smoking. Vegetarian by arrangement. Children welcome. Pets by arrangement.

Dalchonzie, 28 Burrell Street, Crieff, Perthshire, PH7 4DT (0764) 3423
Open Apr. to Oct. No smoking. Vegetarian standard. Children welcome. Tea/coffee making & T.V. in lounge.

St Ninian's Centre, Comrie Road, Crieff, PH7 4BG (0764) 3766
Open all year. No smoking ex. in lounge. Vegetarian by arrangement. Children welcome. Tea-making & T.V.

DUNKELD
**Heatherbank, 1 Guthrie Villas, St Marys Road, Birnam, Dunkeld, PH8 0BJ (0350) 727413**

Heatherbank is an attractive 3-storey bay fronted Victorian house which used to be a hotel run by the Temperance Society at the turn of the century! It has been restored since that time and now offers very comfortable accommodation with all mod cons, but retains the interesting features of the original building (corniced ceilings, stained woodwork, etc). The cooking is imaginative and wholesome, a typical evening menu featuring Smoked Salmon Paté followed by Ginger Beef with fresh vegetables and a delicious Highland dessert, such as Caledonian Cream; tea or freshly made coffee with chocolate mints would complete the meal. Heatherbank is situated in the heart of the peaceful village of Birnam close to the River Tay; you are at the start of the Highlands in Birnam & can enjoy the wealth of hills, woodlands, rivers & flowers which make up the scenery of this beautiful part of the world. *Open April - Dec. No smoking in the house. Vegetarian by arrangement. Children welcome. Pets by arrangement. Tea/coffee making in bedrooms. B. & B. from £12.50.*

 Oronsay House, Oak Road, Birnam, Dunkeld, PH8 0BL (0350) 727294

 Oronsay house is an elegant Victorian villa which stands in an attractive garden close to the River Tay. It has been beautifully furnished and appointed - three of the large bedrooms have views of the hills - and there is a comfortable lounge for guests. Although breakfast is the only meal to be served at Oronsay, it is a very generous meal and features home-made preserves, oakcakes, wholemeal bread and porridge as well as a choice of fresh trout or a grilled platter of bacon, sausage and tomato. This beautiful area of Perthshire is steeped in history and places of interest to visit, as well as being rich in scenic beauty; additionally the area is perfect for walkers, and salmon/trout fishing and golf may be organised for you prior to your holiday should you wish. *Open Apr. to Oct. No smoking throughout. Vegetarian & other diets by arrangement. En suite & tea/coffee making in bedrooms. B & B from £18.50 (reductions for 3 days or more). AA Listed QQQ*

KILLIECRANKIE

 Druimuan House, Killiecrankie, PH16 5LG Tel: (0796) 3214 Fax (0796) 2692
   Open Apr. to Oct. No smoking in the house. Vegetarian diets. Children welcome. En suite, tea/coffee making & TV in all bedrooms. B & B from £17.50.

KINLOCH RANNOCH

 Cuilmore Cottage, Kinloch Rannoch, PH16 5QB (08822) 218
   Open all year. No smoking in the house. Vegetarian and most other special diets by arrangement. Children welcome. Pets by arrangement. Tea/coffee making in rooms. No T.V.

KIRRIEMUIR

Purgavie Farm, Lintrathen, Kirriemuir (05756) 213
Beautful old stone-built farmhouse at the foot of Glen Islaall; food is home-prepared.
Open all year. No smoking in dining room & bedrooms. Vegetarian by arrangement. Children welcome. Pets by arrangement. En suite in 1 room. Tea/coffee making in bedrooms. T.V. B & B from £10.

LOCHEARNHEAD

Stronvar Country House Hotel, Balquhidder, Lochearnhead, FK19 8PB (08774) 688

 Stronvar Country House Hotel is an elegant 19th C. mansion standing on the shores of Loch Voil overlooking the Braes O'Balquhidder. It has had a very interesting history and indeed much of the Stronvar brochure is dedicated to describing it and the activities of its founding family, the Carnegies. These days the house has been completely renovated and restored to its former glory and offers first-class accommodation to guests: bedrooms are sympathetically furnished - many have brass beds or fourposters - and all have spectacular views over the surrounding mountains and countryside; within the house is a fascinating museum of bygones. Stronvar Country House is an excellent base for exploring the Trossachs and central Scotland; additionally fishing (brown trout and salmon) can be arranged on Loch Voil beween mid-March and October, and there are 30 golf courses within easy reach including, of course, Gleneagles.
Open Mar. to Oct. No smoking in dining room & bedrooms. Vegetarian & diabetic by arrangement. Licensed. Children welcome. En suite, tea/coffee making & T.V. in all bedrooms. Access, Visa. B. & B. from £29.

PERTH   Cost/train?

Almond Villa, 51 Dunkeld Rd, Perth, PH1 5RP   (0738) 29356

Almond Villa is a small, family-run guest house which has been commended by the Scottish Tourist Board for its high standard of accommodation and friendly, efficient service. It is a Victorian villa - centrally heated and double-glazed throughout - which is situated just a few minutes'walk from the banks of the River Tay and just 10 minutes'walk from the centre of Perth. A traditional cooked breakfast is served between 7.30 and 8.30 a.m. and a 3-course evening meal is available with advance booking. Perth lies at the very heart of Scotland and here, at the nation's cross-roads, has evolved an attractive, prosperous and compact city with some excellent leisure facilities, including an ice rink, leisure pool and an indoor bowling centre. The surrounding area boasts some of Scotland's most magnificent mountains and there are countless places of interest to be visited including castles, distilleries, craft workshops, museums and gardens.
Open all year. No smoking in the house. Vegetarian & other diets by arrangement. Children & well-behaved pets welcome. 1 room en suite. TV & tea/coffee-making in bedrooms. B. & B. £14-17.

---?

St Leonard's Manse, 112 Dundee Rd, Perth, PH2 7BB   (0738) 27975

B. & B. establishment with 1 twin, 1 double & 1 family room. Adjoins National Trust gardens. Lovely views. 2 bathrooms. Residents' lounge. Private parking. 15 mins walk town centre.
Open all year. No smoking in the house. Vegetarian & other diets by arrangement. Children welcome. Pets by arrangement. Tea/coffee-making facilities, own TV. B. & B. £13.50, single £17.

PITLOCHRY

Burnside Apartments, 19 West Moulin Road, Pitlochry, PH16 5EA   (0796) 2203
Converted Victorian building offering award-winning serviced apartments & coffee shop.
Open all year. No smoking in coffee shop & some apartments. Vegetarian standard. Licensed. Disabled access. Children welcome. Pets by arrangement. En suite bathrooms, galley kitchens & T.V. in all bedrooms.

Kinnard House, Kirkmichael Rd, Pitlochry   (0796) 472843
Situated on the hillside above Pitlochry with wonderful scenery yet within easy reach of all local attractions. Commended for warm welcome. Food & accommodation of the highest quality.
Open all year. No smoking in the house. Vegetarian & other diets by arrangement. TV & tea/coffee-making in bedrooms. Children: over 12s only. B. & B. from £16.50.

Silverhowe, Perth Road, Pitlochry, PH16 5LY   (0796) 2181
Open all year. No smoking in the house. Vegetarian by arrangement. Pets by arrangement. En suite in some rooms. Tea/coffee making & TV in all bedrooms. B & B from £13.50.

Tigh-Na-Cloich Hotel, Larchwood Road, Pitlochry, PH16 5AS   (0796) 472216

Tigh-Na-Cloich (its name means 'house on the sentinel stone') is a beautiful stone-built Victorian villa, southfacing and peacefully situated in its own lovely gardens just a short walk from the centre of Pitlochry. It has been beautifully restored and furnished in keeping with the original period features of the building with its high ceilinged-rooms, and all bedrooms have been exceptionally well-appointed (each has an electric blanket just in case what they say about the Scottish weather turns out to be true!) The food is exceptionally good: everything is home-made from fresh and local ingredients, and a typical evening menu would feature Broccoli and Stilton Soup followed by Lamb Cutlets in a fresh herb crust or Fishy Parcels with Vermouth Sauce, and a delicious dessert, such as Iced Chocolate Souffle with Orange Cream. The proprietors are not only very helpful to those with special dietary needs, but will even offer to cook a favourite dish for you on request! Pitlochry is Scotland's premier inland

tourist resort and as such offers something for everyone, from sailing on rivers and lochs or walking amidst the beautiful hill scenery to visiting the many woollen mills, distilleries or craft centres in the region.

Open Mar. to end Oct. No smoking in the house. Vegetarian & other diets by arrangement. Licensed. Children welcome. En suite in most rooms. Tea/coffee making & T.V. in all bedrooms. B & B from £25.

 "Tom-na-Monachan" Vegetarian B. & B., Cuilc Brae, Pitlochry (0796) 473744
Large family house quietly situated in 1 acre of wooded garden 10 mins'walk from station & shops.

Open all year. No smoking in the house. Exclusively vegetarian/vegan/wholefood. Most other special diets by arrangement. Disabled access: '1 ground floor bedroom & bathroom. Ramp'. Children welcome. Pets by arrangement. Tea/coffee making in bedrooms. B & B from £14.50, childrens'rates available.

SCONE

 Sandabel House, Netherlea, Scone, Perthshire, PH2 6QA (0738) 51062
Highly acclaimed guest house near Scone.

Open all year. No smoking in the house. Vegetarian & other diets by arrangement. Disabled access. Children welcome. En suite, TV & tea/coffee making in bedrooms. B & B from £17.50.

STRATHYRE

Creagan House, Restaurant with Accommodation, Strathyre, FK18 8ND (08774) 638
17th C. farmhouse which has been sympathetically restored and renovated to provide excellent accommodation; the baronial style dining hall with its grand fireplace is the perfect setting for celebratory occasions; excellent cuisine prepared from fresh local produce.

Open Mar. to Jan. No smoking in bedrooms & dining room. Vegetarian & other diets by arrangement. Licensed. Disabled access. Children & pets welcome. En suite in 3 rooms. Tea/coffee making in bedrooms. Visa, Mastercard. B. & B. from £22.50.

Restaurants

CRIEFF

Glenturret Distillery Ltd, The Hosh, Crieff, Perthshire, PH7 4HA (0764) 2424
Large restaurant serving Scottish fare and forming part of Scotland's oldest distillery.
No smoking ex. in bar & 50 seats in restaurant. Vegetarian standard. Licensed. Disabled access. Children

DUNDEE

 Debenhams, 15 Whitehall Crescent, Dundee (0382) 21212
Freebodys Coffee Shop, where waitresses serve popular food & drinks throughout the day.
Open store hours. No smoking throughout. Vegetarian meals. Children very welcome. Credit/debit cards.

KINROSS

Granada Motorway Services, Kincardine Road, (Junction 6 M90), Kinross, KY13 7NQ (0577) 63123/64646
50% no-smoking. Vegetarian standard. Disabled access. Children welcome. Credit cards.

STRATHYRE

Creagan House, Restaurant with Accommodation, Strathyre, FK18 8ND (08774) 638
No smoking. Vegetarian on request. Restricted licence. Disabled access. Visa, Mastercard.

Western Isles Accommodation

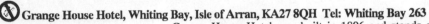

ISLE OF ARRAN

Glencloy Farmhouse, Brodick, Isle of Arran, KA27 8BZ (0770) 2351
Open 1 Mar. to 7 Nov. No smoking ex. in bedrooms. Vegetarian, vegan and diabetic by arrangement. Children welcome. Pets by arrangement. En suite in 2 out of 6 rooms. Tea/coffee making in bedrooms. B. & B. from £25.

Grange House Hotel, Whiting Bay, Isle of Arran, KA27 8QH Tel: Whiting Bay 263

Grange House Hotel was built in 1896 and stands amidst delightful gardens overlooking the sea with views to the Ayrshire coast and out towards Holy Island. Recently refurbished to a very high standard, and in a style in keeping with the period features of the house, Grange House Hotel has every modern convenience including (for those who wish to pamper themselves a little!) a sauna and spa bath suite; on cooler evenings a log fire welcomes you in the lounge. The cooking is first rate: your hosts, Janet and Clive Hughes, base the evening's menu selection around the availability of good, fresh local produce: accordingly, while dishes are often Victorian or Scottish in flavour (Steak Kidney and Oyster Pie followed by Bread and Butter Pudding with whisky cream), everything has been expertly prepared on the premises from fresh, organic (wherever possible) produce; the proprietors also have a sound awareness of healthy nutritional principles: wholefoods are used wherever possible, and cream and animal fats are only used in moderation. Arran is popularly known as 'Scotland in miniature' - within the confines of this small island you will find no less than 7 golf courses, 4 pony-trekking centres, and numerous opportunities for mountaineering and fishing.
Open March to Oct. incl. No smoking throughout. Vegetarian & other diets avail. Licensed. Disabled facilities including converted downstairs bedroom. Children welcome. Tea/coffee making and T.V. in all rooms. Access, Visa. B. & B. from £25. D. £15. 3 Crown Commended.

Kilmichael House Hotel, Glen Cloy, by Brodick, Isle of Arran, ZA23 14PQ (0770) 2219
Small historic mansion set in 4 acres of grounds; beautifully furnished with old & antique furniture.
Open all year. No smoking in dining room & bedrooms. Vegetarian standard. Table licence. Children welcome. Pets by arrangement. T.V. in lounge. B. & B. from £13.

ISLE OF HARRIS

Scarista House, Isle of Harris, PA85 3HX Tel: (085 985) 238 Fax: (085 985) 277
Charming Georgian dwelling, formerly the Church of Scotland manse for Harris.
Open Easter to mid Oct. No smoking in the house except in two sitting rooms. Vegetarian and most other special diets by arrangement. Licensed. Disabled access: '4 bedrooms, dining rooms and library on ground floor'. Children: over 8s only. Pets by arrangement. En suite & tea/coffee making in bedrooms. B. & B. from £44.

ISLE OF IONA

Argyll Hotel, Isle of Iona, PA76 6SJ (068 17) 334
This beautiful sea-facing hotel (the front lawn runs down to the shore and jetty) is one of the hotels

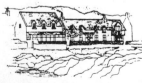

about which I invariably receive a large number of recommendations throughout the year; guests comment on the peace and tranquility which seems to pervade the place - a sense doubtless partly attributable to the fact that the beautiful louges (with their open fires), spacious dining room and plant-filled sun lounge all look out over the Sound of Iona to the hills of Mull; external beauty recreating inner peace. I am sure that the excellence of the food is also an inexorable part of the lure of the place, too: wholefood and organically home-grown vegetables and produce are used in the preparation of excellent meals which would typically feature Hummus followed by Chicken Paprika and Lemon and Blackberry Sponge; the vegetarian options are excellent.

Open Easter to mid Oct. No smoking in dining room & lounge. Vegetarian & other diets by arrangement. Licensed. Children welcome. Pets by arrangement. En suite in 10 rooms. Tea/coffee making in bedrooms. Access, Visa. B. & B. from £24.50.

ISLE OF ISLAY

Ceol-na-Mara, Bruichladdich, Isle of Islay, PA49 7UN (049 685) 419
    Open all year. No smoking in the house. Vegetarian, vegan and most other special diets by arrangement. Children welcome. Pets by arrangement. T.V. in residents'lounge. B & B from £20, D. £7.

Taigh-Na-Creag, 7 Shore Street, Port Charlotte, Isle of Islay, PA48 7TR (049 685) 261
    Lovely guest house, with magnificent views over Loch Indaal, situated opposite the jetty.
Open all year. No smoking in the house. Vegetarian standard. Children. Pets by arrangement. B. & B. £15.

ISLE OF LEWIS

Baile-na-Cille, Timsgarry, Isle of Lewis, PA86 9JD (085 175) 241
Beautifully remote converted manse and stables on the shore at Timsgarry; great food.
Open mid-Mar. to mid-Oct. No smoking in dining room, 2 sitting rooms & bedrooms. Vegetarian by arrangement. Licensed. Children & pets welcome. En suite. Tea/coffee making. T.V. lounge. B. & B. from £26.

Eshcol Guest House, Breasclete, Isle of Lewis, PA86 9ED (0851 72) 357
    Open Mar. to Oct. No smoking in the house. Vegetarian by arrangement. Children welcome. Pets by arrangement. En suite in most rooms. Tea/coffee making & T.V. in all bedrooms. B. & B. from £16.50.

ISLE OF MULL

Druimard Country House, Dervaig, Isle of Mull, PA75 6QW (06884) 345
    Award winning country house hotel & restaurant serving first-class cuisine prepared from fresh, local produce. STB Highly Commended, AA Red Rosette & 1992 Catering & Care Award. *No smoking. Vegetarian standard. Other diets on request. Licensed. Disabled access. Children. Access, Visa.*

Druimnacroish, Dervaig, Isle of Mull, PA75 6QW (06884) 274
Open mid-Apr. to mid-Oct. No smoking ex. bedrooms & smoking lounge. Vegetarian by arrangement. Licensed. Disabled access. Children: over 12s only. Pets by arrangement. En suite, tea/coffee making & T.V. in all rooms.

Keeper's Cottage, Torloisk, Ulva Ferry, Isle of Mull, PA74 6NH (06885) 265
    Open all year. No smoking. Vegetarian by arrangement. Children welcome. T.V. B. & B. from £15.

ISLE OF RAASAY

Isle of Raasay Hotel, Raasay, by Kyle of Lochalsh, Ross-shire, IV40 8PB (047862) 222/226
Open Apr. to Oct. No smoking in dining room & T.V. lounge. Vegetarian by arrangement. Licensed. Disabled access. Children welcome. Pets by arrangement. En suite, TV & tea-making in bedrooms. B. & B. from £26.

ISLE OF SKYE

Langdale Guest House, Waterloo, Breakish, Isle of Skye, IV42 8QE (047 12) 376
Open all year. No smoking ex. lounge. Vegetarian by arrangement. Licensed. Children welcome. Pets by arrangement. Tea/coffee making in bedrooms. T.V. in lounge.B. & B. from £15.

The Tables Hotel & Restaurant, Dunvegan, Isle of Skye, IV55 8WA (047 022) 404
A traditional 19th C. merchant's house overlooking Loch Dunvegan & MacLeod's Tables Mountains. Homely & welcoming with good food, wines & malt whiskies. Relax by peat fires. *Open all year. No smoking in dining room & bedrooms. Vegetarian standard. Other diets by arrangement. Restricted licence. Children welcome. Pets by arrangement. 1 room en suite. Credit cards. B. & B. from £18.*

Restaurants

The majority of hotels and guest houses on the Western Isles which are listed above are also open to non-residents for dinner. It is suggested that you phone in advance to check the evening meal arrangements for each establishment. We were unable to find any other restaurants or cafés in the Western Isles with good smoke-free facilities. If you can find any - do please let us know!

Wales

Clwyd
Accommodation

BRYNEGLWYS

Cae Crwn Farm, Bryneglwys, LL21 9NF (049085) 243
Lovely old detached farmhouse overlooking the village of Bryneglwys.
Open all year. No smoking in the house. Vegetarian standard. Children welcome. Pets by arrangement. Tea/coffee-making in bedrooms. T.V. in lounge. B. & B. from £12.50. D. from £7.50. Reductions for children.

COLWYN BAY

The Haven Guest House, 14 Canning Rd, Colwyn Bay (0492) 531779
Open all year. No smoking. Vegetarian by arrangement. Children welcome. Room service.

DENBIGH

Fron Haul, Bodfari, Denbigh, LL16 4DY (074 575) 301
Charming house with large balconies with superb views. *'Taste of Wales' Commended.*
Open Feb. to Nov. No smoking in dining room, sitting room & bedrooms. Vegetarian by arrangement. Children welcome. Pets by arrangement. En suite. Tea-making in bedrooms. T.V. in lounge. B. & B. from £15.50.

HANMER

Buck Farm, Hanmer, SY14 7LX (094 874) 339
Beautiful half-timbered 16th C. farmhouse in 8 acres of woodland & paddocks. Fabulous food.
Open all year. No smoking in the house. Vegetarian by arrangement. Children welcome. Tea/Coffee available on request. T.V. in lounge. B. & B. from £13.50.

LLANGOLLEN

Hillcrest, Hill Street, Llangollen, LL20 8EU (0978) 860208
Hillcrest is a lovely Victorian house which stands in an acre of pretty gardens just three minutes' walk from both the centre of Llangollen and the River Dee. It is primarily a guest house but your hosts, Joan and Colin Lloyd, will prepare evening meals on request. Llangollen is situated in the beautiful Dee Valley - the home of the International Musical Eisteddfod - and the imposing Dinas Bran castle overlooks the town; Valle Crucis Abbey is only two miles away, and other local attractions include the nearby steam train, trips on a horse-drawn canal boat, visits to the motor museum and a round of golf at the nearby course.
Open all year. No smoking in the house. Vegetarian & other diets by arrangement. Disabled access: 1 downstairs double room. Children welcome. Licensed. En suite & tea/coffee-making in all bedrooms. T.V. lounge. B. & B. from £18. D. from £9. W.T.B 3 Crowns Commended.

MOLD

The Old Mill, Melin-y-Wern, Denbigh Rd, Nannerch, Mold, Clwyd, CH7 5RH (0352) 741542

The Old Mill is a beautifully converted complex of rural water-mill buildings which stands in a conservation area adjacent to an area of Outstanding Natural Beauty. Your hosts, Neil and Susan Evans, offer accommodation of a very high standard: each of the 7 en suite bedrooms is centrally heated and double glazed, and some have external access; there is a choice of family, double, twin or single-bedded rooms and each has been beautifully furnished in pine and has an excellent range of helpful amenities including TV, radio alarm, phone and hairdryer. Efficient friendly service is clearly an important priority at The Old Mill: there is a same-day laundry and dry-cleaning service, and snacks and other refreshments may be ordered throughout the day in your room. The food is tasty and wholesome: local and seasonal ingredients are used in cooking, and there is a good choice of wines to accompany the meal. Melin-y-Wern is an excellent touring base: central for all the major coastal resorts, visitors will also find themselves within easy reach of Chester and Offa's Dyke; you are also in close proximity to Snowdonia with its medieval castles and National Trust properties and gardens.

Open all year ex. Xmas. No smoking. Special diets by arrangement. Licensed. Children welcome. Pets by arrangement. En suite, TV & tea/coffee-making in bedrooms. Credit cards. B. & B. from £22.50.

RHOS-ON-SEA

Sunnydowns Hotel, 66 Abbey Rd, Rhos-on-Sea, LL28 4NU Tel & Fax: (0492) 544256
Hotel just 2 mins walk to the beach & shops, & just 5 mins drive to the towns of Llandudno & Colwyn Bay. Car park, bar, restaurant, games room, sauna. All rooms en suite.

Open all year. No smoking in dining room, some bedrooms & games room. Special diets by arrangement. Children & pets welcome. En suite, TV & tea/coffee-making in bedrooms. Credits cards. D., B. & B. £25.

Restaurants

COLWYN BAY

Good Taste Bistro and Gifts Gallery, 18 Seaview Road, Colwyn Bay (0492) 534786
Charming bistro, faithfully decked out in 30s style, which also has a gallery with crafts and gifts. Imaginative, freshly prepared food (the bistro is a longstanding winner of the Heartbeat Wales Award).

Meals served from 12 - 4.30. Prices L. from £2.50. Main course £4. No smoking in over 80% of the restaurant; totally smoke-free 12 - 2pm. Good selection of vegetarian food and other special diets on request. Licensed. Disabled access. Children welcome.

HANMER

 Buck Farm, Hanmer, SY14 7LX (094 874) 339
Non - resident diners are accommodated with 24 hrs notice.
For further details please see under the entry in the accommodation section.

LLANGOLLEN

 Good Taste, Market Street, Llangollen, LL20 8PT (0978) 861425
Vegetarian restaurant serving a variety of wholesome meat-free meals.
Open 10 - 6. No smoking throughout. Vegetarian exclusively. Disabled access. Children welcome.

Pubs & Wine Bars

BODFARI

Dinorben Arms Inn, Bodfari, Nr Denbigh LL16 4DA (0745 75) 309
A 17th C. free house with restaurants; good value bar food.
Open 12 - 2.30, 6 - 10.30. No smoking in one room. Vegetarian standard. Wheelchair access 'reasonable'. Children welcome. Credit cards accepted.

Dyfed
Accommodation

ABERAERON

Moldavia, 7 & 8 Bellevue Terrace, Aberaeron, SA46 0BB (0545570) 107
A warm welcome at this award-winning guest house overlooking Aberaeron Harbour. Town & beach just 2 mins walk away. Relax in a flower-filled conservatory! Send for brochure.
Open all year. No smoking in dining room & 1 bedroom. Wheelchair access. Vegetarian by arrangement. En suite 2 bedrooms. TV & tea/coffee-making in bedrooms. B. & B. £16 - 20.

ABERYSTWYTH

Glyn-Garth Guest House, South Road, Aberystwyth, SY23 1JS (0970) 615050

A pleasantly appointed family-run guest house situated close to the South Promenade of Aberystwyth; bedrooms have been comfortably furnished and tastefully decorated and many enjoy sea views. Your hosts, Mr & Mrs Evans, offer wholesome food in the pleasant dining room, and the comfortable lounge, with its colour television, has drinks available at most times; the service is excellent and Glyn-Garth has received the Highly Commended status by the Mid Wales Tourism Council together with several other high acclamations.
Open all year ex. Xmas. No smoking in dining room & some bedrooms. Vegetarian & other diets by arrangement. Children. En suite in most rooms. Tea/Coffee-making & T.V. in all bedrooms. B. & B. from £15.

Yr Hafod, 1 South Marine Terrace, Aberystwyth, SY23 1JX (0970) 617579
Guest house situated on the promenade; most rooms have panoramic sea views.
Open all year. No smoking in all public areas & some bedrooms. Vegetarian by arrangement. Children welcome. Some rooms en suite. Tea/coffee-making & colour T.V. in all bedrooms. B. & B. from £15.

BONCATH

 Gwelfor Country Guest House, Blaenffos, Boncath, Pembrokeshire, SA37 0HZ (0239) 831599
Small guest house in an enviable position amidst the beautiful Preseli Hills. Good, wholesome food with imaginative traditional and vegetarian dishes; home-grown, local or organic produce used in cooking. Great for birdwatchers, country lovers and painters. WTB 2 Crowns.
Open all year. No smoking. Vegetarian & vegan standard. Other diets by arrangement. Children welcome. Pets by arrangement. En suite some rooms. Tea/coffee-making in bedrooms. T.V. lounge. B. & B. from £16. D. avail.

CARDIGAN

Trellacca Guest House, Tremain, Cardigan, SA43 1SJ (0239) 810730
Superbly converted from two slate and stone cottages; beautifully furnished with handcrafted pine furniture and fittings; lovely rural setting. Studio flat for self-caterers £140 pw.
Open all year ex. Xmas. No smoking in bedrooms & dining room. Children welcome. Tea/coffee-making in bedrooms. T.V. in lounge & in bedroom on request. B. & B. £15 D. £7. Weekly rates & reductions for children.

FISHGUARD

Coach House Cottage, Glendower Square, Goodwick, Fishguard, Pembrokeshire, SA64 0DH (0348) 873660
Traditional Pembrokeshire stone cottage in secluded location next to mountain stream; vegetarian, vegan and wholefood fare a speciality; organic produce wherever possible.
Open all year. No smoking in the house. Vegetarian standard. Most other special diets by arrangement. Not licensed but guests welcome to bring a bottle. Children welcome. Pets by arrangement. Tea/coffee-making in bedrooms. T.V. in lounge. B. & B. from £11. D. £7.50.

Tregynon Country Farmhouse Hotel, Gwaun Valley, Nr Fishguard, SA65 9TU Tel: (0239) 820531 Fax: (0239) 820808

It is over a decade since Peter Heard decided to abandon the stress-filled London rat race for a more peaceful way of life in a Welsh farmhouse cum smallholding. A tremendous amount of renovation work had to be done on Tregynon but, with a lot of hard work and enthusiasm, the run-down farmhouse soon became a thriving smallholding and a guest house which has won several awards and received much national acclaim. Such is the extent of Tregynon's success that nowadays all energies are devoted to looking after guests. Much of the recognition is due not just to the wonderfully comfortable surroundings (log fires in the inglenook fireplace in the oakbeamed lounge, beautiful bedrooms) but to the superlative quality of Jane's cuisine: fresh produce - much of it local - is used wherever possible in the preparation of all meals: free-range eggs, organic and unpasteurised cheeses, home-smoked bacon and gammon are all part of the Tregynon gastronomic experience - as are the range of speciality additive-free breads and rolls. But Tregynon's surroundings provide the enduring lure for guests who return year after year...situated on the edge of the Gwaun Valley with its ancient oak forest, this beautiful part of the world is a haven for wildlife - badgers, buzzards and herons are regularly seen, whilst red kites and peregrine falcons are also spotted from time to time.

Open all year. Smoking discouraged throughout. Vegetarian & other diets standard and on request. Licensed. Disabled access. Children welcome. En suite, tea/coffee making & T.V. in all rooms. B. & B. from £22.50.

NEWQUAY

Ty Hen Farm Country Hotel & Cottages, Llwyndafydd, Newquay, SA44 6BZ (0545) 560346

This charming stone-built farmhouse (Ty Hen means simply 'Old House') offers a very high standard of accommodation to guests and stands in spacious gardens in a peaceful location just 2 miles from the rocky cliffs and sandy beaches of the Cardiganshire coast. Health is a priority at Ty Hen where the generous breakfast features a number of very laudable items such as yoghurt, muesli and fresh fruit as well as a huge platter of bacon, eggs, mushrooms and anything else breakfasty you care to name. The restaurant in the centre offers a 4-course evening menu and specialises in fish and vegetarian options. The leisure centre at Ty Hen has an indoor heated pool where private lessons, particularly for adults, are available, and also contains a gymnasium, sauna, sunbed and bowls/skittles alley; conference and further leisure facilities are planned.

Open all year. No smoking in the house and leisure centre. Vegetarian standard. Other diets by arrangement. Licensed. Disabled access. Children welcome. Pets by arrangement. En suite, tea/coffee-making, T.V. plus video channel in all bedrooms. Visa, Mastercard. B. & B. from £21.

Nanternis Farm, Nanternis, Newquay, SA45 9RP (0545) 560181
Open Easter to end Sept. No smoking in bedrooms & dining room. Vegetarian by arrangement. Children welcome. Tea/coffee-making in bedrooms. T.V. in lounge. B. & B. from £13

PENCADER

Argeod Fach, Pencader, SA39 9AG (0559) 384800
Secluded single-storey cottage 2m. from Pencader; vegan cuisine. Grid ref: SN433382.
Open Apr. to end Sept. No smoking in the house. All food vegan, other special diets by arrangement. Disabled access. Children welcome. Pets by arrangement. T.V. in lounge. B. & B. from £11. D. £6.

RHYDLEWIS

Broniwan, Rhydlewis, Llandysul, SA44 5PF (023975) 261
Open all year. No smoking in the house. Vegetarian & other diets by arrangement. Children welcome. Pets by arrangement. En suite in 1 room. Tea/coffee available. T.V. in lounge. B. & B. from £12. D. £7.

TENBY

Fairway, The Golf Links, South Beach, Tenby, Dyfed, SA70 7EL   (0834) 842141
Situated just 200 yards from Tenby's South Beach (which stretches some 1½ miles), Fairway is an attractive detached house which guests describe as being "out of town but in town" (Tenby is just 5 minutes'walk away but the house is in a lovely sheltered position on the doorstep of the Pembrokeshire Coastal Path and Tenby's 18-hole Championship Golf Links). Fully centrally heated, the house is very comfortable: each of the en suite double or twin-bedded rooms has been equipped with a radio alarm and tea-making facilities, and there are good, comfortable beds and duvets; additionally there is a large lounge with picture windows overlooking the sand dunes. Tenby is a beautiful old walled town with quaint narrow streets and lovely houses overlooking the picturesque harbours and sandy beaches; it is an ideal base from which to explore the special beauty of Pembrokeshire - whether by car or on foot.
Open Easter - Sept. inc. No smoking in the house. Not licensed but bring your own wine. En suite & tea/coffee-making in bedrooms. Regret no children or pets. TV in lounge. B. & B. from £17, D. £7.

Myrtle House Hotel, St Mary's Street, Tenby, SA70 7HW   (0834) 2508
Open Mar. to Nov. No smoking in the house. Vegetarian & other diets by arrangement. Licensed. Children welcome. Most rooms en suite. Tea/coffee-making & T.V. in rooms. Access, Visa. B. & B. from £15.

TREGARON

The Edelweiss Country Guest House, Penuwch, Tregaron, SY25 6QZ   (0974) 821601
The Edelweiss is a charming oak-beamed house set in 1½ acres of grounds in the beautiful Ceridigion countryside; the proprietors find that the stunning scenery with which their home is surrounded makes it a natural magnet for artists, walkers, ornithologists, flower arrangers, botanists and naturalists as well as holiday-makers in search of peace, tranquillity and good food. On the latter point it is worth noting that all meals served at The Edelweiss have been home-prepared (including the soups) and the traditional English/Welsh menu would also feature such hearty fare as home-made Turkey and Leek Pie (made with fresh vegetables) and a filling pudding such as Apple Crumble with cream. The Edelweiss is 6 miles from both the coastal road and Tregaron, the pony-trekking centre of Mid-Wales. A beautiful self-contained caravan for up to 6 people is also available, with all amenities provided plus meals in the guest house if required.
Open all year. No smoking in the house. Vegetarian & other diets by arrangement. Bring your own wine. Children welcome. Tea/coffee served 7 - 11. T.V. in all bedrooms. B. & B. from £12-£14, £73 weekly. B., B. & D. £17-£19.50, £111 weekly. Caravan £100 weekly. 3-day special Sept. - June. £55.

YSTRAD MEURIG

Hillscape Walking Hols., Blaen-y-ddol, Pontrhydygroes, Ystrad Meurig (097422) 640
Self-guided walking holidays based at cosy guest house in the Ystwyth Valley.
Open Feb. to Nov. No smoking in the house. Vegetarian by arrangement. Bring your own. Children: over 11s only. En suite in all rooms. Tea/coffee-making in lounge. B. & B. from £15.50. D. £6.50.

Restaurants

LLANWRDA

Felin Newydd - the Mill at Crugybar, Llanwrda, SA19 8UE   (05585) 375
One of the last working watermills in Wales with converted milking parlour as tea shop
No smoking throughout including mill and craft workshop. Disabled access. Children welcome.

Glamorgan
Accommodation

CARDIFF

Ⓝ Annedd Lon Guest House, 3 Dyfrig Street, Pontcanna, CF1 9LR (0222) 223349
Annedd Lon Guest house is a lovely Victorian town house which is situated in a quiet residential close off Cathedral Road just a short walk from a frequent bus route, and a few minutes' stroll from Cardiff's shopping centre, castle, the National Sports Centre and Arms Park. Although furnished and decorated in keeping with its original period, Annedd Lon has every modern comfort including colour T.V., tea-making facilities and central heating in the bedrooms. The breakfasts are delicious (witness the repeated commendations in the visitors' book), and from Annedd Lon you will find yourself within easy reach of the Wye Valley, Bath, Bristol & the Forest of Dean.
Open all year. No smoking in the house. Vegetarian and most other special diets by arrangement. Children welcome. En suite in some rooms. Tea/coffee-making & T.V. in all bedrooms. B. & B. from £15.

Holiday Inn, Cardiff Marriot, Mill Lane, Cardiff, CF1 1EZ (0222) 399944
Well-appointed business-class hotel, with a wide range of leisure amenities, in the centre of Cardiff.
Open all year. No smoking in part of dining room & some bedrooms. Vegetarian standard. Other diets by arrangement. Licensed. Disabled access. Children welcome. En suite, tea-making & T.V. in rooms. Credit cards. B. & B. from £44.

RHOOSE

Ⓝ Lower House Farm Guest House & Cottage, Rhoose Rd, Rhoose (0446) 710010
Open all year. No smoking. Vegetarian. Children welcome. Tea-making. T.V. B. & B. from £15.

SWANSEA

Ⓝ The Bays Guest House, 97 Mumbles Road, Mumbles, Swansea (0792) 404775
Open all year. No smoking. Vegetarian. Children: over 10s. En suite. Tea-making. B. & B. from £16.

Restaurants & Pubs

CARDIFF

Ⓝ Debenhams, 46 - 50 St David's Way, Cardiff (0222) 399789
Intermission, a friendly self-service restaurant serving lunches, snacks and hot & cold drinks.
Open store hours. No smoking. Vegetarian meals. Disabled access. Children welcome. Credit/debit cards.

NEATH

Penscynor Wildlife Park, Cilfrew, Nr Neath, West Glamorgan, SA10 8LF (0639) 642189
No smoking inside. Disabled access. Children welcome.

LLANTRISANT

Talbot Grill, J. Lobb & Sons (1891) Ltd, 41-45 Talbot Rd, Talbot Green, Llantrisant
50% no-smoking. Bring your own wine. Wheelchairs no problem. Children welcome. Access, Visa.

SWANSEA

Ⓝ Debenhams, 22 The Quadrant, Swansea (0792) 462500
Springles, a friendly self-service restaurant serving lunches, snacks and hot & cold drinks.
Open store hours. No smoking. Vegetarian. Disabled access. Children welcome. Credit/debit cards

TREORCHY

Red Cow, High St, Treorchy, Mid Glamorgan (0443) 773032
No smoking in lounge bar.

Gwent
Accommodation

ABERGAVENNY

Pentre House, Llanwenarth, Abergavenny, NP7 7EW (0873) 853435
Small, pretty country house set in lovely award-winning gardens; comfortably furnished and offering generous breakfasts with a variety of options. Commended by W.T.B. Large parking area.
Open all year. No smoking in dining room & bedrooms. Vegetarian & other diets by arrangement. Children by arrangement. Pets by arrangement. Tea/coffee-making in bedrooms. T.V. in sitting room. B. & B. from £15.

CHEPSTOW

Roadside Cottage, Caerwent, Nr Chepstow, NP6 4AZ (0291) 420184

Roadside Cottage was built some 300 years ago and stands in the ancient village of Caerwent which was founded around 75 A.D. as the Roman town 'Venta Silurium'. The village is currently undergoing an archaeological dig and the cottage stands alongside one of the completed excavations. The cottage has plenty of character - there are exposed stone walls and an open log burner fire - and there are plenty of interesting local history books to browse through in the lounge! The two pretty guest rooms have all the comforts of home and your hostess, June Goulding, prides herself on her high standards (she has just been awarded a Highly Commended status by the Wales Tourist Board). A full Welsh breakfast is always provided and excellent evening meals may be enjoyed at the local inn (just two minutes' walk away). You are well placed for exploring Chepstow and the Wye Valley, and June's husband Keith, who is a forester, is very knowledgeable about nearby Wentwood Forest and will gladly advise you about how to make the most of your stay.
Open Feb. to Oct. No smoking in the house. Children welcome. Pets by arrangement. H. & C. tea-making & T.V. in rooms. Hairdryer, radio/alarm & iron available. B. & B. from £18. WTB 1 Crown Highly Commended.

CWMBRAN

Glebe Farm, Croesyceiliog, Cwmbran, NP44 2DE
100 acre family farm with a modern bungalow in a lovely parkland.
Open all year ex. Xmas and New Year. No smoking in the house. Disabled access. Children welcome. Tea/coffee-making offered. T.V. available. B. & B. from £13.

The Parkway Hotel and Conference Centre, Cwmbran Drive, Cwmbran (0633) 871199
Open all year. No smoking in dining room & some bedrooms. Vegetarian by arrangement. Licensed. Disabled access. Children welcome. Pets by arrangement. En suite, TV & tea-making in bedrooms. Credit cards.

NEWPORT

Anderley Lodge Hotel, 216 Stow Hill, Newport, NP9 4HA (0633) 266781
Award-winning family-run 19th C. hotel offering spacious, elegant accommodation; beautifully furnished and well-appointed rooms; evening meal by arrangement prepared from fresh produce.
Open all year. No smoking ex. 2 bedrooms. Children welcome. Tea-making & T.V. in rooms.B. & B. from £15.

Chapel Guest House, Church Road, St Brides, Wentloog, Nr Newport, NP1 9SN (0633) 681018
Converted chapel in a small country village adjacent to the Church House Inn and Elm Tree Restaurant; breakfast only. 3m. from M4 junction 28.
Open all year. No smoking in the house. Vegetarian & other diets by arrangement. Children welcome. Pets by arrangement. En suite in 2 rooms. Tea/coffee & T.V. all bedrooms. B. & B. from £14.

The West Usk Lighthouse, St Brides, Wentlodge, Nr Newport, NP1 9SF (0633) 810126
Light house with magnificent views of Bristol Channel. B'fast only. High standards all round.
Open all year. No smoking. Vegetarian. Children welcome. En suite. Tea/coffee & T.V. in all bedrooms.

PONTYPOOL

 Ty'r Ywen Farm, Mamhilad, Pontypool, NP4 8TT (049 528) 200
Charming white-washed, slate-tiled longhouse with oak beams, inglenook fireplaces and
oak panelling standing in a pretty cottage garden with magnificent views down the Usk
valley.
*Open all year. No smoking throughout. Vegetarian and some other special diets by arrangement. Pets by
arrangement. En suite, tea/coffee-making & T.V. in all bedrooms. B. & B. from £16. D. £8.80.*

TINTERN

The Old Rectory, Tintern, NP6 6SG (0291) 689519
Lovely old house, once used as a rectory for the Church of St Mary's (now in ruins on the hillside
opposite the Abbey); architectural extensions and additions over the years have added to its charm;
fresh natural spring water for most of the year; own produce used in home-made cuisine.
*Open all year. Smoking allowed only in the sitting room. Vegetarian and most other special diets by
arrangement. Children welcome. Pets by arrangement. B. & B. from £12.50 D. £7.50.*

Valley House, Raglan Road, NP6 6TH (0291) 689652
Charming Georgian residence opposite picturesque woods within a mile of Tintern Abbey; its rural
setting is exquisite - and many beautiful forest walks begin literally from the Valley House doorstep.
*Open all year. No smoking in dining room & most bedrooms. Vegetarian food by arrangement. Pets by
arrangement. En suite, TV & tea/coffee-making in bedrooms. B. & B. from £15, D. £12.50.*

USK

Glen-yr-Afon House, Pontypool Road, Usk, NP5 1SY Tel: (02913) 2302 Fax: (02913) 2597
Elegant country house set in mature, secluded grounds just 5 mins walk from the historic village
of Usk; tastefully decorated throughout and offering excellent home-cooked food.
*Open all year. No smoking in dining room. Vegetarian and most other special diets by arrangement. Licensed.
Disabled access. Children welcome. Pets by arrangement. En suite in all rooms. T.V. facilities. Access, Amex,
Visa. B. & B. from £21.*

Restaurants

ABERGAVENNY
Bagan Tandoori, 35 Frogmore Street, Abergavenny (0873) 4790
Outstanding Indian Restaurant in Abergavenny. Wide selection of indian sweets, lagers, wines.
*36 seats. Open 12 - 2.30, 6 - 11.30. 95% of clientèle do not smoke. Vegetarian standard. Licensed. Disabled
access. Children welcome. Access, Visa, Amex.*

Gwynedd
Accommodation

ABERDOVEY

The Harbour Hotel, Aberdovey, LL35 0EB (0654) 767250
The Harbour Hotel is a lovely, award-winning, Victorian hotel which stands on the seafront in the heart of the picturesque village of Aberdovey overlooking miles of golden sandy beaches. Owned and run by the resident proprietors, the Harbour Hotel has been beautifully restored and its furnishing and decor are of an exceptionally high standard; bedrooms are very comfortable and family suites are available (with separate children's and parents' bedrooms). Excellent, home-cooked food may be enjoyed in the Alacarte (*sic.*) Restaurant, and there is a family restaurant, 'Rumbles', which has good children's options; there is also a basement wine bar.
Open all year. No smoking in dining room, sitting room & some bedrooms. Vegetarian standard. Other diets by arrangement. Licensed. Children welcome. Pets by arrangement. En suite , tea/coffee-making & T.V. in all bedrooms. Credit cards. B. & B. from £32.50.

One Trefeddian Bank, Aberdovey, LL35 0RU (0654) 767487
Lovely house in quiet, elevated position with stunning views over the Dovey Estuary.
Open all year. No smoking in the house. Vegetarian and most other special diets by arrangement. Children welcome. Tea/coffee-making in bedrooms. T.V. in lounge and conservatory. B. & B. from £13. D. £8.50.

BANGOR

Rainbow Court, Pentir, Nr Bangor, LL57 4UY (0248) 353099
Excellent restaurant outside Bangor on B4366 at Caerhun turnoff; with accommodation.
Open all year. No smoking in the house. Vegetarian by arrangement. Bring your own wine. Children by arrangement. En suite in most rooms. Tea/coffee & T.V. in all bedrooms. Credit cards. B. & B. from £12.50.

Pen Parc Guest House, Park Rd, Barmouth, LL42 1PH (0341) 280150
Small guest house in a quiet location overlooking the bowling & putting green, & tennis court.
Open all year. No smoking throughout. Vegetarian standard. Other diets by arrangement. Bring your own drinks. Older children by arrangement. Tea/coffee making. T.V. in lounge. B. & B. from £14. D. £7.

BETWS-Y-COED

The Ferns Guest House, Holyhead Rd, Betws-y-Coed, LL24 0AN (0690) 710587
The Ferns Guest House is situated in in the popular village of Betws-y-Coed and is owned
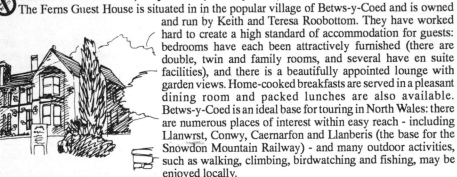
and run by Keith and Teresa Roobottom. They have worked hard to create a high standard of accommodation for guests: bedrooms have each been attractively furnished (there are double, twin and family rooms, and several have en suite facilities), and there is a beautifully appointed lounge with garden views. Home-cooked breakfasts are served in a pleasant dining room and packed lunches are also available. Betws-y-Coed is an ideal base for touring in North Wales: there are numerous places of interest within easy reach - including Llanwrst, Conwy, Caernarfon and Llanberis (the base for the Snowdon Mountain Railway) - and many outdoor activities, such as walking, climbing, birdwatching and fishing, may be enjoyed locally.
Open all year. No smoking in the house. Vegetarian & other diets by arrangement. Children: over 4s welcome. En suite in some rooms. Tea/coffee making & TV in all bedrooms. B. & B. from £16.

Swn-y-Dwr, Pentrefelin, Betws-y-Coed, LL24 0BB (0690) 710648
Traditional Welsh stone farmhouse centrally situated on the banks of the River Llugwy at the famous Pont y Pair Bridge; lovely views of river and woods.
Open all year. No smoking in the house. Tea/coffee-making & T.V. in all bedrooms. B. & B. from £13.

Tan-y-Foel Country House, Capel Garman, Nr Betws-y-Coed, Gwynedd, LL26 0RE Tel: (0690) 710507 Fax: (0690) 710681

A recent and highly deserving winner of the WTB Best Small Hotel Award, Tan-y-Foel

(whose name means The House under the Hillside) is a 16th C. country manor which stands high above the beautiful Conwy Valley enjoying fabulous views of both the valley and the high peaks of Snowdonia. Its owners, Peter and Janet Pitman, have worked hard to create an interior in harmony with the tranquil beauty surrounding the house: bedrooms are beautifully furnished with antiques, there are crisp linen sheets on firm beds, fresh flowers and lovely views; lots of lovely little extras have been provided to make you feel special - bath robes, toiletries, even chocolates - and winter guests may curl up in the cosy lounge in front of a log fire (summer visitors have use of the heated pool). The food is fabulous - fresh fish straight from the sea, local Welsh lamb and home-made bread all feature on the menu: there is a bumper breakfast to set you up for the day, and a delicious selection of dishes on the evening menu such as Fresh Asparagus with Chive Hollandaise followed by Poached Assorted Sea Fish in Creamy Wine Sauce; a tempting dessert - perhaps Almond Biscuit Basket filled with fresh strawberries and cream - together with local cheeses, biscuits, tea or coffee would complete the meal.

Open all year. No smoking in the house. Vegetarian & other diets by arrangement. Licensed. En suite & tea/coffee in bedrooms. Children: over 9s welcome. Credit cards. D., B. & B. from £57.50 per person.

Ty'n-y-Celyn House, Llanrwst Rd, Betws-y-Coed, Gwynedd, LL24 0HD Tel: (0690) 710202 Fax: (0690) 710800

Ty'n-y-Celyn is a large Victorian house which nestles in a quiet elevated position overlooking the picturesque village of Betws-y-Coed. It has been very comfortably furnished: there are 8 bedrooms - 3 of which are family rooms - and each has been tastefully refurbished with new beds and fitted furniture, together with a range of helpful amenities including TV, hairdryer, radio-cassette and tea-making facilities; most bedrooms have magnificent views of the Llugwy Valley, surrounding mountains or the Conwy River. Your hosts, Maureen and Clive Muskus, will do all they can to make your stay a happy and comfortable one - including picking you up from the station if you are arriving by rail. Betws-y-Coed is a perfect touring base: it is in the heart of the Snowdonia National Park, yet is also within easy reach of the fine coastlines; in addition to walking and climbing, it is an excellent centre for other outdoor pursuits such as fishing (which can be arranged in the nearby streams, rivers and reservoirs) and horse riding.

Open all year. No smoking in the dining room. Vegetarian & other diets by arrangement. Licensed. Children & pets welcome. En suite, TV & tea/coffee-making in bedrooms. B. & B. £18 - 20.

CAERNARFON

 Ty Mawr Farmhouse, Saron, Llanwnda, Caernarfon, Gwynedd, LL54 5UH (0286) 830091

Charming farmhouse with country antiques & modern comforts. 3 pretty bedrooms with coastal /mountain views. Peaceful countryside 3m. Caernarfon close to Snowdonia. Parking. Easy to find.

Open Jan. - Oct. No smoking in the house. Vegetarian & other diets by arrangement. Children: over 3s only. Pets by arrangement. En suite, TV & tea/coffee-making in bedrooms. B. & B. £14-17

Ty'n Rhos, Seion, Llanddeiniolen, Caernarfon, LL55 3AE (0248) 670489

Modern farmhouse with traditional furnishings and accoutrements; home-produce includes eggs, milk, yoghurt and cheese.

Open all year. No smoking in dining room. Vegetarian, vegan and other special diets by arrangement. Licensed. Disabled access. Children: over 6s only. Pets by arrangement. En suite, tea/coffee-making & T.V. in all bedrooms. B. & B. from £18.

CONWY

Castle Bank Hotel, Mount Pleasant, Conwy, Gwynedd, LL32 8NY (0492) 593888

 Castle Bank Hotel is an impressive stone-built Victorian house which stands in its own grounds close to Conwy town walls overlooking the estuary of the river and the surrounding countryside. It has been comfortably furnished throughout: each of the en suite bedrooms has a range of helpful amenities including tea/coffee-making and a hairdryer, and there is an attractive well-stocked bar in which to enjoy a pre-dinner drink. The menus are imaginative and varied: everything is prepared from fresh local produce wherever possible, and the home-cooked evening meal would typically feature a choice of such dishes as Local Smoked Trout followed by Honey-Roast Duckling (with a selection of imaginative fresh vegetables) and an exotic dessert such as home-madePassion Fruit Ice-cream with Strawberries. Conwy is considered to be one of the best preserved mediaeval walled towns in Europe: it is possible to walk round most of the walls (3 of the original gates remain), and there are a number of interesting historic buldings to be visited including Edward I's fortress castle, Plas Mawr (a fine Elizabethan mansion), 15th C. Aberconwy House and the smallest house in Great Britain.

Open mid Feb. - mid Dec. No smoking. Vegetarian & other diets by arrangement. Licensed. Children welcome. En suite, TV & tea/coffee-making in bedrooms. Credit cards. B. & B. from £25, D. £14. 2-day breaks £75.

Castle Hotel, High Street, Conwy, LL32 8DB (0492) 592324

Open all year. No smoking in dining room. Vegetarian standard. Other diets by arrangement. Licensed. Children welcome. Pets by arrangement. En suite, TV & tea/coffee in bedrooms. Credit cards. B. & B. from £35.

The Old Rectory, Llansanffraid Glan Conwy, Nr Conwy, LL28 5LF (0492) 580611

 There has been a rectory on this beautiful site on the Conwy Estuary with its spectacular views from Conwy Castle to Snowdonia, for the last 5 centuries. Sadly, in 1740, the Tudor House was burnt down, but the elegant Georgian replacement is a splendid house - skilfully restored by the Vaughan family and now functioning as a comfortable and charming small country house: sympathetically decorated and furnished with antiques (the collection of Victorian watercolours is a delight) and all the individually styled bedrooms have excellent facilities (including bathrobes, ironing centres & hairdryers). The cuisine is exceptionally good: the finest local produce is used in imaginative dishes, and a typical evening menu would feature Mediterranean Vegetable & Herb in Strudel Pastry with Tomato Sauce followed by Spinach & Salmon Terrine, Lamb with Leek Garnish & a delicious dessert, such as Chocolate & Raspberry Roulade, and a selection of Welsh Cheeses.

Open Feb. to Dec. No smoking in the house. Vegetarian and some other special diets by arrangement. Licensed. Children: over 10s only. En suite & TV in all rooms. Room service. Credit cards. B. & B. from £56.

The Whins, Whinacres, Conwy, LL32 8ET (0492) 593373

The Whins was designed by the well-known local artist, Hubert Coop at the turn of the century, and it is a charming house with lots of character and original features, including the interesting wood panelling in the lounge. Good home-cooking is served in the cosy dining room, and a log fire blazes welcomingly in the lounge in cooler weather. The Whins is conveniently situated close to Conwy town with its spectacular and historic castle and you are perfectly placed for touring the many beautiful attractions of the North Wales Coast.

Open Mar. to Oct. No smoking in the house. Vegetarian & other diets by arrangement. Well-behaved children welcome. Pets by arrangement. En suite in 2 rooms. Tea/coffee-making in bedrooms. T.V. lounge. B. & B. from £16. D. £9.50.

CRICIETH

Ⓧ Muriau, Cricieth, LL52 0RS (0766) 522337
Open all year. No smoking in the house. Vegetarian & other diets by arrangement. Children welcome. Some en suite rooms. Tea/coffee-making in bedrooms. T.V. in drawing room. B. & B. from £15.

DOLGELLAU

Penmaenuchaf Hall, Penmaenpool, Dolgellau, Gwynedd, LL40 1YB Tel & Fax: (0341) 422129
It would be difficult to imagine a more beautiful and idyllic situation than the one enjoyed by this lovely country manor hotel which nestles in the foothills of Cader Idris overlooking the famous Mawddach Estuary. Upon entering the hall you are instantly transported back to an age of gracious living: the oak panelling, exquisite furnishings, fresh flowers and blazing log fires encourage a feeling of relaxation and well-being. Lulled thus into a condition of happy anaesthesia with respect to 20th C. concerns, the most stressful decision you are likely to have to make is whether your choice of afternoon tea will spoil your appetite for the superb evening meal: the food is fabulous and not to be missed, an evening menu choice perhaps featuring Tomato Consommé with Coriander, Madeira and Herb Dumplings followed by Pan-fried Pork with Apple and Rosemary and some outstandingly irresistible desserts (Apricot Soufflé and Orange Caramel Sauce, Mille Feuilles of Chocolate on a Compote of Cherries).
Open all year. No smoking in dining room, 2 lounges & bedroom. Vegetarian standard. Other diets by arrangement. Licensed. Children. En suite, TV & tea/coffee in rooms. Credit cards. B. & B. from £47.50.

HARLECH

Ⓧ Aris Guest House, Pen-y-Bryn, Harlech, LL46 2SL (0766) 780409
Open all year. No smoking throughout. Vegetarian, vegan and most other special diets by arrangement. Children welcome. Pets by arrangement. Tea/Coffee-making & T.V. in all bedrooms. B. & B. from £12.50.

Hotel Maes-y-Neuadd, Talsarnau, Nr Harlech, LL47 6YA (0766) 780200
Ancient Welsh manor on a wooded mountainside in 8 acres of landscaped grounds.
Open all year ex. 2 weeks mid Dec. No smoking in dining room. Vegetarian by arrangement. Licensed. Disabled access. Children & pets by arrangement. En suite all rooms. T.V. facilities. Credit cards. B. & B. from £48.

Ⓧ Tremeifion Vegetarian Country Hotel, Talsarnau, Near Harlech (0766) 770491
Charming house, with beautiful views of Portmeirion, the estuary & Snowdonia.
Open all year. No smoking in the house. Exclusively vegetarian and vegan; other meat-free special diets by arrangement. Licensed. Children welcome. Pets by arrangement. En suite in some rooms. Tea/Coffee-making in bedrooms. T.V. in lounge. Access, Visa. D., B. & B. from £27.

LLANBERIS

Ⓧ Maesteg, High St, Llanberis, Caernarfon, LL5 4HB (0286) 871187
Maesteg is a privately owned house with a very friendly atmosphere which nestles at the foot of Mount Snowdon in the heart of Llanberis village. Breakfast is the only meal to be served at Maesteg, but packed lunches are available if required and there is a good choice of eating places in Llanberis where you may enjoy your evening meal. As well as being surrounded by some of the finest mountain and hill walking to be had in the British Isles, Maesteg is also an excellent base from which to enjoy pony-trekking, fishing and water sports; venturing a little further afield you will find yourself within easy reach of a number of castles, fine country houses and even narrow gauge railways which are well worth a visit; private guided car and walking tours can be arranged.
Open all year. No smoking in the house. Vegetarian & some other diets by arrangement. Disabled access. Children: over 12s only. Tea/coffee-making in bedrooms. T.V. in some bedrooms. B. & B. from £13.

LLANDUDNO

Ⓧ Bodnant Guest House, 39 St Mary's Road, Llandudno, LL30 2UE (0492) 876936
Small, elegant Edwardian guest house in a pleasant residential area of Llandudno.
Open Jan. to end Nov. No smoking in the house. Licensed. Children: over 12s only. En suite, tea/coffee-making & T.V. in all bedrooms. B. & B. from £15. AA Listed. WTB 3 Crowns Commended.

Brin-y-Bia Lodge Hotel, Craigside, Llandudno, LL30 3AS (0492) 549644
Charming 18th C. hotel in walled grounds on the Little Orme overlooking the town and the sea.
Open all year ex. Xmas & New Year. No smoking in dining room. Vegetarian by arrangement. Licensed. Children welcome. Pets by arrangement. En suite, TV & tea/coffee in bedrooms. Access, Visa, Amex. B. & B. from £25.

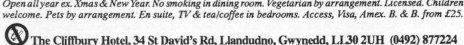

The Cliffbury Hotel, 34 St David's Rd, Llandudno, Gwynedd, LL30 2UH (0492) 877224

The Cliffbury is a small, non-smoking, licensed, family-run hotel just 5 minutes' walk from all the main attractions of Llandudno. It is run by Janet and Michael Cook who aim to offer a real home-from-home welcome to guests: Michael will collect you from the station if you arrive by coach or rail and Janet does all her own home-cooking - and delicious home-cooking it is, too, a typical evening menu featuring Melon followed by Fresh Salmon with Hollandaise Sauce and a choice of home-made desserts, cheese, biscuits, tea and coffee. Llandudno is a large, thriving holiday centre with a huge assortment of leisure pursuits including a ski/toboggan slope, bowls, horse-riding and golf; the secret of its success lies in its safe, sandy beach & its proximity to so many other places of interest such as Snowdonia and Conwy.
Open all year. No smoking in the house,. Vegetarian & other diets by arrangement. Licensed. Children & pets welcome. En suite, TV & tea/coffee-making in bedrooms. B. & B. from £12.50.

Cranberry House, 12 Abbey Rd, Llandudno, Gwynedd, LL30 2EA (0492) 879760

Cranberry House is a small, elegant Victorian house which stands just a few minutes' walk

from the pier, promenade and shops of Llandudno. Your hosts, Mr and Mrs Aldridge, offer a very high standard of comfort and service, and have taken tremendous trouble to furnish and decorate their lovely home in a manner which complements its period origins: each of the bedrooms is beautifully equipped and there is a comfortable lounge for guests' use. The dining room is particularly attractive - a perfect setting in which to enjoy the delicious home-cooked meals which have been prepared from fresh ingredients: the Aldridges will meet guests' special dietary needs wherever possible, and a typical evening meal would feature home-made Cream of Leek Soup followed by Fresh Chicken breasts with Herb Stuffing (with fresh vegetables) and a choice of tempting desserts; cheese, biscuits and coffee would complete the meal.
Open mid Mar. - mid Oct. No smoking in the house. Vegetarian & other diets by arrangement. En suite, TV & tea/coffee-making in bedrooms. Credit cards. B. & B. from £16. WTB Commended. AA QQQ

The Grafton Hotel, Promenade, Craig-y-Don, Llandudno, LL30 1BG (0492) 876814
Open Feb. to Nov. No smoking in dining room and some bedrooms. Vegetarian by arrangement. Licensed. Disabled access. Children welcome.En suite, TV & tea/coffee in bedrooms. Credit cards. B. & B. from £16.25.

Oakwood Hotel, 21 St Davids Road, Llandudno, LL30 2UH (0492) 879208
Family hotel situated in the beautiful garden area of Llandudno within walking distance of the promenade and all amenities; attractive gardens in which tea may be served.
Open all year. No smoking in dining room. Vegetarian & other diets by arrangement. Licensed. Children welcome. Pets by arrangement. En suite in 2 rooms. Tea/coffee-making & T.V. in bedrooms. B. & B. from £11.

Plas Madoc Private Hotel, 60 Church Walks, Llandudno, LL30 2HL (0492) 76514
Open all year. No smoking in dining room bedrooms. Vegetarian and most other special diets by arrangement. Licensed. Children welcome. En suite, tea/coffee-making & T.V. in bedrooms. B. & B. from £15.

Summer Hill Luxury Apartment, c/o 10 Crescent Court, Llandudno, LL30 1AT (0492) 879300

Summer Hill accommodation is spotlessly clean and has been awarded the Wales Tourist Board's top grade 5 for the sixth consecutive year.
Open Jan. to mid Dec. No smoking. Children: over 8s only. Some pets by arrangement. One bedroom apartment, fully self-contained, with separate lounge, kitchen, bathroom and toilet. T.V. Tariff £89 to £239 per week.

LLANFAIRFECHAN

Rhiwiau Riding Centre, Llanfairfechan, Gwynedd, LL33 0EH (0248) 680094

Family owned & run riding centre with friendly, relaxed atmosphere; good home-cooking.
Open all year. No smoking in the house. Vegetarian and other diets by arrangement. Licensed. Children welcome. Tea/coffee-making facilities. T.V. in 2 lounges. W/E full board and riding from £75.

LLWYNGWRIL

Bryn-y-Mor Guest House, Fairbourne, Llwyngwril, LL37 2JQ (0341) 250043

Bryn-y-Mor is a large, red-brick Victorian house which stands amidst a large, colourful garden and enjoys extensive sea views of beautiful Cardigan Bay and, to the rear of the house, wooded hillsides; the three en suite bedrooms (one double, one twin, one family room) have been very comfortably appointed with a good range of facilities, and there is a safe, private car park to the rear of the house. Whilst full evening meals are prepared to order, a wide range of hot or cold snack meals is always available and there are several pubs and restaurants nearby which offer a range of food to suit all tastes. Llwyngwril (pronounced 'Thlew-in-Gooril'and meaning literally 'Grove of green leaves') lies half way between Dolgellau and Tywyn on the A493 coast road in the heart of Snowdonia National Park and is an excellent base from which to explore Meirionnyddshire's most popular tourist attractions and to enjoy coastal and hill walking, pony trekking, golf and water sports.

Open March to Nov. Smoking banned throughout the house. Vegetarian and other special diets by arrangement. Children and pets welcome. En suite & tea/coffee making in rooms. T.V. in lounge. Visa. B. & B. from £14.

Pentre Bach, Llwyngwril, LL37 2JU (0341) 250294

A former manor house, Pentre Bach is splendidly situated in a secluded (but not isolated!) position and has wonderful views of the sea and the mountains. There is a great emphasis on the use of healthy produce and guests can also buy free-range eggs, organic fruit and vegetables and preserves, all produced on the premises. Llwyngwril is a pretty coastal village with a British Rail station and regular bus service. There is no need to leave the house during the day - guests can just sit and enjoy the glorious scenery with its wealth of wildlife (including cormorants, buzzards and herons), all with the sea as a backdrop. The more energetic can stagger the 20 yards to play table tennis, 330 yards to the local pub or around the same to go pony-trekking; those who wish to travel further afield by car, public transport or Pentre Bach mountain bikes, will find themselves within easy reach of castles, craft centres, steam railways and the Centre for Alternative Technology. Packed lunches and evening meals may also be ordered by arrangement. Private parking.

Open all year ex. Xmas. No smoking in the house. Vegetarian & trad. b'fast standard. Other diets by arrangement. Children welcome. En suite, TV & tea/coffee making in all bedrooms. B. & B. from £18.

NEFYN

Craig y Mor, Ffordd Dewi Sant, Nefyn, LL53 6EA (0758) 721412

Open all year. No smoking in the house. Vegetarian by arrangement. Bring your own wine. Children welcome. Pets by arrangement. Tea/Coffee in bedrooms. T.V. in lounge. B. & B. from £15. D. from £7.50.

PORTHMADOG

Bwlch-y-Fedwen Country House Hotel, Penmorfa, LL49 9RY (0766) 512975

Beautifully renovated coaching inn.

Open Apr. to Oct; closed Aug. No smoking in the house. Vegetarian by arrangement. Licensed. En suite & tea/coffee-making in bedrooms. Separate T.V. room. D., B. & B. from £32.

TALSARNAU

Tegfan, Llandecwyn, Talsarnau, LL47 6YG (0766) 771354
Lovely old detached house in an elevated position & surrounded by panoramic views.
Open all year ex. Xmas. No smoking in the house. Tea/Coffee available. B. & B. from £12.

TREFRIW

Crafnant Guest House, Main St, Trefriw, LL27 0JH (0492) 640809
Open all year. No smoking in the house. Vegetarian food a speciality. Most other special diets by arrangement. Children & groups welcome. Pets by arrangement. En suite. Tea/coffee & T.V. in all rooms.

Restaurants

ANGLESEY

Bodeilio Craft centre, Bodeilio, Talwrn, Nr Llangefni, Anglesey (0248) 722535
No smoking throughout. Vegetarian standard. Licensed. Children welcome. Credit cards.

BALA

Y Radell, 81 High St, Bala (0678) 520203
No smoking throughout. Access, Visa.

BANGOR

Rainbow Court, Pentir, Nr Bangor, LL57 4UY (0248) 353099

BARMOUTH

The Old Tea Rooms, 'Walsall House', Church St, Barmouth, LL42 1EG (0341) 280194
No smoking throughout.

BEAUMARIS

Welsh Dresser Tea Shop, 30 Castle St, Beaumaris (0248) 810851
No smoking throughout.

HARLECH

The Cemlyn Restaurant, High Street, Harlech (0766) 780425
Separate room for smokers. Vegetarian. Licensed. Disabled access. Children: over 8s only.

LLANBERIS

Y Bistro, 43-45 High St, Llanberis, LL55 4EU

LLANGEFNI

The Whole Thing, 5 Field St, Llangefni (0248) 724832

PORTHMADOG

Blossom's Restaurant, Both y Gest, Porthmadog, LL49 9TP (0766) 513500
No smoking throughout. Vegetarian standard. Licensed. Children welcome. Access, Visa.

TREFRIW

Chandler's Brasserie, Trefriw, Gwynedd, LL27 0JH (0492) 640991
No smoking throughout. Vegetarian standard. Licensed. Children welcome. Access, Visa.

Pembrokeshire Accommodation

CAREW

 Old Stable Cottage, Carew, Pembs., SA70 8SL (0646) 651889

A Grade II listed stone cottage, Old Stable Cottage was originally a stable and carthouse for

Carew Castle, one of Pembrokeshire's finest castles which is reflected idyllically in the tidal waters of the River Carew which it overlooks. The entrance porch to the cottage was a trapshed and leads into the old stable and from thence to the large lounge with its low beams and inglenook (there is a log fire and bread oven therein). A wrought iron spiral staircase leads to three double en suite bedrooms which have been well-equipped with colour TV, a tea and coffee-making tray and bathrobes. There is an attractive conservatory adjoining the country kitchen where delicious meals, prepared from fresh produce and cooked on the Aga by Joyce, are temptingly and creatively presented (Lionel specializes in the bread making). Breakfast is a healthy feast of muesli, oats, almonds, yoghurts, seeds and fresh fruit followed by the traditional English platter. Your hosts, Joyce and Lionel Fielder, are keen sailors who now, having sailed across the Atlantic, keep their yacht in the British Virgin Islands where they sail during the winter months.

Open 10 Mar. - 30 Nov. No smoking in the house. Vegetarian & other diets by arrangement. Children: over 5s welcome. En suite, TV & tea/coffee-making in bedrooms. B. & B. £22.50, D. £17.50, single £30.

CRYMYCH

Felin Tygwyn Farm, Crymych, SA41 3RX (023 979) 603

Felin Tygwyn is a traditional earth and slate farmhouse which nestles at the foot of the Preseli Mountains, some 9 miles from Cardigan and Newport beach. It is very welcoming and has lots of character including beamed ceilings from which are hung bunches of home grown dried flowers, and an inviting open fire in the lounge. The farmhouse forms part of an organic smallholding in which your hosts, Tom and Beryl Hazelden, do everything they can to preserve the habitat for all forms of wildlife: they even allow dandelions to grow in the spring to provide a feast for gold finches and linnets! The house has a very friendly and relaxed atmosphere, and the freshly cooked meals are prepared from home-grown vegetables and herbs or local produce. You will find much at Felin Tygwyn to help you relax and unwind - the surrounding countryside is rich in different varieties of flora and fauna - and there are many places to visit nearby, including nature reserves, castles, standing stones and craft workshops.

Open all year. No smoking in the house. Vegetarian and most other special diets by arrangement. Licensed. Children welcome. Pets by arrangement. Tea/coffee available. T.V. in lounge. D., B. & B. from £20.80.

FISHGUARD

Coach House Cottage, Glendower Square, Goodwick, Fishguard, Pembrokeshire, SA64 0DH (0348) 873660

Traditional Pembrokeshire stone cottage in secluded location next to mountain stream; vegetarian, vegan and wholefood fare a speciality; organic produce wherever possible.

Open all year. No smoking in the house. Vegetarian standard. Most other special diets by arrangement. Not licensed but guests welcome to bring a bottle. Children welcome. Pets by arrangement. Tea/Coffee-making in bedrooms. T.V. in lounge. B. & B. from £11. D. £7.50.

Powys
Accommodation

BRECON

Beacons Guest House, 16 Bridge St, Powys, LD3 8AH (0874) 623339
Friendly Georgian guest house close to town centre & River Usk. 4-poster bed. Coffee shop too!
Open all year. No smoking in the dining room. Vegetarian & other diets by arrangement. Chidren & pets welcome. Licensed. En suite, TV & tea/coffee-making in bedrooms. Credit cards. B. & B. £16 - 19.

The Coach Guest House, Orchard St, Brecon, Powys, LD3 8AN (0874) 623803
The Coach Guest House is a totally smoke-free town house in Brecon. The standard of accommodation is very high indeed (Highly Commended, 4 Crown & Dragon Award by the WTB and has a RAC Highly Acclaimed and QQQ status from the AA), and each of the six en suite bedrooms has been equipped with clock radio, telephone, hairdryer, TV & beverage-making in addition to the usual amenities. Excellent accommodation & an ideal centre for touring the Brecon Beacons National Park.
Open all year. No smoking in the house. Vegetarian & other diets by arrangement. En suite, tea/coffee-making & TV in all bedrooms. B. & B. from £18.

Forge Farm House, Hay Road, Brecon, LD3 7SS (0874) 611793
Beautiful 17th C. house of historical interest in a quiet, secluded position in the valley of the River Honddu; good home-cooking including bread and jams.
Open all year ex. Xmas. No smoking in the house. Vegetarian and most other special diets by arrangement. Children welcome. Tea/coffee-making in sitting room. T.V. in sitting room. B. & B. from £12.50. D.£8.

BUILTH WELLS

The Court Farm, Aberedw, Nr Builth Wells, LD2 3UP (0982) 560277
Spacious farmhouse in peaceful, picturesque valley. Home-produce used in cooking including meat, poultry, eggs, honey and organically home-grown vegetables and fruit. Farm, riverside and hill walking, with 3 golf courses nearby.
Open Easter to Nov. No smoking in the house. Vegetarian by arrangement. Children: over 12s only. Tea/coffee-making on request. T.V. in lounge. B. & B. from £13.50.

Nant-y-Derw Farm, Builth Wells, LD2 3RU (0982) 553675
Working sheep farm 4m N. of Builth Wells on a south-facing slope amidst 45 acres of farmland. Home from home in which to relax & unwind. One-level accommodation.
Open May to Dec. ex. Xmas. No smoking in the house. Vegetarian by arrangement. Disabled access. Children: over 7s only. Pets by arrangement. Tea/Coffee-making in bedrooms. T.V. lounge. B. & B. from £14. D. from £5.

HAY-ON-WYE

York House, Victorian Guest House, Cusop, Hay on Wye, Hereford, HR3 5QX (0497) 820705
For details please see the entry in the Herefordshire section.

LLANDRINDOD WELLS

Corven Hall, Howey, Llandrindod Wells, LD1 5RE (0597) 823368
Large Victorian house in 4 acres of peaceful gardens, bounded by open country. Disabled suite.
Open Feb. to Nov. No smoking in dining room & lounge. Vegetarian by arrangement. Licensed. Disabled access. Children welcome. Pets by arrangement. En suite. Tea/coffee. T.V. lounge. B. & B. from £16. D. £10.

LLANGAMMARCH WELLS

The Lake Country House Hotel, Llangammarch Wells, LD4 4BS (05912) 202
Exceptional award-winning hotel.
Open mid Jan. to end Dec. No smoking in dining room and some bedrooms. Vegetarian by arrangement. Licensed. Disabled access. Children welcome. Pets by arrangement. En suite & T.V. in all bedrooms.

MACHYNLLETH

Ⓝ Gwalia, Cemmaes, Machynlleth, SY20 9PU (0650) 511377
Exclusively vegetarian, family-run 10 acre smallholding; lovely house with beautiful views outside Snowdonia National Park; virtually all food home-grown/produced. Therapeutic massage. *Open all year. No smoking in the house. Vegetarian and vegan diets. Children welcome. Pets by arrangement. Tea/coffee on request. B. & B. from £13. D. £7*

Ⓝ Ty Bach, Cwm Einion, Artists Valley, Furnace, Machynlleth, SY20 8PG (0654) 781298
Ty Bach (Little House) offers fully equipped self-catering accommodation high above the Dyfi Estuary in the heart of beautiful countryside; wonderful wildlife and walks. *Open all year ex. Xmas. No smoking in the house. Sleeps 2/3. W.T.B. 5 Dragon Grade. From £150 per week.*

The Wynnstay Arms Hotel, Machynlleth, SW20 8AE (0654) 702941
Open all year. No smoking in part of dining room, 2 lounges and some bedrooms. Vegetarian standard. Licensed. Children welcome. En suite, tea & coffee-making, & T.V. in all rooms. Credit cards.

RHAYADER

Ⓝ Tre Garreg, St Harmon, Nr Rhayader, LD6 5LU (0597) 88604
Converted stone barn offering comfortable accomm. with log fires & wholesome food. *Open Easter to Oct. No smoking. En suite. Tea/coffee-making & T.V. in lounge.B. & B. from £15. D. £10.*

Restaurants

MACHYNLLETH

Ⓝ Felin Crewi (Amanda's Tearooms) Penegoes, Machynlleth, SY20 8NH
No smoking. Vegetarian, vegan and low-fat food standard. Disabled access. Children welcome.

Ⓝ The Old Station Coffee Shop, Dinas Mawddwy, Machynlleth, SY20 9LS (06504) 338
No smoking. Mainly vegetarian food. Licensed. Disabled access. Well behaved children welcome.

Ⓝ The Quarry Shop, Wholefood Café and Store. 13 Maengwyn Street, Machynlleth
Part of the Centre for Alternative Technology at Machynlleth
No smoking throughout. Vegetarian and vegan wholefoods served.

MIDDLETON, WELSHPOOL

Ⓝ Border Restaurant, Middletown, Welshpool, Powys, SY21 8EN (0938570) 201
The Border Restaurant is thus named because it straddles the border of Shropshire and Powys on the A458 gateway to Mid-Wales. It is run by Brenda and Dennis Hickman, late of the Tables Hotel in Skye, who have bought their culinary skills to a more southern audience: those who remember them from their time at Skye will recall such delicious delights as Cidered Pork Steak (with apple and sage) or Port and Redcurrant Lamb followed by Squidgy Chocolate Log (rich dark chocolate roll filled by chocolate mousse and cream) or Bannoffee Shortbread (home-made shortbread topped with banana, caramel and coffee cream). The Border Restaurant is comprised of a Coffee Shop and a Cellar Bistro incidentally, so you may break your journey to or from Wales with either home-made tea and cakes or a full 3-course meal! *Open all year. No smoking throughout. Vegetarian standard (there is an extensive menu). Wheelchair access. Children welcome. Licensed.*

RHAYADER

Ⓝ Carole's Cake shop and Tea room, South Street, Rhayader, LD6 5BH (0597) 811060
No smoking throughout. Vegetarian standard. Children welcome.

Index

The following index lists the names of regions, counties, cities, towns and villages in alphabetical order. The pages in the guide on which they appear are listed under three columns: H (hotels & guest houses), R (restaurants) and P (pubs and wine bars).

READER'S OBSERVATIONS

I would be very glad to hear your comments about the establishments you have visited as a result of *Eat, Drink & Sleep Smoke-free*. If you think I have ommitted anyone who ought to be included - do please let me know. Write to me at Saddlers Cottage, York Rd, Elvington, York, YO4 5AR (no phone calls please!).

Hotel/ Guest House

. . . .
. . . .
. . . .
. . . .

Comments

. . . .
. . . .
. . . .
. . . .
. . . .
. . . .
. . . .
. . . .
. . . .
. . . .
. . . .
. . . .
. . . .
. . . .
. . . .
. . . .
. . . .
. . . .
. . . .
. . . .
. . . .
. . . .
. . . .
. . . .
. . . .
. . . .
. . . .
. . . .
. . . .